OUTLINE OF
HUMAN ANATOMY

BLAKISTON OUTLINE SERIES

Published

In Preparation

OUTLINE OF HUMAN ANATOMY

By SAUL WISCHNITZER, Ph.D.

Assistant Professor of Anatomy
New York Medical College
New York City

Illustrated by PAUL SINGH-ROY

The Blakiston Division
McGRAW-HILL BOOK COMPANY, INC.

New York   Toronto   London

6880

OUTLINE OF HUMAN ANATOMY

71121

Dedicated to

PROFESSOR EUGENE LUDWIG

Formerly Director, Department of Anatomy, University of Basel, Switzerland, *who provided me a most stimulating introduction to the beauty of human morphology.*

Late REVEREND ROBERT J. SHEEHAN, C.S.C.

Formerly Director, Department of Biology, University of Notre Dame, Indiana, *who provided me the opportunity to complete my academic studies.*

PROFESSOR J. CLIFFORD HAYNER

Formerly Director, Department of Anatomy, New York Medical College, New York, *who provided me the teaching opportunity that led to the development of this book.*

PREFACE

Anatomy is the first discipline of medical education that the student must master. The subject matter is voluminous, and the time allotted to the study of anatomy is continually being decreased. As a result, the student needs a book on anatomy which will facilitate his orientation to the subject matter prior to lecture and dissection and subsequent review of the material presented. *Outline of Human Anatomy* has been written to fill this need.

The presentation used in this book is based essentially on the regional approach to dissection used in American and Canadian medical colleges. The placement of illustrations as close as possible to the appropriate text material is an arrangement intended to make it possible for the student to conveniently locate the anatomic parts described in the text.

The illustrations are line drawings and are semischematic. For maximum clarity the number of labels has been restricted to the pertinent anatomic terms under discussion; not all landmarks are labeled on each illustration.

The author believes that anatomic information can be more readily assimilated when it is summarized in tabular form, and he has utilized this approach.

The nomenclature used in *Outline of Human Anatomy* is usually the English equivalent of the Latin anatomic term and was selected in the light of the current standard nomenclature (PNA) accepted at the Sixth International Congress of Anatomists (Paris, 1955) and revised at the Seventh Congress (New York, 1960).

The Format

The text is divided into the eight major *areas* of the body (e.g., head, neck, etc.). The study of gross anatomy can be initiated with any of these areas. Each of the major areas is subdivided into smaller *regions*, and under the caption of each region is the numerical list of grouped structures (e.g., muscles, nerves, etc.) to be studied. The presentation of these grouped structures is from superficial to deep, as they appear during dissection. The grouped structures have the same number as indicated in the region summary. The bones and joints are discussed collectively, since they are usually studied in this manner in the laboratory. The running heads on the left-hand page indicate the area, and, on the right, the region of the body under discussion.

The Glossary

I to XII: Cranial nerves.

V^1, V^2, V^3: The three major divisions of the trigeminal (V) nerve; ophthalmic, maxillary, and mandibular nn., respectively.

Cv, Tv, Lv: Cervical, thoracic, and lumbar vertebrae, respectively. The specific vertebra will be indicated (e.g., Cv 6)

Cn, Tn, Ln: Cervical, thoracic, and lumbar spinal nerves, respectively. The specific nerve will be indicated (e.g., Cn 6)

The Abbreviations

a., aa.: artery, arteries
v., vv.: vein, veins
n., nn.: nerve, nerves
m., mm.: muscle, muscles (in tables)

The Acknowledgments

The volume and quality of the anatomic illustrations used in this book represent the untiring efforts of Paul Singh-Roy and reflect both his talent and devotion. The author is also deeply indebted to Martin Zane for his able assistance with the many phases of the preparation of this book, and to Dr. Homer Blincoe, Associate Professor of Anatomy, New York Medical College, for his critical reading of the text and illustrations.

Saul Wischnitzer

CONTENTS

LOWER EXTREMITY 291

BACK 351

OUTLINE
OF
HUMAN ANATOMY

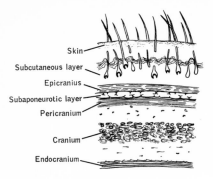

Skin
Subcutaneous layer
Epicranius
Subaponeurotic layer
Pericranium

Cranium

Endocranium

1-1   LAYERS OF THE SCALP

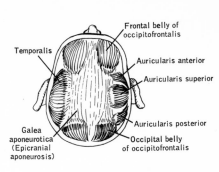

Temporalis

Frontal belly of
occipitofrontalis

Auricularis anterior

Auricularis superior

Auricularis posterior

Galea
aponeurotica
(Epicranial
aponeurosis)

Occipital belly
of occipitofrontalis

1-2   MUSCULOAPONEUROTIC LAYER OF SCALP

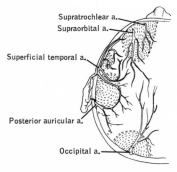

Supratrochlear a.
Supraorbital a.

Superficial temporal a.

Posterior auricular a.

Occipital a.

1-3   ARTERIES OF THE SCALP

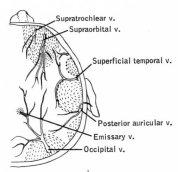

Supratrochlear v.
Supraorbital v.

Superficial temporal v.

Posterior auricular v.
Emissary v.
Occipital v.

1-4   VEINS OF THE SCALP

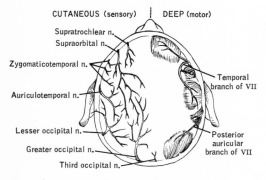

CUTANEOUS (sensory)   DEEP (motor)

Supratrochlear n.
Supraorbital n.

Zygomaticotemporal n.

Auriculotemporal n.

Lesser occipital n.

Greater occipital n.

Third occipital n.

Temporal
branch of VII

Posterior
auricular
branch of VII

1-5   NERVES OF THE SCALP

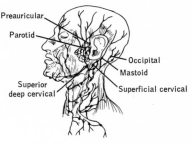

Preauricular

Parotid

Superior
deep cervical

Occipital
Mastoid

Superficial cervical

1-6   LYMPH NODES OF HEAD AND NECK

Plate 1

HEAD

The head contains the brain and the special sensory organs. These are protected by a bony framework, the skull. The integument covering the dome of the skull is the scalp.

SCALP

1. Layers	3. Veins
2. Arteries	4. Nerves
5. Lymphatics	

The scalp covers the cranium and extends from the eyebrows to the superior nuchal lines and from one temporal line to the other.

1. Layers (Fig. 1-1)

The scalp may be subdivided into five layers:

SKIN. It is very thick and contains numerous hairs and sebaceous glands.

SUBCUTANEOUS LAYER. Consisting of dense, fibrous connective tissue which firmly unites the skin with the aponeurotic layer, it contains the superficial nerves and vessels, as well as a small amount of fat.

EPICRANIUS MUSCLE (Fig. 1-2). It consists of the occipitofrontalis muscle, the bellies of which are connected by the galea aponeurotica.

Frontal Bellies. They are long, wide, and united.

Origin: Galea aponeurotica.

Insertion: Skin of eyebrows and root of nose.

Action: Raises eyebrows and wrinkles forehead.

Nerve supply: Temporal branch of the facial n. (VII).

Occipital Bellies. They are small and separate.

Origin: Lateral two-thirds of the superior nuchal line.

Insertion: Galea aponeurotica.

Action: Draws scalp backwards.

Nerve supply: Posterior auricular branch of the facial n. (VII).

Galea Aponeurotica (Epicranial Aponeurosis). Extending from the frontal bellies of the occipitofrontalis muscle to and between the occipital bellies, it attaches to the external occipital protuberance. Laterally it is attached to the temporal line, but it extends down as a thin membrane over the temporal fascia to the zygomatic arch.

3

Table 1

Artery	Branch of:	Course	Region supplied
Supratrochlear.....	Ophthalmic	Exits orbit via its upper medial angle	Scalp of forehead
Supraorbital.......	Ophthalmic	Exits orbit via supraorbital foramen	Forehead and vault of skull
Superficial temporal	External carotid	Divides in front of auricle	Scalp of frontal and parietal regions
Posterior auricular.	External carotid	Divides near mastoid process	Scalp above, behind, and back of ear
Occipital..........	External carotid	Occipital groove to mastoid temporal	Scalp of occiput

Table 2

Nerve	Course	Skin innervated
Supratrochlear...........	Exits orbit and pierces frontal belly of occipitofrontalis m.	Medial part of eyelid and forehead
Supraorbital.............	Exits orbit and pierces frontal belly of occipitofrontalis m.	Forehead to vertex
Zygomaticotemporal.......	Exits orbit via zygomaticotemporal foramen	Anterior part of temple
Auriculotemporal..........	Ramifies on surface at upper end of parotid gland	Side of head, auricle, meatus, tympanic membrane
Lesser occipital............	Ascends along posterior border of sternomastoid m.	Neck and behind auricle
Greater occipital..........	Ascends to pierce trapezius m.	Posterior part of scalp
Third occipital............	Ascends to pierce trapezius m.	Back of neck

Table 3

Group name	Nodes	Region drained	Draining nodes
Occipital......	1–3	Occipital	Superior deep cervical
Preauricular...	1	Anterior temporoparietal	Parotid
Mastoid.......	2	Posterior temporoparietal	Superficial cervical
Parotid.......	3	Frontal	Superior deep cervical

SUBAPONEUROTIC LAYER. Consisting of loose connective tissue, it contains the emissary veins, which connect the venous sinuses of the skull with the veins of the subcutaneous layer.

PERICRANIUM. This is the external periosteum of the skull. It is relatively loosely attached to the surface of the skull bones, except at the suture lines, where it dips between the skull bones as the suture membrane, becoming continuous with the internal periosteum of the skull (outer layer of dura mater).

2. Arteries (Fig. 1-3)

Five arteries on each sipe of the scalp anastomose freely with one another and with the arteries of the opposite side (see Table 1).

3. Veins (Fig. 1-4)

The terminal veins of the scalp anastomose with each other and form a network within the subcutaneous layer. This network is drained by veins that accompany the arteries in the scalp and diverge near their terminations.

SUPRATROCHLEAR AND SUPRAORBITAL VV. Both drain the forehead, communicate with the ophthalmic vv., and unite at the medial angle of the eye to form the facial v.

SUPERFICIAL TEMPORAL V. It descends from the temple to the upper part of the parotid gland, where it unites with the maxillary v. to form the retromandibular v. The latter descends through the parotid gland to terminate, after branching, in the external jugular v. and common facial v.

POSTERIOR AURICULAR V. Draining the back parts of the temporal region, it descends behind the auricle. Below the parotid gland it joins the posterior division of the retromandibular v. to form the external jugular v.

OCCIPITAL V. Draining the posterior parietal and occipital regions, it pierces the trapezius muscle, and diverges from its corresponding artery to terminate in the suboccipital plexus, located beneath the muscles of this triangle (p. 355).

4. Nerves (Fig. 1-5)

The nerves of the scalp are sensory and have a distribution similar to that of the blood vessels that accompany them (see Table 2).

5. Lymphatics (Fig. 1-6 and Table 3)

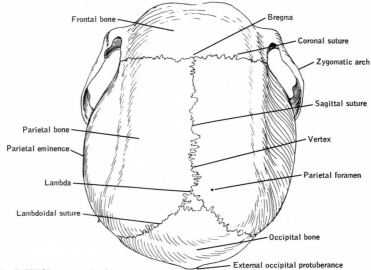

Frontal bone — Bregma — Coronal suture — Zygomatic arch — Sagittal suture — Parietal bone — Vertex — Parietal eminence — Lambda — Parietal foramen — Lambdoidal suture — Occipital bone — External occipital protuberance

2-1   SUPERIOR ASPECT OF SKULL

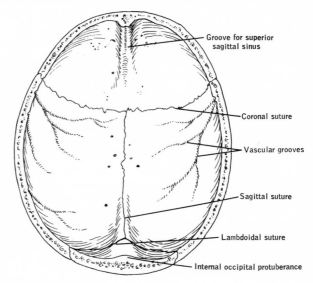

Groove for superior sagittal sinus — Coronal suture — Vascular grooves — Sagittal suture — Lambdoidal suture — Internal occipital protuberance

2-2   INTERNAL SURFACE OF CALVARIA

Plate 2

SKULL

1. Superior aspect	*4. Posterior aspect*
2. Anterior aspect	*5. Inferior aspect*
3. Lateral aspect	*6. Floor of cranial cavity*
	7. Roof of cranial cavity

The *skull* is the skeleton of the head. It consists of a fixed composite of bones, the *cranium,* and a movable single bone, the *mandible.* The roof, or cap, of the cranium is the *calvaria.* The skull, in addition to its protective function, provides the respiratory and digestive systems with openings to the outside.

1. Superior Aspect (Fig. 2-1)

The top of the skull is ovoid and consists of four bones: frontal, occipital, and two parietal. It presents the following landmarks:

sagittal suture. In the midline between the parietal bones.
coronal suture. Transverse between the frontal and parietal bones.
lambdoidal suture. Between the occipital and parietal bones.
bregma. Junction of the sagittal and coronal sutures.
lambda. Junction of the sagittal and lambdoidal sutures.
vertex. Highest point on the sagittal suture.
parietal eminence. The most convex portion of each parietal bone.
parietal foramen. Near the sagittal suture a little in front of the lambda.

2. Anterior Aspect (Fig. 3-1)

The anterior aspect of the skull consists of the forehead, orbits, cheeks, bony dorsum of the nose, and the upper and lower jaws.

Forehead

frontal bone. The skeleton of the forehead; smooth and convex.
supraciliary arches. The curved ridges above each orbit.
glabella. The smooth depressed area between the supraciliary arches.
nasion. The junction of the frontonasal sutures.

Orbits

Each orbit is a four-sided pyramid, the base of which forms the opening on the front of the skull. See also eye, p. 29.

supraorbital margin. The superior margin of the orbit; it has a *supraorbital notch,* or *foramen,* medially.

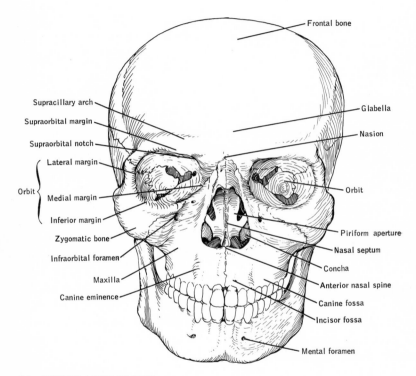

Frontal bone

Supraciliary arch

Supraorbital margin

Supraorbital notch

Lateral margin

Orbit

Medial margin

Inferior margin

Zygomatic bone

Infraorbital foramen

Maxilla

Canine eminence

Glabella

Nasion

Orbit

Piriform aperture

Nasal septum

Concha

Anterior nasal spine

Canine fossa

Incisor fossa

Mental foramen

3-1   ANTERIOR ASPECT OF SKULL

Plate 3

lateral margin. Formed by the zygomatic bone and zygomatic process of the frontal bone.

medial margin. Formed by the frontal process of the maxilla and the maxillary process of the frontal bone.

inferior margin. Formed by the maxilla and zygomatic bones.

Cheeks

The bony prominence of each cheek is formed by the zygomatic bone together with the zygomatic process of the maxilla.

zygomatic bone. Has a *frontal process* projecting upwards and a *temporal process* projecting backwards.

infraorbital foramen. Slightly below the inferior orbital margin.

zygomaticofacial foramen. On the lateral surface of the zygomatic bone.

Dorsum of Nose

The bony part of the dorsum of the nose consists of the nasal bones and the frontal processes of the maxillae and fits in between the orbits.

piriform aperture. The opening of the bony nose; it leads into the nasal cavity, which is divided by the vertical *nasal septum.* Along the lateral wall of the nasal cavity are curled bony plates, the *conchae,* each separated from the other by a *meatus.*

anterior nasal spine. Projecting forward, in the median line, from the inferior border of the nasal aperture.

Upper Jaw

MAXILLAE. Forming the upper jaw, each bone consists of a *body* from which project upward, its *frontal process;* lateralward, its *zygomatic process;* and downward, its *alveolar process.*

canine eminence. The bulge on the alveolar process above the canine tooth that separates the *incisive fossa,* medially, from the *canine fossa,* laterally.

Lower Jaw (p. 65)

3. Lateral Aspect (Fig. 4-1)

The lateral aspect of the skull includes the temporal fossa, external acoustic meatus, and mastoid region, above; the zygomatic arch, infratemporal fossa, and lateral aspects of the maxilla and mandible, below.

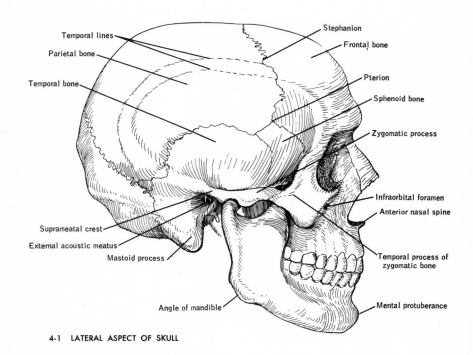

Temporal lines

Parietal bone

Temporal bone

Stephanion

Frontal bone

Pterion

Sphenoid bone

Zygomatic process

Infraorbital foramen

Anterior nasal spine

Temporal process of
zygomatic bone

Suprameatal crest

External acoustic meatus

Mastoid process

Angle of mandible

Mental protuberance

4-1   LATERAL ASPECT OF SKULL

Plate 4

10

Temporal Fossa

The temporal fossa is an oval space on the side of the skull. It has four boundaries:

Superior boundary: the temporal line, which is usually double. It arches backward from the zygomatic process of the frontal bone and becomes continuous with the suprameatal crest and posterior root of the zygomatic process.

Inferior boundary: the infratemporal crest, extending across the greater wing of the sphenoid bone. It is continuous with a ridge that extends backwards across the squamous part of the temporal bone to the anterior root of the zygomatic process.

Medial wall: consisting of parts of the frontal and parietal bones, the temporal squama, and the greater wing of the sphenoid bone.

Lateral wall: formed by the zygomatic arch (and temporal fossae).

Two landmarks of the temporal fossa are the pterion and stephanion.

pterion. The junction of the greater wing of the sphenoid bone and the parietal and temporal bones.

stephanion. The junction of the upper temporal line and the coronal suture.

External Acoustic Meatus

The external aperture of the meatus is surrounded by the root of the zygomatic arch, above, and by the roughened free margin of the tympanic part of the temporal bone on the other three sides. The cartilaginous portion of the meatus is attached to the temporal bone. The *suprameatal triangle* is the depression just above and behind the meatus.

Mastoid Region

The mastoid region consists of the mastoid part of the temporal bone, which lies below the suprameatal crest. It is prolonged downward as the *mastoid process.* The latter is separated from the tympanic plate by the *tympanomastoid suture.*

Zygomatic Arch

The zygomatic arch (zygoma) consists of the temporal process of the zygomatic bone and the zygomatic process of the temporal bone. The latter arises from two roots: the anterior root curves medially and terminates as the articular eminence; the posterior root continues backward as the *suprameatal crest.*

Infratemporal Fossa

The infratemporal fossa is the irregularly shaped space behind the maxilla, below and deep to the zygomatic arch.

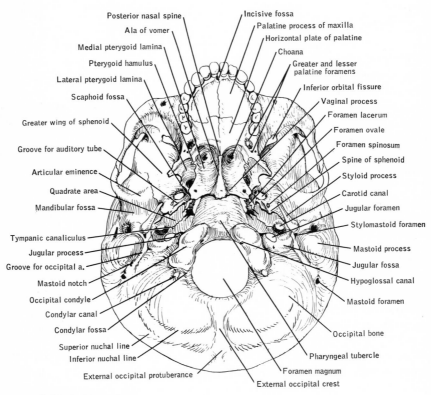

Posterior nasal spine
Ala of vomer
Medial pterygoid lamina
Pterygoid hamulus
Lateral pterygoid lamina
Scaphoid fossa
Greater wing of sphenoid
Groove for auditory tube
Articular eminence
Quadrate area
Mandibular fossa
Tympanic canaliculus
Jugular process
Groove for occipital a.
Mastoid notch
Occipital condyle
Condylar canal
Condylar fossa
Superior nuchal line
Inferior nuchal line
External occipital protuberance

Incisive fossa
Palatine process of maxilla
Horizontal plate of palatine
Choana
Greater and lesser palatine foramens
Inferior orbital fissure
Vaginal process
Foramen lacerum
Foramen ovale
Foramen spinosum
Spine of sphenoid
Styloid process
Carotid canal
Jugular foramen
Stylomastoid foramen
Mastoid process
Jugular fossa
Hypoglossal canal
Mastoid foramen
Occipital bone
Pharyngeal tubercle
Foramen magnum
External occipital crest

5-1 INFERIOR ASPECT OF SKULL

Plate 5

12

Lateral Aspect of Maxilla

This is the convex infratemporal surface of the maxilla. It is bounded anteriorly by the origin of the zygomatic process of the maxilla and by a ridge that descends downward from the process toward the first molar tooth. It ends above at the infraorbital fissure, behind at the pterygopalatine fossa, and posteroinferiorly in a rounded eminence, the *maxillary tuberosity*. On its surface are two *posterior superior alveolar foramens*.

4. Posterior Aspect (Fig. 5-1)

This surface is convex and consists of the parietal bones above, the occipital squama below, and the mastoid temporal bone at each side.

external occipital protuberance. A projection near the center of the occipital squama, from which the *external occipital crest* extends towards the foramen magnum.

superior nuchal line. Arching sideways from the protuberance. Above it, lies the faintly marked *highest nuchal line*.

5. Inferior Aspect (Fig. 5-1)

This aspect will be described in terms of four areas.

Anteromedian Area

bony palate. Forming the roof of the mouth and the floor of the nasal cavity. It consists of the palatine process of the maxillae in front and of the horizontal plates of the palatine bones behind.

posterior nasal spine. Projecting from the middle of the free posterior margin of the palate.

incisive fossa. The depression behind the sockets for the incisor teeth; it presents the four *incisive foramens*.

greater palatine foramens. At each posterolateral angle of the palate.

lesser palatine foramens. May be doubled; are located behind each of the greater palatine foramens.

choanae. The posterior bony apertures of the nose, through which the nasal cavities are continuous with the nasopharynx. Each is bounded, below, by the posterior free margin of the palatine plate; above, by the ala of the vomer and the vaginal process of each medial pterygoid plate, which meet and cover the base of the sphenoid bone; medially, by the vomer; and laterally, by the medial pterygoid plate.

SPHENOID BONE. Made up of a cuboidal *body* and three pairs of processes, or "wings": greater wings, lesser wings, and pterygoid processes. The greater wings and pterygoid processes are fused to the lateral surfaces of the body. The *lesser wings* are attached to the upper and front parts of the body by two roots, between which is an optic canal. The anterior and inferior surfaces of the body of the sphenoid bone form part of the roof of the nose and pharynx, respectively. The posterior end is fused with the basilar part of the occipital bone. The *greater wing* of the sphenoid presents cerebral, orbital, temporal, and infratemporal surfaces.

pterygoid process. A winglike structure on either side of the nasal aperture, consisting of a narrow *medial lamina* and a broad *lateral lamina;* the laminae or plates are fused anteriorly at their upper parts and are free behind and below.

pterygoid fossa. A V-shaped area enclosed by the fused parts of the laminae; above it is a small depression, the *scaphoid fossa*.

pterygoid hamulus. The hooklike process at the lower end of the medial lamina.

vaginal process. Extending medially from the upper end of the medial plate to articulate with the ala of the vomer.

pharyngeal canal. On the undersurface of the vaginal process.

pterygoid tubercle. Projecting from the upper end of the posterior border of the medial plate.

pterygoid canal. Above and laterad to the pterygoid tubercle.

Anterolateral Area

foramen ovale. At the base of the lateral pterygoid lamina.

foramen spinosum. Smaller than the foramen ovale and posterolaterad to it. Posterolaterad to this foramen is the *spine of the sphenoid*.

inferior orbital fissure. Between the sphenoid bone and the maxilla.

Posteromedian Area

OCCIPITAL BONE. It is made up of four parts arranged around the oval *foramen magnum:* the basilar part anteriorly, the squamous part posteriorly, and two condylar parts laterally.

Basilar Part. A wide bar of bone joining the base of the sphenoid bone. Near its center it has an elevation, the *pharyngeal tubercle*.

Condylar Part. Consisting of the condyles which lie at the anterolateral margin of the foramen magnum. The convex articular surface of each articulates with the lateral mass of the atlas.

condylar fossa. The depression behind each condyle which may become a canal.

hypoglossal canal. In front of each condyle.

jugular process. Extending laterally from each condyle to the petrous part of the temporal bone and with a concave anterior border, the *jugular notch*. The notch forms the posterior boundary of the jugular foramen.

Posterolateral Area

TEMPORAL BONE. It consists of four parts: squamous part, above and anteriorly; petrous part, medially; styloid part, posteriorly; tympanic part, below.

Petrous Part. The base of this three-sided pyramid is fused with the mastoid bone; its apex is directed anteromedially. Its anterior and posterior surfaces face the cranial cavity; its inferior surface presents the following landmarks:

jugular foramen. Between the petrous part of the temporal bone and the jugular process of the occipital bone. The wide depression on the anterolateral wall of the foramen is the *jugular fossa*.

carotid canal. In front of the jugular foramen.

tympanic canaliculus. A passage opening on the ridge of bone between the carotid canal and the jugular foramen.

mastoid canaliculus. A passage opening on the lateral wall of the jugular fossa.

foramen lacerum. The irregular opening above the apex of the petrous temporal bone. The inferior surface of the gap is closed by fibrocartilage in the living state.

quadrate area. Between the carotid canal and the foramen lacerum.

groove for auditory tube. A depression containing the cartilaginous part of the auditory tube during life. It runs between the petrous bone and the greater wing of the sphenoid bone anteromedially from the pterygoid tubercle to the spine of the sphenoid bone. The groove is continuous behind with the bony part of the canal which runs in the temporal bone to the tympanic cavity.

mastoid process. This lies behind the stylomastoid foramen and it presents the *mastoid notch,* medial to which is the *occipital groove*.

Squamous Part. This is evident on the lateral aspect of the skull. Its inferior surface is very small and articulates with the greater wing of the sphenoid bone.

articular eminence. A smooth, convex surface continuous with the anterior root of the zygomatic process. Behind the eminence is the *mandibular fossa;* both articulate (with a disk intervening) with the head of the mandible.

Tympanic Part. This curved plate appears as a ring of bone on the lateral aspect of the skull. It forms the anterior and posterior walls and the floor of the external acoustic meatus. The upper border of the plate is separated from the squamous part of the temporal bone by the squamotympanic fissure. Behind, the tympanic plate fuses with the petrous part and forms a sheath for the styloid process.

squamotympanic fissure. It extends from the anterior margin of the meatus, behind the mandibular fossa to the groove for the auditory tube. This fissure is

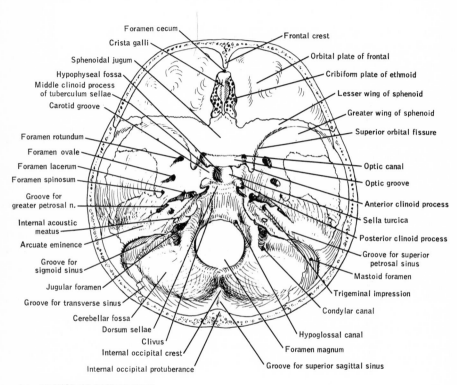

Foramen cecum

Crista galli

Sphenoidal jugum

Hypophyseal fossa

Middle clinoid process of tuberculum sellae

Carotid groove

Foramen rotundum

Foramen ovale

Foramen lacerum

Foramen spinosum

Groove for greater petrosal n.

Internal acoustic meatus

Arcuate eminence

Groove for sigmoid sinus

Jugular foramen

Groove for transverse sinus

Cerebellar fossa

Dorsum sellae

Clivus

Internal occipital crest

Internal occipital protuberance

Frontal crest

Orbital plate of frontal

Cribiform plate of ethmoid

Lesser wing of sphenoid

Greater wing of sphenoid

Superior orbital fissure

Optic canal

Optic groove

Anterior clinoid process

Sella turcica

Posterior clinoid process

Groove for superior petrosal sinus

Mastoid foramen

Trigeminal impression

Condylar canal

Hypoglossal canal

Foramen magnum

Groove for superior sagittal sinus

6-1   INTERIOR OF BASE OF SKULL

Plate 6

16

divided into two parts by the *tegmen tympani,* a sliver of bone which belongs to the petrous temporal bone. The anterior part is the *petrosquamous fissure;* the posterior part is the *petrotympanic fissure.*

Styloid Part. This part consists of the *styloid process,* a slender projection of variable length, which is directed downward and forward. At the root of this process is the *stylomastoid foramen;* both really belong to the petrous temporal.

6. Floor of Cranial Cavity (Fig. 6-1)

The upper surface of the base of the skull is divided into three areas, the anterior, middle, and posterior cranial fossae.

Anterior Cranial Fossa

The floor of the anterior cranial fossa is formed by the orbital plates of the frontal bone, the cribriform plate of the ethmoid bone, and the lesser wings and forepart of the body of the sphenoid bone.

frontal crest. In the midline on the cerebral surface of the frontal bone. At its base is a blind pit, the *foramen cecum.*

crista galli. The median process behind the foramen cecum; it divides anteriorly into a pair of alae. On either side of the crest are the perforated cribriform plates.

sphenoidal jugum. The anterior part of the upper surface of the body of the sphenoid bone; it connects the two lesser wings. From its anterior margin the ethmoid spine projects forward. This articulates with the posterior edge of the cribriform plates. Its free posterior margin is the *sphenoidal limbus.*

orbital plates. Convex portions of the frontal bone; they present the impressions of the cerebral gyri and sulci.

lesser wings (of the sphenoid bone). Articulating with the frontal plates. They have a sharp posterior border, which overhangs the middle cranial fossa and terminates medially in the *anterior clinoid processes.*

Middle Cranial Fossa

The floor of the middle cranial fossa consists of the body and greater wing of the sphenoid bone, the anterior surface of the petrous and squamous parts of the temporal bone, and the anteroinferior angle of the parietal bone.

optic groove. A shallow, transverse, furrow coursing parallel to the sphenoidal limbus and just behind it. On each side this groove leads to the *optic canal.*

sella turcica. The upper surface of the body of the sphenoid bone; it begins just behind the optic groove. It is bounded in front by the *tuberculum sellae,* posterolaterad to which are small tubercles, the *middle clinoid processes.* The sella is

Table 4

Opening in skull	*Content of opening*
Anterior ethmoidal foramen........	Anterior ethmoidal a., v., and n.
Carotid canal..................	Internal carotid a. and carotid plexus
Cochlear aqueduct..............	Piece of dura mater
Condylar canal (inconstant).......	Emissary v.
External acoustic meatus..........	Facial n. (VII), statoacoustic (VIII), and labyrinthine a. and v.
Foramen lacerum................	Internal carotid a., carotid plexus, n. of pterygoid canal
Foramen lacrimale (inconstant).....	Anastomosis between middle meningeal and lacrimal aa.
Foramen ovale..................	Mandibular n. (V³), accessory meningeal a., lesser petrosal n.
Foramen rotundum..............	Maxillary n. (V²)
Foramen spinosum...............	Recurrent branch of V³, middle meningeal a. and v.
Foramen of Scarpa (inconstant)....	Nasopalatine n.
Greater palatine canal.............	Greater palatine a., v., and n.
Hiatus of facial canal.............	Greater petrosal n., petrosal branch of middle meningeal a.
Hypoglossal canal................	Hypoglossal n., meningeal branch of ascending pharyngeal a.
Incisive foramen and canal.........	Greater palatine aa., nasopalatine n.
Infraorbital fissure................	(V²), infraorbital a. and v., zygomatic n., orbital branch from pterygopalatine ganglion, vv. from orbit to pterygoid plexus
Innominate canaliculus (inconstant).	Lesser petrosal n.
Jugular foramen..................	Glossopharyngeal n. (IX), vagus n. (X), accessory n. (XI), inferior petrosal sinus
Lesser palatine foramens...........	Middle and posterior palatine nn.
Mandibular foramen..............	Inferior alveolar a., v., and n.
Mastoid canaliculus...............	Auricular branch of vagus n.
Mastoid foramen.................	Emissary v.
Nasal slit.......................	Anterior ethmoid a. and n.
Optic canal.....................	Optic n. (II), ophthalmic a., sympathetic fibers of internal carotid plexus
Petrosquamous fissure.............	Tympanic branch of middle meningeal a.
Petrotympanic fissure.............	Chorda tympani, anterior tympanic a., tympanic branch of maxillary a.
Pharyngeal canal.................	Pharyngeal a. and v., pharyngeal branch of pterygopalatine ganglion
Posterior ethmoidal foramen.......	Posterior ethmoidal a., v., and n.
Posterior superior alveolar foramen..	Posterior superior alveolar a., v., and n.
Pterygoid canal..................	A., v., and n. of pterygoid canal
Pterygomaxillary fissure...........	Maxillary a. and v.
Pterygopalatine canal.............	Descending palatine a. and v., anterior palatine n.
Squamotympanic fissure...........	Tympanic branch of middle meningeal a.
Stylomastoid foramen.............	Facial n. (VII), stylomastoid branches of posterior auricular a.
Superior orbital fissure............	Oculomotor n. (III), trochlear n. (IV), abducent n. (VI), ophthalmic n. (V¹), frontal n., lacrimal n., sympathetic plexus from internal carotid plexus, ophthalmic v., recurrent branch of lacrimal a., orbital branch of middle meningeal a.
Supraorbital foramen.............	Supraorbital a., v., and n.
Tympanic canaliculus.............	Tympanic branch of vagus n.
Tympanomastoid suture...........	Auricular branch of vagus n.
Vestibular aqueduct...............	Endolymphatic duct
Zygomaticofacial foramen..........	Zygomaticofacial a., v., and n.
Zygomaticotemporal foramen.......	Zygomaticotemporal n.

bounded behind by an upright plate of bone, the *dorsum sellae,* which bears the *posterior clinoid processes* on its upper angles. The concavity of the sellae is the *hypophyseal fossa.* On the side of the body of the sphenoid bone, laterad to the fossa, are the *carotid grooves.*

superior orbital fissure. A slit between the greater and the overhanging lesser wings of the sphenoid bone.

foramen rotundum. Below and behind the medial end of the superior orbital fissure.

foramen ovale. Somewhat posterolaterad to the foramen rotundum.

foramen spinosum. Small and posterolaterad to the foramen ovale.

foramen lacerum. Medial to the foramen ovale.

Anterior Surface of the Petrous Temporal Bone. This surface presents a shallow concavity near its apex, the *trigeminal impression.* More laterally, in the middle of the same surface, is a rounded elevation, the *arcuate eminence.* Below and medial to this eminence is the *groove for the greater petrosal n.* Laterad to this groove is the groove for the *lesser petrosal n.* The smooth bone posterolaterad to the eminence is the *tegmen tympani,* which roofs over the tympanic antrum and cavity.

Posterior Cranial Fossa

The floor of the posterior cranial fossa consists of the dorsum sellae of the sphenoid bone, the posterior surface of the petrous part of the temporal bone, and the occipital squama.

clivus. The sloping inner surface of the basilar part of the occipital bone, presenting on each of its lateral sides, the *groove for the inferior petrosal sinus,* which leads back to the jugular foramen.

Posterior Surface of the Petrous Temporal Bone. This surface presents the *internal acoustic meatus* in its middle. Behind and laterad to this conspicuous opening is a slit, the *external opening of the vestibular aqueduct,* overhung by a lip of bone. The *subarcuate fossa* lies above the meatus. Along the upper border of this surface is the *groove for the superior petrosal sinus.*

internal occipital crest. The median ridge extending up from the foramen magnum to the *internal occipital protuberance.* On each side of the crest is a *cerebellar fossa.* Extending laterally on each side from the protuberance is a *groove for the transverse sinus.* At the posteroinferior angle of the parietal bone this becomes the *groove for the sigmoid sinus,* near which opens the *mastoid foramen.* The *anterior condylar foramen* opens into the sinus just before it terminates at the jugular foramen.

hypoglossal canal. Near the margin of the anterior part of the foramen magnum.

Table 5

Artery	Site of origin	Region supplied
Inferior labial..........	Opposite angle of mouth	Muscles and labial glands of lower lip
Superior labial.........	Just above inferior labial a.	Muscles and labial glands of upper lip
Septal branch........	....	Anterior inferior nasal septum
Lateral nasal...........	Just above ala of nose	Ala and dorsum of nose
Angular...............	(Terminal part of facial a.)	Orbicularis oculi and lacrimal sac

Table 6

Artery	Branch of:
Supraorbital..........	Ophthalmic a.
Supratrochlear........	Ophthalmic a.
Lateral palpebral......	Lacrimal a.
Medial palpebral......	Ophthalmic a.
Dorsal nasal..........	Ophthalmic a.
Zygomaticotemporal...	Lacrimal a.
Zygomaticofacial......	Lacrimal a.
Infraorbital...........	Third part of maxillary a.
Superficial temporal....	External carotid a.
Buccal...............	Second part of maxillary a.
Mental...............	First part of maxillary a.

Table 7

Branches	Site of emergence with regard to parotid gland	Area innervated
Temporal.......	Superior border	Muscles near orbit
Zygomatic......	Anterior border, above duct	Muscles of nose and between eye and mouth
Buccal.........	Anterior border, below duct	Buccinator muscle and muscles inside mouth
Mandibular.....	Anterior border	Muscles of chin and lower lip
Cervical........	Inferior border	Platysma

7. Roof of Cranial Cavity (Fig. 2-2)

The inner aspect of the calvaria exhibits the same sutures that were described on its external surface. It also presents:

digital impressions. For cerebral gyri.

groove for the superior sagittal sinus. Extending from the frontal crest along the sagittal suture to the internal occipital protuberance, where it usually joins the right transverse groove. On both sides of this sinus are pits for the arachnoid granulations. On one side is the *parietal foramen.*

vascular grooves. Markedly evident on the surface of the parietal bones; they carry meningeal vessels.

CONTENTS OF CRANIAL CAVITY

The gross anatomy of the brain and of the cranial meninges, nerves, and blood vessels is considered in textbooks of neuroanatomy. That portion of each cranial nerve situated outside the cranial cavity is discussed in the appropriate places in this book.

The cranial nerves are:

I	Olfactory n.	VII	Facial n.
II	Optic n.	VIII	Vestibulocochlear (statoacoustic) n.
III	Oculomotor n.	IX	Glossopharyngeal n.
IV	Trochlear n.	X	Vagus n.
V	Trigeminal n.	XI	Accessory n.
VI	Abducent n.	XII	Hypoglossal n.

FACE

1. Arteries *3. Nerves*

2. Veins *4. Muscles*

5. Lymphatics

The face extends from ear to ear and from the point of the chin to the roots of the hair. The skin of the face is thick and vascular. Beneath the skin is the superficial fascia, which contains blood vessels and nerves. The *buccal fat pad* lies between the superficial fascia and the buccinator muscle. The many small mucous glands present in the submucous layer of the lips and cheek are known as the *labial* and *buccal glands,* respectively. Their ducts open into the vestibule of the mouth. About five *molar glands* lie around the parotid duct on the buccopharyngeal fascia. Their ducts also open into the mouth.

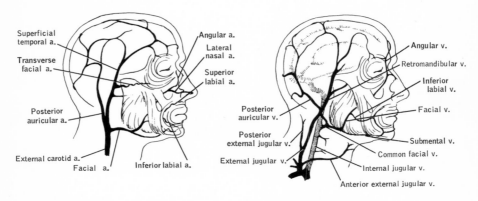

Superficial temporal a.
Transverse facial a.
Posterior auricular a.
External carotid a.
Facial a.
Inferior labial a.
Angular a.
Lateral nasal a.
Superior labial a.

7-1 ARTERIES OF THE FACE

Posterior auricular v.
Posterior external jugular v.
External jugular v.
Angular v.
Retromandibular v.
Inferior labial v.
Facial v.
Submental v.
Common facial v.
Internal jugular v.
Anterior external jugular v.

7-2 VEINS OF THE FACE

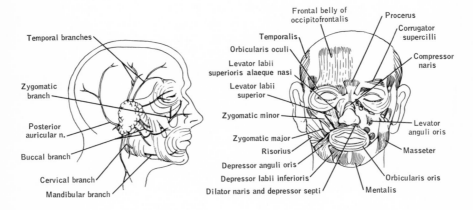

Temporal branches
Zygomatic branch
Posterior auricular n.
Buccal branch
Cervical branch
Mandibular branch

7-3 SUPERFICIAL BRANCHES OF FACIAL NERVE

Frontal belly of occipitofrontalis
Temporalis
Orbicularis oculi
Levator labii superioris alaeque nasi
Levator labii superior
Zygomatic minor
Zygomatic major
Risorius
Depressor anguli oris
Depressor labii inferioris
Dilator naris and depressor septi
Procerus
Corrugator supercilli
Compressor naris
Levator anguli oris
Masseter
Orbicularis oris
Mentalis

7-4 MUSCLES OF THE FACE

Plate 7

1. Arteries (Fig. 7-1)

These are principally the facial a. and its branches.

FACIAL A. This branch of the external carotid a. passes on to the face at the anterior inferior angle of the masseter muscle, ascends sinuously, and terminates near the medial angle of the eye. Its branches are divided into two groups, arising in the neck (p. 103) and on the face. The latter are shown in Table 5.

Other arteries that supply the face (see Table 6) are the transverse facial a., a branch of the superior temporal a., and the accompanying branches of the trigeminal n. (compare Tables 6 and 9).

2. Veins (Fig. 7-2)

The veins of the face form a network that is drained by the common facial v.; they communicate with the ophthalmic vv. (via the nasofrontal v.) and the pterygoid plexus (via the deep facial v.)

FACIAL V. The supratrochlear and supraorbital vv. unite to form the angular v., which continues as the facial v. at the lower margin of the orbit. It passes downward and backward and receives the tributaries that correspond to branches of the artery. It leaves the face at the anterior inferior angle of the masseter muscle, pierces the deep cervical fascia, and joins the anterior division of the retromandibular v. to form the common facial v.

3. Nerves

The nerves of the face are derived from three sources:

FACIAL N. (VII) (Fig. 7-3). This nerve leaves the cranial cavity via the internal acoustic meatus, facial canal, and stylomastoid foramen, where it gives off the posterior auricular n. and a branch to the posterior bellies of the digastric and the stylohyoid muscles. The facial n. curves, enters the posterior border of the parotid gland, and ramifies into its terminal motor branches (see Table 7).

FACIAL BRANCHES OF GREATER AURICULAR N. These branches innervate the skin over the lower part of the parotid gland and the masseter muscle.

BRANCHES OF TRIGEMINAL N. ON THE FACE. These branches arise from the three divisions of the trigeminal n. (see Table 9).

4. Muscles (Fig. 7-4)

The deep fascia is thin over most of the muscles but is thickened posteriorly to form the parotideomasseteric fascia and buccopharyngeal fascia. The muscles of facial expression are divided into the five groups shown in Table 8.

Table 8

Muscles	Origin	Insertion	Action
Scalp:			
Occipitofrontalis			
Frontal bellies.............	Epicranial aponeurosis	Skin of eyebrows	Raise eyebrows
Occipital bellies...........	Superior nuchal line	Epicranial aponeurosis	Retract scalp
Temporoparietalis...........	Superficial temporal fascia	Skin above ear	Retract scalp
Ear:			
Auricularis (superior, anterior, posterior)	Primarily epicranial aponeurosis	Root of auricle	Usually none
Eye:			
Orbicularis oculi			
Palpebral part.............	Medial palpebral ligament	Lateral palpebral raphe	Closes lids lightly
Orbital part...............	Medial orbital margin	Forms an ellipse	Closes lids forcibly
Lacrimal part.............	Orbital surface of lacrimal bone	Superior and inferior tarsi	Compresses lids to eyeball
Corrugator supercilii.........	Medial end of superciliary arch	Skin of eyebrows	Draws eyebrow downward and medially
Nose:			
Procerus...................	Nasal bone	Skin between eyebrows	Depresses medial end of eyebrow
Compressor naris............	Canine eminence	Dorsum of nose	Compresses nostril
Dilator naris..............	Maxilla above lateral incisor	Ala of nose	Widens nostril
Depressor septi.............	Subnasal fossa	Nasal septum	Narrows nostril
Mouth:			
Orbicularis oris.............	Muscles converging on mouth	Forms an ellipse	Closes lips
Buccinator................	Pterygomandibular ligament Alveolar process of maxilla and mandible	Orbicularis oris; upper and lower lips	Flattens cheeks
Risorius...................	Fascia over masseter muscle	Skin of angle of mouth	Helps widen mouth
Depressor anguli oris........	Oblique line of mandible	Skin of angle of mouth	Draws angle downward and laterally
Depressor labii inferioris.....	Front of body of mandible	Lower lip	Depresses lower lip
Levator labii superioris......	Above infraorbital foramen	Skin of angle of mouth	Elevates and everts upper lip
Levator labii superioris alaeque nasi	Frontal process of maxilla	Ala of nose	Everts upper lip and dilates nostril
Zygomaticus major..........	Zygomatic bone	Skin of angle of mouth	Draws angle upward and laterad
Zygomaticus minor..........	Orbicularis oculi	Upper lip	Elevates upper lip
Mentalis..................	Incisor fossa of mandible	Skin of chin	Draws up skin of chin
Caninus...................	Below infraorbital foramen	Skin of angle of mouth	Raises angle of mouth

All the muscles shown in Table 8 are supplied by the facial n. (VII). Note that the masseter muscle, although located on the face, is not included in the table as it is a muscle of mastication.

5. Lymphatics

The lymphatics of the face consist of the three groups shown in Table 10.

Table 9

Division	Nerve	Branch of:	Area innervated
V¹	Supraorbital	Frontal n.	Scalp
	Supratrochlear	Frontal n.	Forehead
	Palpebral branch of supratrochlear	Lacrimal n.	Lateral part of upper eyelid
	Infratrochlear	Nasociliary n.	Eyelid
	External nasal	Anterior ethmoidal n.	Lower half of nose
V²	Zygomaticotemporal	Zygomatic n.	Skin on bony part of cheek
	Zygomaticofacial	Zygomatic n.	Skin on bony part of cheek
	Infraorbital	Maxillary n.	Palpebral branch: eyelids
			Nasal branch: side of nose
			Labial branch: skin of upper lip
V³	Auriculotemporal	Mandibular n.	Auricle, meatus, tympanic membrane
	Buccal	Mandibular n.	Skin of cheek
	Mental	Inferior alveolar n.	Skin of lower lip

Table 10

Group name	Region drained	Draining nodes
Parotid........	Face above level of nose	Superior deep cervical
Submental.....	Lower lip and chin	Submandibular
Facial.........	Rest of face	Deep cervical

ORBITAL REGION

1. *Eyelids*   3. *Orbit and its contents*
2. *Lacrimal apparatus*   4. *Eyeball*

The eyes are the most valuable of the sense organs. They lie deep in the bony orbits enveloped by fat and protected also by the curtaining eyelids and tear-secreting lacrimal apparatus.

1. Eyelids (Fig. 8-1)

The eyelids (palpebrae) are the two movable folds which are attached to the orbit and which serve to protect the eye.

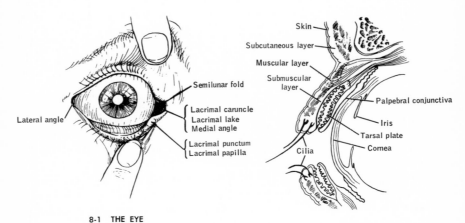

8-1 THE EYE

Semilunar fold

Lacrimal caruncle
Lacrimal lake
Medial angle

Lacrimal punctum
Lacrimal papilla

Lateral angle

Skin

Subcutaneous layer

Muscular layer

Submuscular layer

Palpebral conjunctiva

Iris

Tarsal plate

Cornea

Cilia

8-2 THE EYELID

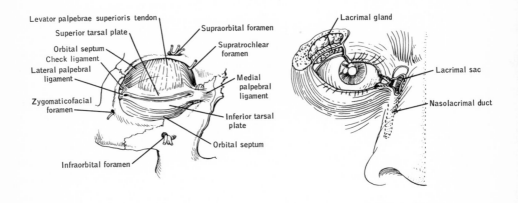

Levator palpebrae superioris tendon

Superior tarsal plate

Orbital septum
Check ligament
Lateral palpebral ligament

Zygomaticofacial foramen

Infraorbital foramen

Supraorbital foramen

Supratrochlear foramen

Medial palpebral ligament

Inferior tarsal plate

Orbital septum

8-3 TARSOFASCIAL LAYER

Lacrimal gland

Lacrimal sac

Nasolacrimal duct

8-4 LACRIMAL APPARATUS

Plate 8

Superficial Features

palpebral fissure. The elliptical space between the margins of the eyelids. Its lateral angle, or *canthus,* is more acute than its medial angle.

lacrimal lake. The triangular area at the medial angle.

semilunar fold. The fold of conjunctiva that forms the lateral margin of the lacrimal lake.

lacrimal caruncle. The red mass of modified skin lying in the lacrimal lake.

lacrimal papilla. The elevation at the medial end of the lids.

lacrimal punctum. The opening at the summit of the papilla.

Structure of Eyelid (Fig. 8-2)

Each eyelid consists of six layers.

SKIN. The skin of the eyelid is thin and hairless except for the eyelashes, or cilia. It is continuous with the conjunctiva.

SUBCUTANEOUS LAYER. This areolar tissue contains large sebaceous glands and modified sweat (ciliary) glands.

MUSCULAR LAYER. This is the palpebral part of the orbicularis oculi.

SUBMUSCULAR LAYER. This loose areolar tissue contains sensory nerves. It is continuous with the musculoaponeurotic layer of the scalp (p. 3) and is pierced by superficial fibers of the levator palpebrae superioris muscle.

TARSOFASCIAL LAYER (Fig. 8-3). This layer is made up of the tarsal plate and the orbital septum.

Tarsal Plate (Fig. 8-3). A compact mass of connective tissue supports each lid. Embedded in each plate are the sebaceous *tarsal glands,* the ducts of which open by minute foramens at the edge of the eyelids. The medial and lateral ends of the upper and lower tarsal plates are anchored to the margin of the orbit by the *medial* and *lateral palpebral ligaments.*

Orbital Septum. This consists of the *superior* and *inferior palpebral fascia.* These membranes are continuous with each other at the medial angle of the eye behind the lacrimal sac and at the lateral angle by means of the lateral palpebral ligament, which is fused with the fascia. This fascia is continuous with the periosteum of the orbit.

PALPEBRAL CONJUNCTIVA. Lining the inner surface of the eyelid, this conjunctiva is continuous with the bulbar conjunctiva at the superior and inferior fornices.

2. Lacrimal Apparatus (Fig. 8-4)

The lacrimal apparatus consists of the tear-secreting organ and its duct system.

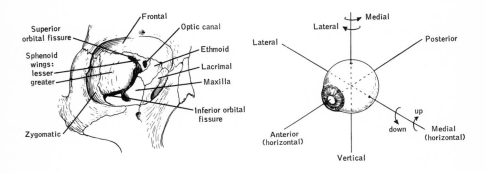

9-1 THE ORBIT

9-2 MOTION OF THE BULB

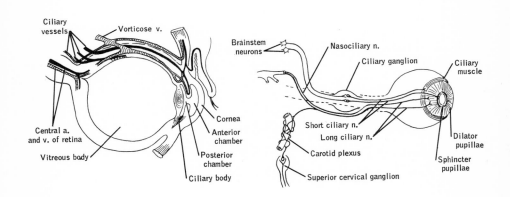

9-3 ARTERIES OF THE BULB

9-4 AUTONOMIC INNERVATION OF THE BULB

Plate 9

LACRIMAL GLAND. This serous gland is located in a depression in the supero-lateral angle of the orbit. The gland is divided into a larger, superior orbital portion and a smaller, inferior palpebral portion by the lateral border of the tendon of the levator palpebral superioris muscle. The gland is supplied by the lacrimal a., lacrimal n. (sensory), and parasympathetic fibers (secretory).

The lacrimal secretion flows down medially under pressure of the eyelids. Most of the secretion evaporates; the rest is drained off by the canaliculi. Excess fluid appears as tears.

LACRIMAL CANALICULI. Two slender ducts lie in the medial edge of the eyelids. They receive the secretion at the lacrimal puncta and drain into the lacrimal sac.

LACRIMAL SAC. Lying behind the medial palpebral ligament in the lacrimal fossa, this sac represents the dilated upper end of the nasolacrimal duct.

NASOLACRIMAL DUCT. This duct descends through the nasolacrimal canal and enters the nasal cavity. At this entrance a *lacrimal fold* often acts as a valve to prevent upward flow of nasal secretions.

3. Orbit and Its Contents (Fig. 9-1)

Each orbit is a four-sided pyramid lined by periosteum. Its boundaries are:
Apex: medial part of superior orbital fissure
Base: open and bounded by orbital margin
Roof: orbital plate of frontal bone and lesser wing of sphenoid bone
Floor: maxilla, zygomatic bone, and orbital process of palatine bone
Lateral wall: frontal process of zygomatic and greater wing of sphenoid bone
Medial wall: orbital plate of ethmoid, lacrimal, frontal process of maxilla; part of body of sphenoid bone

The orbit contains the eyeball, its related muscles, blood vessels, and nerves. These structures are embedded in a large amount of fat.

Ocular Muscles (Fig. 10-1)

There are seven ocular muscles. One elevates the eyelid; the others move the eyeball.

LEVATOR PALPEBRAE SUPERIORIS
Origin: Roof of orbit in front of optic canal.
Insertion:

Superficial layer: Pierces the orbital septum to become attached to the skin of the upper lid.

Middle layer: Joins the upper border of the superior tarsus.

Deep layer: Fuses with the sheath of the superior rectus muscle and inserts into the superior fornix of the conjunctiva.

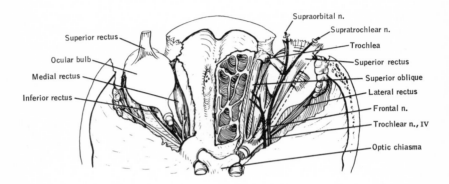

10-1 MUSCLES OF THE ORBIT

Superior rectus
Ocular bulb
Medial rectus
Inferior rectus

Supraorbital n.
Supratrochlear n.
Trochlea
Superior rectus
Superior oblique
Lateral rectus
Frontal n.
Trochlear n., IV
Optic chiasma

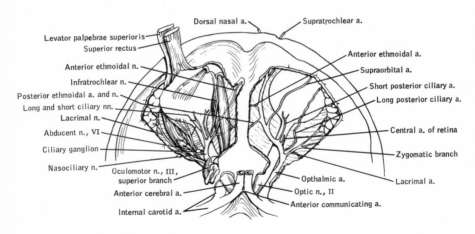

10-2 ARTERIES AND NERVES OF ORBIT

Dorsal nasal a.
Supratrochlear a.

Levator palpebrae superioris
Superior rectus
Anterior ethmoidal n.
Infratrochlear n.
Posterior ethmoidal a. and n.
Long and short ciliary nn.
Lacrimal n.
Abducent n., VI
Ciliary ganglion
Nasociliary n.
Oculomotor n., III, superior branch
Anterior cerebral a.
Internal carotid a.

Anterior ethmoidal a.
Supraorbital a.
Short posterior ciliary a.
Long posterior ciliary a.
Central a. of retina
Zygomatic branch
Opthalmic a.
Optic n., II
Anterior communicating a.
Lacrimal a.

Plate 10

30

Action: Raises eyelid.

Nerve supply: Oculomotor n. (III).

RECTI. Four muscles are named according to their location with reference to the eyeball: superior, inferior, medial, or lateral rectus.

Origin: Common fibrous ring surrounding the optic canal and medial part of the superior orbital fissure. The lateral rectus has two heads of origin, from the upper and lower parts of the lateral portion of the ring.

Insertion: On the eyeball by wide tendons, a little behind the sclerocorneal junction.

Nerve supply: Lateral rectus muscle by the abducent n. (VI); the others by the oculomotor n. (III).

SUPERIOR OBLIQUE

Origin: Orbital roof adjacent to the optic canal. The tendon passes through the trochlea, a fibrocartilaginous ring attached to the trochlear fossa, and passes under the superior rectus muscle.

Insertion: Sclera behind the equator of the eyeball.

Nerve supply: Trochlear n. (IV).

INFERIOR OBLIQUE. It passes below the eyeball and the inferior rectus muscle.

Origin: Floor of the orbit laterad to the lacrimal fossa.

Insertion: Sclera beneath the lateral rectus muscle.

Nerve supply: Oculomotor n. (III).

Action of intrinsic ocular muscles: Can be resolved relative to three primary axes at right angles to each other (see Table 11 and Fig. 9-2).

FASCIA. The fascia envelopes the muscles and is continuous with the periosteum posteriorly and with the bulbar fascia anteriorly. The *check ligaments* are fibrous expansions from the lateral rectus muscle to the zygomatic bone and from the medial rectus muscle to the lacrimal bone.

Arteries

OPHTHALMIC A. This arises from the intracranial part of the internal carotid a. It enters the orbit through the optic canal inferolaterad to the optic n. It passes over the optic n. to the medial side of the orbit and terminates at the medial angle of the eye in the supratrochlear and dorsal nasal aa. The branches of the ophthalmic a. are divided into two groups, orbital and ocular, as shown in Table 12 and Figs. 9-3 and 10-2.

Table 11

| Muscle | Motion relative to axis: | |
	Horizontal	Vertical
Superior rectus......	Up	Medial
Inferior rectus.......	Down	Medial
Medial rectus.......	.....	Medial
Lateral rectus.......	.....	Lateral
Superior oblique.....	Down	Lateral
Inferior oblique......	Up	Lateral

Veins

SUPERIOR OPHTHALMIC V. Formed by the union of the supraorbital and supratrochlear vv., it anastomoses with the facial v. It passes out of the orbit through the superior orbital fissure and empties into the cavernous sinus.

INFERIOR OPHTHALMIC V. Beginning on the floor of the orbit, it empties into the superior ophthalmic v.

Nerves (Fig. 10-2)

The nerves of the orbit may be grouped as follows:

Special sensory: optic n.

Motor: oculomotor, trochlear, abducent nn.

Sensory: branches of the ophthalmic n.

Autonomic:

   Sympathetic fibers from the carotid plexus

   Parasympathetic fibers traveling with the oculomotor n.

OPTIC N. (II). It originates from the ganglion cells of the retina, the axons of which pierce the sclera to become myelinated and enclosed by the cranial meninges. The nerve and its meninges pass backward and medially and leave the orbit through the optic canal.

OCULOMOTOR N. (III). Entering the orbit as two branches through the superior orbital fissure between the heads of the lateral rectus muscle.

Superior Branch. This branch passes across II and terminates by innervating the superior rectus and levator palpebrae superioris muscles.

Inferior Branch. Passing forward on the floor of the orbit, it provides branches to the medial and inferior recti muscles and terminates in the inferior oblique muscle. It provides preganglionic parasympathetic fibers to the ciliary ganglion, where they

Table 12

Branch	Course	Area supplied or branch joined
Orbital branches		
Lacrimal a..........	Along lateral rectus muscle to lateral angle of eye	Lacrimal gland
Zygomatic branches	Exits via zygomaticotemporal and zygomaticofacial foramens	Side of face
Recurrent branch...	Exits via superior orbital fissure	Joins branch of middle meningeal a.
Lateral palpebral branches........	Circle the eyelids	Join medial palpebral aa.
Supraorbital a.......	Exits via supraorbital foramen	Superficial and deep branches to scalp
Posterior ethmoidal a.	Exits via posterior ethmoidal canal	Posterior ethmoidal cells.
Anterior ethmoidal a.	Exits via anterior ethmoidal canal	Middle and anterior ethmoidal cells and frontal sinuses
Medial palpebral aa...	Circle the eyelids	Join lateral palpebral branches
Supratrochlear a......	Exits via supratrochlear notch	Terminal branch to forehead and scalp
Dorsal nasal a........	Exits above medial palpebral ligament	Lacrimal sac and dorsum of nose
Muscular branches....	....	Muscles around eyeball
Ocular branches		
Central a. of retina...	Pierces and runs in the optic n.	Retina
Short ciliary a........	Pierces sclera near the optic n.	Choroid and sclera
Long ciliary a........	Pierces sclera beyond the optic n.	Ciliary body and iris
Anterior ciliary a.....	Pierces sclera near cornea	Iris

synapse. The postganglionic fibers pass via the short ciliary n. to the eyeball, where they innervate the ciliary and sphincter pupillae muscles (Fig. 9-4).

TROCHLEAR N. (IV) (Fig. 10-1). Entering the orbit through the superior orbital fissure, it passes above the levator palpebrae superioris muscle and innervates the superior oblique muscle.

ABDUCENT N. (VI). This nerve also enters the orbit through the superior orbital fissure; it passes forward on the surface of the lateral rectus muscle and innervates that muscle.

The sensory nerves of the orbit are the branches of the ophthalmic n. (V^1); they arise near and pass through the superior orbital fissure individually.

LACRIMAL N. Following the upper border of the lateral rectus muscle, it innervates the lacrimal gland, conjunctiva, and upper eyelid. It innervates the gland via postganglionic secretory fibers originating in the pterygopalatine ganglion. These fibers are transmitted via V², the zygomatic n., and a communicating branch to the lacrimal n.

FRONTAL N. (Fig. 10-1). This is the largest branch of the ophthalmic n. It lies on the levator palpebrae superioris muscle beneath the roof of the orbit and divides into two branches:

Supraorbital N. Leaving the orbit through the supraorbital foramen, this nerve innervates the forehead and scalp.

Supratrochlear N. This nerve leaves the orbit to supply the upper eyelid and forehead.

NASOCILIARY N. Passing towards the medial wall of the orbit, it ramifies as follows:

Communicating Branch. This branch carries sensory fibers to the ciliary ganglion.

Long Ciliary Nn. These nerves pierce the sclera with its corresponding arteries. They carry sensory fibers from the internal carotid plexus as well as the sympathetic (motor) fibers, which innervate the dilator pupillae muscle.

Posterior Ethmoidal N. Passing into the posterior ethmoidal canal, it innervates the sphenoidal and posterior ethmoidal cells.

Infratrochlear N. This nerve passes forward on the medial wall of the orbit, beneath the trochlea, emerges above the medial angle of the eye, and innervates the eyelids, the upper part of the nose, and the lacrimal sac.

Anterior Ethmoidal N. The continuation of the nasociliary n., it passes through the anterior ethmoidal canal into the anterior cranial fossa. It courses on the cribriform plate to the side of the crista galli, where it passes through the nasal slit into the nose.

CILIARY GANGLION (Fig. 9-4). Located in the orbital fat on the lateral side of the optic n., the ciliary ganglion has branches known as the *short ciliary nn.* (see Table 13).

4. Eyeball (Fig. 11-1)

The eyeball is a sphere that bulges anteriorly. It is enveloped by the *bulbar fascia*, which separates the eyeball from the orbital fat. This thin membrane is pierced by the ciliary vessels and nerves and fuses with the sheath of the optic n. It is continuous with the muscular fascia at the points of insertion of the tendons of the ocular muscles.

The eye will be discussed in terms of its three principal layers (see Table 14) and its refractive media.

Table 13

Roots	Synapse	Branches
Sensory branch from nasociliary n.....	No	Sensory branch to eye
Preganglionic parasympathetic from III	Yes	Postganglionic parasympathetic to sphincter pupillae m.
Postganglionic sympathetic from internal carotid plexus	No	Postganglionic sympathetic to dilator pupillae and blood vessels of eye

Table 14

Layer	Structure
Outer: fibrous...........	Sclera and cornea
Middle: vascular........	Choroid, ciliary body, and iris
Inner: nervous..........	Retina

Outer (Fibrous) Coat

SCLERA. This opaque capsule covers most of the eyeball. It is continuous with the cornea at the *sclerocorneal junction*. The sclera is pierced by vessels and nerves and receives the insertions of the ocular muscles. The *lamina cribrosa* is the meshwork formed where the sclera is perforated by the optic n.

CORNEA. The cornea is the transparent anterior sixth of the eyeball; its surface is covered by bulbar conjunctiva. The cornea is avascular and richly supplied with sensory nerve endings.

Middle (Vascular) Coat

CHOROID. Extending from the optic n. as far forward as the ora serrata of the retina (see below), it consists of a pigmented meshwork of areolar tissue in which are embedded nerve plexuses, small arteries (derived from the short posterior ciliary aa.) and veins (derived from five vorticose vv.).

CILIARY BODY (Figs. 11-2, 11-3). This is the elevated area at the anterior end of the choroid. In three-dimensional perspective it is a wedge-shaped ring that serves to connect the choroid with the iris. It consists of:

ciliary processes (Fig. 11-2). About 70 choroid folds are arranged as the *ciliary ring* behind the periphery of the iris.

ciliary muscle. This muscle consists of two sets of fibers: *meridional fibers*, arising from the sclerocorneal junction and passing backward to attach to the ciliary processes and ciliary ring; *circular fibers* form a ring internal to the meridional fibers. The ciliary muscle acts to accommodate for near vision by drawing the choroid and

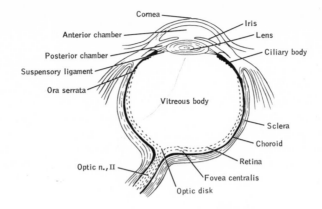

11-1 THE EYE IN CROSS SECTION

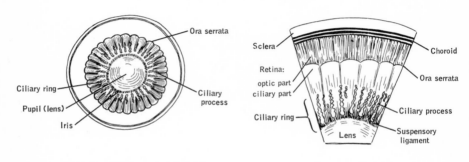

11-2 ANTERIOR BULB (seen from behind)

11-3 THE CILIARY BODY

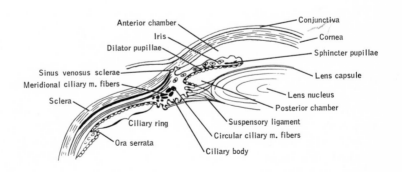

11-4 ANTERIOR BULB IN CROSS SECTION

Plate 11

36

ciliary processes forward. This relaxes the suspensory ligament of the lens, which becomes more convex. The muscle is innervated by the parasympathetic fibers of the short ciliary nn.

IRIS (Fig. 11-4). This contractile, circular curtain, located vertically behind the cornea and in front of the lens, is continuous with the ciliary body. The circular aperture formed by the free ends of the iris is the *pupil.* The iris divides the space in front of the lens into *anterior* and *posterior chambers.* Within the loose stroma of the iris are two involuntary muscles. The *sphincter pupillae* muscle comprises circular fibers located near the pupil. This muscle is innervated by parasympathetic fibers of the short ciliary nn. The *dilator pupillae* muscle comprises radiating fibers located near the posterior surface of the iris. These are innervated by sympathetic fibers of the long ciliary nn.

Inner (Nervous) Coat

RETINA (Fig. 11-1). This layer is divided into three parts.

Optic Part. Containing the nervous elements, it extends from the optic disk to the *ora serrata,* a jagged line. The *optic disk* is the region where the nerve fibers leave the eye.

Ciliary Part. This layer of columnar cells extends from the ora serrata over the ciliary body to the iris.

Iridial Part. Extending on the posterior surface of the iris to its pupillary margin, it is continuous with the ciliary part.

The *macula lutea* is a yellowish area located at the posterior pole of the eye. It contains a central depression, the *fovea centralis,* in which vision is most acute.

Refractive Media

The light entering the eye is bent, or refracted, at the interfaces of the various media through which it passes. These are:

CORNEA (see p. 35).

AQUEOUS HUMOR. Filling both the anterior and posterior chambers of the eye, this clear liquid is secreted by the ciliary processes and exits into the sinus *venosus sclerae* at the iridocorneal angle.

VITREOUS BODY. This transparent gel fills the eyeball behind the lens and ciliary body.

LENS. The lens lies behind the iris and pupil. It is biconvex, transparent, and composed of a structureless membrane, the capsule of the lens; a dense cortex; and a hard nucleus. The lens is held in place by its *suspensory ligament,* which consists of a series of fibers extending from the capsule of the lens to the ciliary body.

The neurovascular system of the eyeball is supplied by:

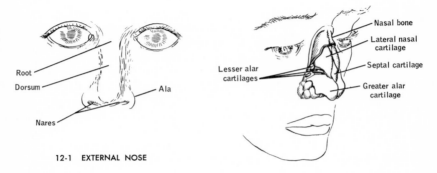

Root

Dorsum

Nares

Ala

12-1 EXTERNAL NOSE

Nasal bone

Lateral nasal cartilage

Septal cartilage

Lesser alar cartilages

Greater alar cartilage

12-2 NASAL CARTILAGES

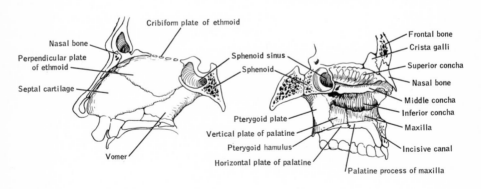

Cribiform plate of ethmoid

Nasal bone

Perpendicular plate of ethmoid

Septal cartilage

Vomer

12-3 MEDIAL NASAL WALL

Sphenoid sinus

Sphenoid

Pterygoid plate

Vertical plate of palatine

Pterygoid hamulus

Horizontal plate of palatine

Frontal bone

Crista galli

Superior concha

Nasal bone

Middle concha

Inferior concha

Maxilla

Incisive canal

Palatine process of maxilla

12-4 LATERAL NASAL WALL

Plate 12

arteries: Long and short posterior and anterior ciliary aa. supply the sclera, choroid, and iris.

veins: Vorticose vv. drain the choroid and merge to form five principal vessels which enter the posterior ciliary and ophthalmic vv.

nerves: Long and short ciliary nn. provide sensory fibers to the sclera and choroid as well as autonomic fibers to the muscles of the ciliary body and iris.

NASAL REGION

1. *External nose*	4. *Veins*
2. *Nasal cavity*	5. *Nerves*
3. *Arteries*	6. *Paranasal sinuses*

The nose is the peripheral organ of smell; it consists of the external nose and the nasal cavities. The most essential element, however, is the olfactory mucous membrane.

1. External Nose (Fig. 12-1)

The framework of the nose consists of skull bones (the nasal and frontal processes of the maxilla) and five significant cartilages (Fig. 12-2): (1) one *septal cartilage* contributes to the partition between the nasal cavities; (2) two *lateral nasal cartilages* are triangular in shape; (3) two *greater alar cartilages* have septal processes that extend backward; (4) three additional small plates, the *lesser alar cartilages,* are embedded in the fibrous membrane connecting the upper nasal cartilage to the frontal process.

2. Nasal Cavity

The nasal cavity has the following boundaries:

Naris: the anterior aperture, kept open by the greater alar cartilages

Choana: the oblong posterior aperture leading from the nose to the nasopharynx

Floor: the superior surface of the hard palate

Roof: the upper nasal cartilages and nasal bone, anteriorly; the anterior and inferior surfaces of the body of the sphenoid bone, posteriorly; and the cribriform plate between

Medial wall (Fig. 12-3): the perpendicular plate of ethmoid, above; the vomer, below; and the septal cartilage, between and in front.

Lateral wall (Fig. 12-4): a complex of bones: the frontal process of the maxilla and the lacrimal bone, anteriorly; the vertical plate of the palatine and medial pterygoid plate of the sphenoid, posteriorly; and the ethmoid, maxilla, and inferior nasal conchae between

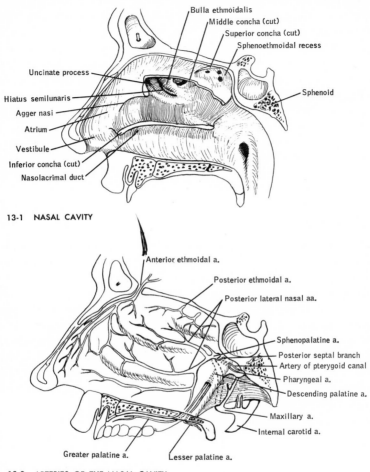

Bulla ethmoidalis

Middle concha (cut)

Superior concha (cut)

Sphenoethmoidal recess

Uncinate process

Hiatus semilunaris

Agger nasi

Atrium

Vestibule

Inferior concha (cut)

Nasolacrimal duct

Sphenoid

13-1 NASAL CAVITY

Anterior ethmoidal a.

Posterior ethmoidal a.

Posterior lateral nasal aa.

Sphenopalatine a.

Posterior septal branch

Artery of pterygoid canal

Pharyngeal a.

Descending palatine a.

Maxillary a.

Internal carotid a.

Greater palatine a.

Lesser palatine a.

13-2 ARTERIES OF THE NASAL CAVITY

Plate 13

40

There are three passageways, the *superior, middle,* and *inferior meatuses,* formed by the corresponding overhanging conchae along the wall of each nasal cavity. The inferior concha is an independent bone; the others are expansions of the ethmoid labyrinth. Beneath the middle concha is a curved fissure, the *hiatus semilunaris,* bounded above by an elevation, the *bulla ethmoidalis,* and below by the *uncinate process.* The space above the superior concha is known as the *sphenoethmoidal recess.* The communications between the nasal cavity and the paranasal sinuses are shown in Fig. 13-1. The *atrium* is the wide space in front of the middle meatus. It is limited posteriorly by a ridge, the *agger nasi.* The *vestibule* is the dilated part of the nasal cavity above the nostril. It is lined with skin bearing hair. The remainder of the nasal cavity is divided into an *olfactory area,* above, and a *respiratory area,* below. The nasal cavity is lined with a thick, vascular mucous membrane continuous with that of the pharynx and adjoining sinuses.

3. Arteries (Fig. 13-2)

OPHTHALMIC A. This artery provides the anterior and posterior ethmoidal aa., the nasal branches of which supply the upper and anterior parts of the lateral wall of the nasal cavity.

MAXILLARY A. This vessel is divided into three parts (p. 59). Branches of its third part include the sphenopalatine and greater palatine aa. The sphenopalatine a. passes through its foramen to enter the nasal cavity and provides *posterior lateral nasal branches* to supply the posterior lateral wall. The sphenopalatine a. continues beneath the body of the sphenoid bone to terminate as the *posterior septal branches* on the nasal septum. The greater palatine a. descends through the pterygopalatine canal, supplies the hard palate, and supplies the soft palate via its *lesser palatine branches.*

4. Veins

An extensive venous network is formed beneath the mucous membrane. The principal pathways are:

Ethmoidal vv. through the cribriform plate to the superior sagittal sinus
Nasal vv. to the ophthalmic vv. and cavernous sinus
Sphenopalatine v. through the foramen to the pterygoid plexus
Others to the facial v.

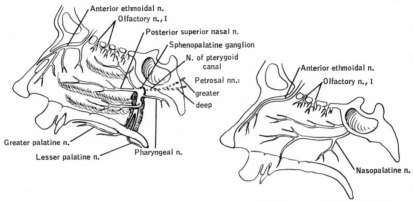

Anterior ethmoidal n.
Olfactory n., I
Posterior superior nasal n.
Sphenopalatine ganglion
N. of pterygoid canal
Petrosal nn.:
greater
deep
Greater palatine n.
Lesser palatine n.
Pharyngeal n.

Anterior ethmoidal n.
Olfactory n., I
Nasopalatine n.

14-1 NERVES OF THE NASAL CAVITY

14-2 NERVES OF THE NASAL SEPTUM

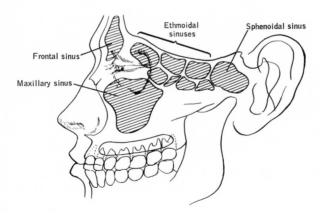

Ethmoidal sinuses
Sphenoidal sinus
Frontal sinus
Maxillary sinus

14-3 PARANASAL SINUSES

Plate 14

5. Nerves (Fig. 14-1)

Special Sensory

OLFACTORY N. (I). Innervating the olfactory area of the nasal cavity, this nerve consists of a number of fibers, ensheathed in meningeal linings, which pass from the olfactory bulb through the cribriform plate into the nose.

General Sensory

ANTERIOR ETHMOIDAL N. This terminal branch of the nasociliary n. enters the cranial cavity from the orbit via the ethmoidal foramen, passes on the cribriform plate and through the nasal slit, and enters the nasal cavity. It descends beneath the nasal bone, provides the *internal nasal branches,* and exits between the nasal bone and upper nasal cartilage as the *external nasal n.* to the skin of the lower half of the nose.

POSTERIOR SUPERIOR NASAL NN. Arising from the pterygopalatine ganglion, these branches pass through the sphenopalatine foramen to the upper and posterior parts of the lateral wall of the nasal cavity.

NASOPALATINE N. (Fig. 14-2). This nerve also arises from the pterygopalatine ganglion. It passes through its foramen, crosses the roof of the nasal cavity, descends along the nasal septum to the palate, and reaches the roof of the mouth through the median incisive foramen. It innervates the nasal cavity and hard palate.

GREATER PALATINE N. Descending from the pterygopalatine ganglion through the pterygopalatine canal, it emerges through the greater palatine foramen to the hard palate. The *posterior inferior nasal branches* arise in the canal and innervate the lower part of the nose.

LESSER PALATINE N. Arising in the canal from the greater palatine n., it emerges from the lesser palatine foramen and innervates the soft palate, uvula, and tonsil.

PHARYNGEAL N. Arising from the pterygopalatine ganglion, it passes back through the pharyngeal canal and innervates the roof and posterior wall of the nasopharynx.

6. Paranasal Sinuses (Fig. 14-3)

These air spaces originate as diverticula from the nasal cavity. They serve to decrease the weight of the skull bones and act as resonating chambers for the voice. They are generally absent at birth and enlarge rapidly at puberty.

FRONTAL SINUS. Paired and located between the vertical and orbital plates of the frontal bone, these sinuses are separated from each other by a bony septum.

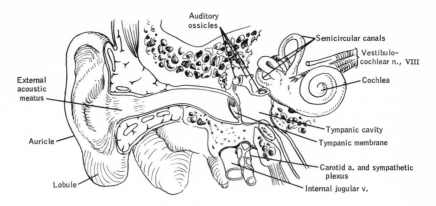

Auditory ossicles

Semicircular canals

Vestibulo-cochlear n., VIII

External acoustic meatus

Cochlea

Auricle

Tympanic cavity

Tympanic membrane

Lobule

Carotid a. and sympathetic plexus

Internal jugular v.

15-1 POSTERIOR PORTION OF EAR (anterior portion removed)

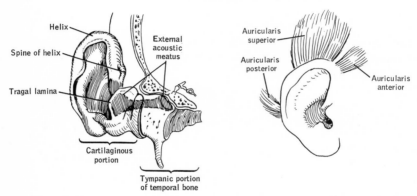

Helix

External acoustic meatus

Spine of helix

Tragal lamina

Cartilaginous portion

Tympanic portion of temporal bone

15-2 EXTERNAL ACOUSTIC MEATUS

Auricularis superior

Auricularis posterior

Auricularis anterior

15-3 EXTRINSIC MUSCLES OF THE EAR

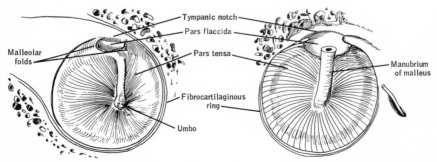

Tympanic notch

Pars flaccida

Malleolar folds

Pars tensa

Manubrium of malleus

Fibrocartilaginous ring

Umbo

15-4 EXTERNAL ASPECT OF TYMPANIC MEMBRANE

15-5 INTERNAL ASPECT OF TYMPANIC MEMBRANE

Plate 15

44

Each sinus opens by a narrow passage, the *infundibulum*, into the upper part of the hiatus semilunaris.

ETHMOIDAL SINUS. Small, numerous, thin-walled cells located between the upper parts of the nasal cavities and orbits, they are divided into three groups: (1) Anterior: opening into the middle of the hiatus semilunaris; (2) Middle: opening on the bulla ethmoidalis; (3) Posterior: opening into the superior meatus.

SPHENOIDAL SINUS. Paired, located in the body of the sphenoid bone, and separated from each other by a bony septum, each of these sinuses opens into the sphenoethmoidal recess of it own side.

MAXILLARY SINUS. The largest sinus, it is a four-sided hollow pyramid that opens from its upper medial wall into the posterior part of the hiatus semilunaris. It is also paired and lies just external to the lateral nasal wall.

EAR

The ear, known also as the *vestibulocochlear organ,* is concerned with equilibration and hearing. It is divided into three major parts (Fig. 15-1; Table 15):

1. External Ear

The external ear serves to conduct sound toward the middle ear.

AURICLE (PINNA). This is composed of and supported by a plate of fibrocartilage covered by tightly adherent skin. The chief landmarks of the lateral surface of the auricle, produced by the underlying cartilage, consist of depressions and elevations, shown on Fig. 15-2. Only the lobule is devoid of cartilage; it is composed of fat and fibrous tissue.

Extrinsic Muscles. Three, small, extrinsic muscles (shown in Table 16) connect the root of the auricle with the side of the head (Fig. 15-3).

The neurovascular system of the extrinsic muscles of the ear are supplied by:

arteries: Superficial temporal and posterior auricular aa.

nerves: Auriculotemporal, great auricular, and lesser occipital nn.

EXTERNAL ACOUSTIC MEATUS. Beginning at the bottom of the concha, it has a sinuous course and terminates at the tympanic membrane. The lateral third, which is continuous with the auricle, is mostly cartilaginous. The medial two-thirds is bony. Fibrous tissue connects the two parts. The firmly adherent skin of the meatus contains modified sweat glands which secrete wax and are known as *ceruminous glands.*

nerves: Auriculotemporal branch of the trigeminal n. and the auricular branch of the vagus n.

Table 15

1. External ear	2. Middle ear	3. Internal ear
Auricle	Tympanic cavity	Bony labyrinth
External acoustic meatus	Ossicles, joints, muscles	Membranous labyrinth
Tympanic membrane	Blood vessels and nerves	Internal acoustic meatus

Table 16

Auricularis	Origin	Insertion	Nerve supply
Superior...	Epicranial aponeurosis	Top of root of auricle	Temporal branch of VII
Anterior...	Epicranial aponeurosis	Front of root of auricle	Temporal branch of VII
Posterior..	Mastoid temporal bone	Back of root of auricle	Posterior auricular branch of VII

TYMPANIC MEMBRANE (Figs. 15-4, 15-5). This membrane has an oblique orientation in the meatus. Its thickened circumference, known as the *fibrocartilaginous ring,* is set in the tympanic sulcus of the tympanic part of the temporal bone. The ring is incomplete superiorly at the *tympanic notch.* Below the notch is the V-shaped *pars flaccida,* or lax part, of the membrane. It is bounded by the *anterior* and *posterior malleolar folds,* which meet where the lateral process of the malleus is attached to the membrane (see below). The remainder of the membrane is the rigid *pars tensa.* The handle of the malleus is attached to the membrane and draws it medially. The point of maximal concavity on its lateral surface is known as the *umbo.* The tympanic membrane is made up of fibrous tissue (absent from the pars flaccida) covered laterally with epidermis and medially with mucous membrane.

nerves. On the medial surface, innervation is supplied by the tympanic branch of IX; on the lateral surface, the nerves are the same as for the meatus.

2. Middle Ear

The middle ear is composed of the tympanic cavity and its contents.

Tympanic Cavity

This air space is lined with mucous membrane and located within the temporal bone between the tympanic membrane and the internal ear. It consists of the *tympanic cavity proper* and the *epitympanic recess*. The latter is that part of the cavity above the level of the tympanic membrane; it contains the greater part of the incus and the upper half of the malleus.

BOUNDARIES OF THE TYMPANIC CAVITY (Figs. 16-1, 16-2)

Roof. Consisting of a portion of the petrous temporal bone, the *tegmen tympani*, the roof is a bony barrier between the middle ear and the middle cranial fossa.

Floor. This consists of the *fundus tympani*, a thin sheet of bone that forms the floor of the jugular fossa, posteriorly; and the posterior wall of the ascending part of the carotid canal, anteriorly.

Anterior Wall. The roof and floor slope toward each other; the anterior wall is represented merely by the openings to two canals, one for the tensor tympani, and the other for part of the auditory tube. The former is located above the latter, and they are separated by a thin bony septum, the *cochleariform process*.

Posterior Wall. This wall consists (from above downwards) of:

aditus ad antrum. Connecting the epitympanic recess with a cavity, the *tympanic antrum*

fossa incudis. A small depression in the back part of the epitympanic recess that lodges the short process of the incus

pyramid. A hollow eminence below the aditus which contains the stapedius muscle

posterior canaliculus of the chorda tympani n. Located near the top of the tympanic membrane and providing entrance for this nerve into the tympanic cavity

Medial Wall. This lateral surface of the internal ear presents:

promontory. A rounded, hollow, prominence resulting from the first turn of the cochlea. Its surface contains fine grooves for the tympanic plexus.

fenestra vestibuli. An oval window above and behind the promontory. It leads into the vestibule of the inner ear and is closed by the base of the stapes.

prominence of the facial canal. Indicating the path of the facial n. as it courses backward in the upper part of the medial wall above the pyramid and fenestra vestibuli towards the lower border of the aditus. The canal continues behind the posterior wall and terminates at the stylomastoid foramen.

sinus tympani. The depression behind the promontory opposite the ampulla of the posterior semicircular canal.

fenestra cochleae. The round window at the bottom of the promontory. It is closed by the secondary tympanic membrane, which intervenes between the middle ear and the scala tympani of the cochlea.

Lateral Wall. This wall consists of the tympanic membrane and a small upper part formed by the squamous temporal bone.

AUDITORY TUBE. Serving to equalize the air pressure on both sides of the tympanic membrane, this tube extends from the anterior wall of the tympanic cavity

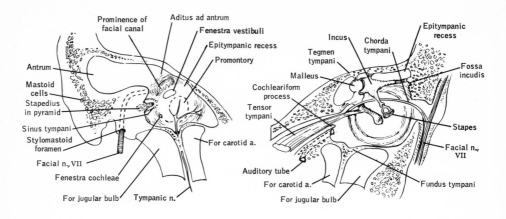

16-1   MEDIAL WALL OF MIDDLE EAR

16-2   LATERAL WALL OF MIDDLE EAR

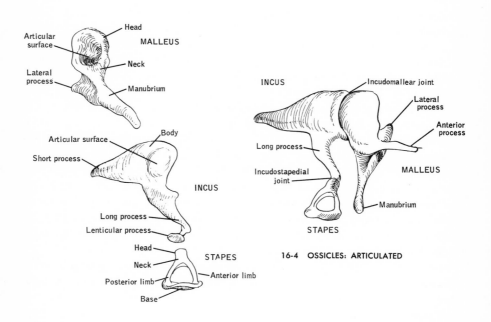

16-3   OSSICLES: DISARTICULATED

16-4   OSSICLES: ARTICULATED

Plate 16

downwards, forwards, and medially, terminating on the lateral wall of the naso-pharynx. The *bony part* is located within the temporal bone below the canal for the tensor tympani muscle. This part of the tube ends at the base of the skull behind and medial to the sphenoidal spine. The *cartilaginous part* is fixed to the inferior surface of the skull in a groove between the greater wing of the sphenoid bone and the petrous temporal bone. It is triangular in shape, with the apex attached to the medial end of the bony part. The free base is curved and forms the tubal elevation behind the pharyngeal opening of the tube. In section, the tube is C-shaped, with its lateral wall composed of fibrous tissue.

Contents of the Tympanic Cavity

MUSCLES (Fig. 16-2). Two muscles are associated with the middle ear.

Tensor Tympani

Origin: Cartilaginous part of the auditory tube and greater wing of the sphenoid bone.

Insertion: Near the root of the manubrium of the malleus.

Action: Draws the tympanic membrane medially.

Nerve supply: Branch of the mandibular n. (V^2).

Stapedius

Origin: Walls of the interior of the pyramid.

Insertion: Neck of the stapes.

Action: Tilts the anterior end of the base of the stapes laterally.

Nerve supply: Branch of the facial n. (VII).

TYMPANIC OSSICLES (Figs. 16-3, 16-4). These ossicles are enveloped by the mucous membrane of the middle ear.

Malleus. The malleus presents a round *head* and a constricted *neck;* both lie in the epitympanic recess. The *anterior process* projects from the neck and is connected by the anterior ligament to the petrotympanic fissure. The *manubrium* extends downwards, medialwards, and backwards from the neck. It is embedded in the upper half of the tympanic membrane. The *lateral process* projects towards the membrane from the root of the manubrium, and the malleolar folds are attached to it.

Incus. Shaped like a molar tooth, the incus has a *short process* projecting from the body towards the fossa incudis, where it is attached to the wall by the *posterior ligament*. The *long process* extends downwards, with its lower end bending medially, and terminates in a knob, the *lenticular process*.

Stapes. The stapes presents a small *head* and *neck*. From the neck, two diverging limbs extend to the oval *base*, which is attached to the fenestra vestibuli by the *annular ligament*.

JOINTS (Fig. 16-4)

Incudomallear Joint

Type: Saddle.

Articulating elements: Body of incus with head of malleus.

Incudostapedial Joint

Type: Ball and socket.

Articulating elements: Long process of incus with head of stapes.

Tympanostapedial Joint

Type: Syndesmosis.

Articulating elements: Membrane of fenestra vestibuli with base of the stapes.

The neurovascular system of the middle ear is supplied by:

arteries: Tympanic branch of the maxillary a. to the tympanic membrane, and the stylomastoid branch of the posterior auricular a. to the tympanic antrum.

veins: The veins parallel the arteries and terminate in the superior petrosal sinus and pterygoid plexus.

nerves: Tympanic branch of the glossopharyngeal n. (IX) and the superior and inferior caroticotympanic nn. (from carotid plexus). The former ascends through the bone between the fossa and canal to enter the tympanic cavity, where it ramifies on the medial wall to contribute to the formation of the tympanic plexus. The caroticotympanic nn. enter the middle ear through the wall of the carotid canal and ramify, together with the tympanic branch of the IX, as the *tympanic plexus.* The chorda tympani merely passes through the middle ear, crossing from the posterior wall, over the upper part of the manubrium, to the anterior wall.

3. Internal Ear

The internal ear is located within the petrous temporal bone between the medial wall of the middle ear and the bottom of the internal acoustic meatus. It contains the essential organs of hearing and equilibrium.

Bony Labyrinth (Figs. 17-1, 17-2)

The bony labyrinth encloses the sacs and ducts that constitute the membranous labyrinth. It consists of the vestibule, the semicircular canals, and the cochlea.

VESTIBULE. This oval cavity has the following boundaries:

Medial boundary: fundus of the internal acoustic meatus

Lateral boundary: fenestra vestibuli

Anterior boundary: communicates with the cochlea

Posterior boundary: communicates with the semicircular canals

A narrow canal, the *vestibular aqueduct*, extends from the posteroinferior surface of the vestibule to the posterior surface of the petrous temporal bone.

SEMICIRCULAR CANALS. Located above and behind the vestibule, each of these canals approximates a circle; they terminate as the enlarged osseous ampullae. There are three canals:

Anterior Canal. Arching laterally in a vertical plane, transverse to the axis of the petrous temporal bone, this canal produces the *arcuate eminence*. Its lateral end is ampullated; the medial end joins the posterior canal to form the *crus commune*.

Posterior Canal. Lying vertically, it arches parallel to the long axis of the petrous temporal bone. Its lower end is ampullated and has a separate opening into the vestibule. Its upper end forms the crus commune.

Lateral Canal. Arching laterally in a horizontal plane, this canal has an ampullated lateral end; both ends have separate openings into the vestibule.

COCHLEA (Figs. 17-3, 17-4). Looking like a snail shell placed on its side, the cochlea has its base at the fundus of the meatus and its apex directed anterolaterally. It is a tapering canal, coiled about two and one-half times around the *modiolus*, a horizontal central core. Projecting sideways from the modiolus, the *osseous spiral lamina* subdivides the cochlear canal into the *scala vestibuli*, above, and the *scala tympani*, below. The scalae communicate with each other near the apex of the modiolus by an aperture, the *helicotrema*, which is bounded by a bony process, the *hamulus* of the spiral lamina. Both the modiolus and the osseous spiral lamina contain numerous canals for passage of nerve fibers of the cochlear part of the statoacoustic n. (VIII). The *cochlear aqueduct* extends from the basal turn of the cochlea through the petrous temporal to open at the anterior margin of the jugular foramen.

Membranous Labyrinth (Fig. 17-5)

The membranous labyrinth is filled with a clear fluid, the *endolymph*. It lies in the bony labyrinth and is bathed by *perilymph*. The parts of the membranous labyrinth are:

UTRICLE. A sac in the upper part of the vestibule receives the ends of the semicircular canals.

SACCULE. A smaller sac is located in front of the utricle and below it. The *ductus reuniens* is the short tube connecting the saccule with the cochlear duct. The *endolymphatic duct* lies in the vestibular aqueduct, indirectly connecting the saccule and utricle by two branches. The other end of this duct ends in a dilatation, the *endolymphatic sac*, in contact with the dura mater at the termination of the aqueduct.

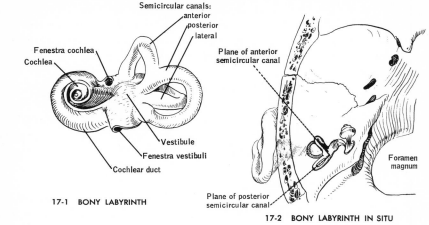

17-1 BONY LABYRINTH

Semicircular canals:
anterior
posterior
lateral

Fenestra cochlea
Cochlea

Plane of anterior
semicircular canal

Vestibule
Fenestra vestibuli
Cochlear duct

Plane of posterior
semicircular canal

Foramen
magnum

17-2 BONY LABYRINTH IN SITU

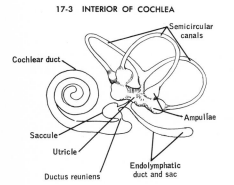

Helicotrema
Hamulus
Scala vestibuli
Scala tympani
Modiolus

17-3 INTERIOR OF COCHLEA

Osseous
spiral
lamina

Scala vestibuli
Modiolus
Scala tympani
Spiral foraminous tract
Internal acoustic
meatus (cut)

17-4 CROSS SECTION OF COCHLEA

Semicircular
canals
Cochlear duct
Ampullae
Saccule
Utricle
Ductus reuniens
Endolymphatic
duct and sac

17-5 MEMBRANOUS LABYRINTH

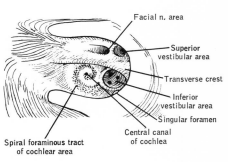

Facial n. area
Superior
vestibular area
Transverse crest
Inferior
vestibular area
Singular foramen
Central canal
of cochlea
Spiral foraminous tract
of cochlear area

17-6 INTERNAL ACOUSTIC MEATUS

52

Plate 17

SEMICIRCULAR DUCTS. These ducts open by ampullae at their ends into the utricle.

COCHLEAR DUCT. Triangular in section and located between the two scalae of the cochlea, this duct is bounded above by the vestibular membrane and below by the basilar membrane, which extends across the duct from the free edge of the osseous spiral lamina.

The neurovascular system of the membranous labyrinth is supplied by:

arteries: Labyrinthine a., a branch of the basilar a. that enters the inner ear through the internal acoustic meatus to divide and ramify with the cochlear and vestibular nn.

veins: Labyrinthine v., which originates from branches similar to those of the artery and drains into the inferior petrosal sinus. Veins also pass out through the vestibular and cochlear aqueducts.

nerves: Vestibulocochlear n. (VIII) consisting of two functionally distinct parts that meet in the internal acoustic meatus. The *cochlear n.* originates from the central processes of the spiral ganglions in the spiral bony lamina. The peripheral fibers extend to the organ of Corti. The ganglion of the *vestibular n.* is located in the internal acoustic meatus. Its peripheral fibers, which enter the inner ear, break up into three branches (see Table 17).

Table 17

Area	Contents
Superior vestibular......	Branch of vestibular n. (to utricle and ampullae of anterior and lateral semicircular ducts)
Facial nerve............	Facial n. (VII)
Inferior vestibular.......	Branch of vestibular n. (to saccule)
Cochlear...............	Cochlear n. (via spiral foraminosus tract and central canal)
Singular foramen........	Branch of vestibular n. (to ampulla of posterior semicircular duct)

Internal Acoustic Meatus (Fig. 17-6)

The internal acoustic meatus is the opening that leads into a short canal in the petrous temporal bone located medial to the internal ear. The lateral end of the canal is closed by a perforated, bony, vertical plate. The *transverse crest* extends across this plate. The various areas of the plate are:

PAROTID REGION

1. *Fascia* 2. *Parotid gland*
3. *Related structures*

The parotid region consists of the parotid gland and its bed (Fig. 18-1).

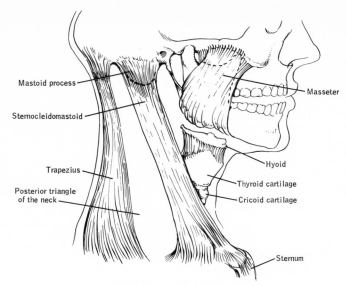

18-1 LATERAL ASPECT OF THE NECK

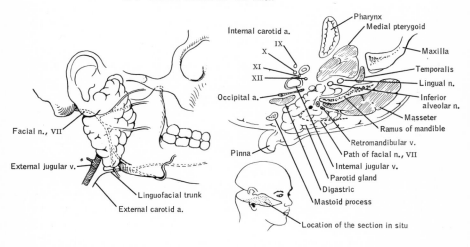

18-2 LATERAL ASPECT OF PAROTID GLAND

18-3 HORIZONTAL SECTION THROUGH PAROTID GLAND

Plate 18

54

1. Fascia

SUPERFICIAL. This fascia covers the gland. It is a part of the fascia of the face and contains lymph glands and the facial branches of the great auricular n.

DEEP. This fascia is the backward continuation of the parotideomasseteric fascia. It covers the lateral surface of the masseter muscle and splits to enclose the parotid gland in a fibrous capsule. It is attached to the zygoma above, continuous with the muscular layer of deep cervical fascia below, and continuous with the investing layer of deep cervical fascia posteriorly.

2. Parotid Gland (Fig. 18-2)

The parotid gland is the largest of the three paired salivary glands. Perforating septums from the fibrous capsule divide the gland into lobules. Its four borders and two surfaces are related to the following structures.

Superior border: next to the external acoustic meatus and the mandibular joint

Inferior border: between the sternocleidomastoid muscle and the angle of the mandible

Anterior border: grooved by the masseter muscle and the ramus of the mandible

Posterior border: next to the mastoid process and the sternocleidomastoid muscle

Lateral surface: covered by the parotideomasseteric fascia

Medial surface: in contact with the digastric and styloid muscles; carotid sheath, IX, X, XI, and XII

A more or less detached portion located above the duct adjacent to the anterior border is known as the *accessory parotid gland.*

The neurovascular system of the parotid gland is supplied by:

arteries and *veins:* From neighboring vessels.

nerves: The sensory nerves are the great auricular and auriculotemporal nn. The secretory nerves are preganglionic parasympathetic fibers in the IX that course via the tympanic n. and lesser petrosal n. to the otic ganglion. Postganglionic fibers via the auriculotemporal n. pass to the parotid gland (see Fig. 18-2). The vasomotor nerves are derived from the sympathetic plexus which envelops the external carotid. These nerves are largely vasoconstrictor in function.

Parotid Duct. This is formed by union of the ducts of the lobules. It appears at the anterior border of the gland, passes forward, and bends around the anterior border of the masseter muscle. It pierces the buccal fat pad, buccopharyngeal fascia, buccinator muscle, and mucous membrane, opening into the vestibule of the mouth opposite the second upper molar tooth.

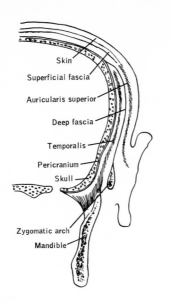

Skin

Superficial fascia

Auricularis superior

Deep fascia

Temporalis

Pericranium

Skull

Zygomatic arch

Mandible

19-1 LAYERS OF THE TEMPORAL REGION

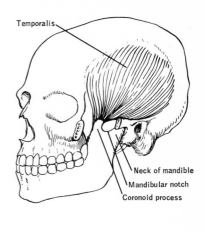

Temporalis

Neck of mandible

Mandibular notch

Coronoid process

19-2 TEMPORALIS MUSCLE

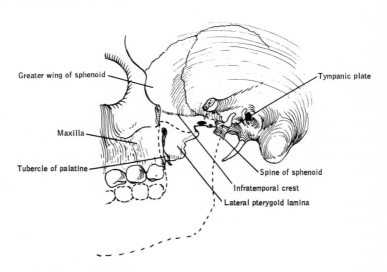

Greater wing of sphenoid

Maxilla

Tubercle of palatine

Tympanic plate

Spine of sphenoid

Infratemporal crest

Lateral pterygoid lamina

19-3 BOUNDARIES OF THE INFRATEMPORAL REGION

Plate 19

3. Related Structures (Fig. 18-3)

Three structures (an artery, a vein, and a nerve) lie partly embedded within the parotid gland. From superficial to deep, they are:

EXTERNAL CAROTID A. Ascending into the parotid gland, it divides into its two terminal branches: the superficial temporal a. provides the transverse facial a. and leaves the gland at its superior border; the maxillary a. passes forward to course behind the neck of the mandible.

RETROMANDIBULAR V. Formed within the gland by the union of the superficial temporal and maxillary vv., it descends and splits into anterior and posterior divisions, which terminate in the common facial and external jugular vv., respectively.

FACIAL N. (VII). Emerging from the stylomastoid foramen, it curves to enter the posterior border of the gland and ramifies into its facial branches (see Table 7).

MASSETER MUSCLE. This muscle is covered by the parotideomasseteric fascia.

Origin: Lower border and medial surface of the zygomatic arch.

Insertion: Lateral surface of the ramus and coronoid process of the mandible.

Action: Muscle of mastication; raises the mandible.

Nerve supply: Masseteric branch of V^3.

TEMPORAL REGION

The temporal region consists of the temporal fossa (p. 11) and its contents. The fossa is bounded by the temporal lines, above; the zygomatic arch, laterally; and the infratemporal crest, below.

Contents (Fig. 19-1)

SKIN. It moves separately from the underlying fascia.

SUPERFICIAL FASCIA. It contains fat, the extrinsic muscle of the ear, and the superficial blood vessels and nerves of this region.

DEEP FASCIA. This strong, dense temporal fascia covers the muscle and is attached to the margins of the temporal fossa.

TEMPORALIS MUSCLE (Fig. 19-2). This muscle is fan-shaped.

Origin: Floor of the temporal fossa; temporal fascia.

Insertion: Coronoid process and anterior border of the ramus of the mandible.

Action: Raises the mandible.

Nerve supply: Deep temporal branches of mandibular n. (V^3).

PERICRANIUM. This periosteum lines the lateral surface of the temporal bone.

INFRATEMPORAL FOSSA

1. *Boundaries*   3. *Arteries*
2. *Muscles*   4. *Veins*
                5. *Nerves*

The infratemporal fossa is the irregularly shaped space behind the maxilla, below and deep to the zygomatic arch.

1. Boundaries (Fig. 19-3)

The infratemporal fossa presents the following six boundaries:

Lateral boundary: ramus and coronoid process of the mandible

Medial boundary: tubercle of the palatine bone, lateral pterygoid lamina, sphenoidal spine

Anterior boundary: posterior surface of the maxilla

Posterior boundary: tympanic plate

Superior boundary: infratemporal surface of the greater wing of the sphenoid bone below the infratemporal crest

Inferior boundary: alveolar border of the maxilla

2. Muscles (Fig. 20-1)

LATERAL PTERYGOID. This muscle has two heads of origin.

Origin:

　Upper head: infratemporal surface and crest.

　Lower head: lateral surface of lateral pterygoid plate.

Insertion: Front of neck of the mandible and capsule of the mandibular joint.

Action: Protrudes and depresses the mandible.

Nerve supply: Branch of mandibular n. (V³).

MEDIAL PTERYGOID. This muscle also has two heads of origin.

Origin:

　Superficial head: small; maxillary tuberosity.

　Deep head: large; medial surface of lateral pterygoid plate.

Insertion: Medial surface of the angle and ramus of the mandible behind the mylo-hyoid groove.

Action: Elevates mandible.

Nerve supply: Branch of mandibular n. (V³).

3. Arteries

MAXILLARY A. (Fig. 20-2). One of the two terminal branches of the external carotid artery, it originates in the parotid gland behind the neck of the mandible,

Table 18

Part	Relation to lateral pterygoid m.	Branches
First: Mandibular........	Before	Run with branches of V^3 through foramens
Second: Pterygoid.........	Behind	Muscular
Third: Pterygopalatine.....	In front of	Run with branches of V^3 through foramens

passes forward and along the lower border of the lateral pterygoid muscle, and terminates in the pterygopalatine fossa. The lateral pterygoid muscle serves to demarcate its three parts (Table 18).

The branches of each of the parts of the maxillary a. are shown in Table 19.

4. Veins

PTERYGOID PLEXUS. This venous network is located around the lateral pterygoid muscle and is formed by vessels corresponding to the branches of the maxillary a. The plexus ends as a short stem, the maxillary v., at the lower border of the lateral pterygoid muscle which terminates in the posterior facial v.

5. Nerves

Trigeminal N. (V)

The largest cranial nerve provides the principal cutaneous innervation to the scalp and face, motor innervation of the muscles of mastication, and sensory innervation to the mucous membrane of the facial cavities. The sensory and motor roots from the pons meet at the trigeminal (semilunar) ganglion, which lies in the trigeminal impression, near the apex of the petrous temporal bone. The three major divisions extend from the ganglion (Table 20).

MANDIBULAR N. (V^3) (Fig. 20-3). This nerve arises from the trigeminal ganglion and emerges from the cranial cavity into the infratemporal fossa via the foramen ovale. It divides behind the lateral pterygoid muscle into two unequal divisions after giving off the meningeal and the medial pterygoid branches.

Table 19

Part	Branch	Course	Part supplied
First.....	Deep auricular a.	Between cartilage and bone of meatus	External auditory meatus (External) tympanic membrane
	Anterior tympanic a.	Through petrotympanic fissure	(Internal) tympanic membrane
	Middle meningeal a.	Enters cranium via foramen spinosum	Anterior and posterior branches to dura
	Accessory meningeal a.	Enters cranium via foramen ovale	Trigeminal ganglion
	Inferior alveolar a.	Via mandibular canal	
	Lingual branch	With corresponding nerve	Mucous membrane of tongue
	Mylohyoid branch	In mylohyoid groove	Mylohyoid m.
	Dental branches	With corresponding nn.	Molar and bicuspid teeth
	Mental branch	Via mandibular canal to mental foramen	Chin
	Incisor branch	Termination of inferior alveolar	Canine and incisor teeth
Second...	Masseteric a.	Via mandibular notch	Masseter m.
	Anterior and posterior deep temporal aa.	Ascend over infratemporal crest	Temporalis m.
	Pterygoid branches	Runs to pterygoid muscles	Medial and lateral pterygoid mm.
	Buccal a.	Descends	Buccinator m.
Third....	Posterior superior alveolar	Descends on tuberosity of maxilla	Upper molar and biscuspid teeth
	Infraorbital a.	Via infraorbital fissure, groove, canal, and foramen	Face
	Orbital branch	Ramifies	Rectus and obliquus inferior mm. and lacrimal gland
	Anterior superior alveolar branch	Via alveolar canals	Upper canine and incisor teeth
	Descending palatine a.	Via pterygopalatine canal	
	Greater palatine a.	Continuation of stem a.	Roof of hard plate
	Lesser palatine branch	Via lesser palatine foramen	Soft palate and palatine tonsil
	A. of pterygoid canal	Via pterygoid canal	Upper part of pharynx
	Pharyngeal a.	Via pharyngeal canal	Roof of pharynx
	Sphenopalatine a.	Via sphenopalatine foramen	Superior meatus of nose
	Posterior lateral nasal branches	Ramifies	Lateral nasal wall
	Posterior septal branches	Ramifies	Upper part of septum

Table 20

Divisions	Fibers	Pathway
Ophthalmic n. (V¹)...	Sensory	Enters orbit via super-orbital fissure
Maxillary n. (V²).....	Sensory	Enters pterygopalatine fossa via foramen rotundum
Mandibular n. (V³)...	Sensory and motor	Enters infratemporal fossa via foramen ovale

Meningeal Branch. A recurrent branch containing sensory fibers passes back through the foramen spinosum to supply the dura mater.

Medial Pterygoid N. This passes through the otic ganglion to innervate the muscle. It also provides the *nerve to the tensor veli palatini* muscle and the *nerve to the tensor tympani* muscle.

Anterior Division

The anterior division is small and has one sensory branch and three motor branches.

MASSETERIC N. Ascending through the mandibular notch, it innervates the muscle from its deep surface and provides a branch to the temporomandibular joint.

DEEP TEMPORAL NN. Two or three nerves ascend out of the infratemporal fossa over its crest and enter the deep surface of the temporalis muscle.

LATERAL PTERYGOID N. Enters the muscle on its deep surface.

BUCCAL N. This nerve passes between the heads of the lateral pterygoid muscle toward the buccinator muscle, where it ramifies to supply the sensory innervation of the skin of the cheek and mucous membrane of the mouth.

Posterior Division

The posterior division has three sensory branches and one motor branch.

AURICULOTEMPORAL N. It arises by two roots which encircle the middle meningeal a. and form a single trunk, passing backwards deep to the lateral pterygoid muscle beneath the parotid gland. It crosses the posterior root of the zygoma and enters the temporal region with the superficial temporal a. The auriculotemporal n. communicates with:

Otic Ganglion. Postganglionic parasympathetic fibers are contributed to the parotid gland.

Facial N. This receives sensory fibers from the auriculotemporal n. in the substance of the parotid.

The auriculotemporal n. provides the branches listed in Table 21.

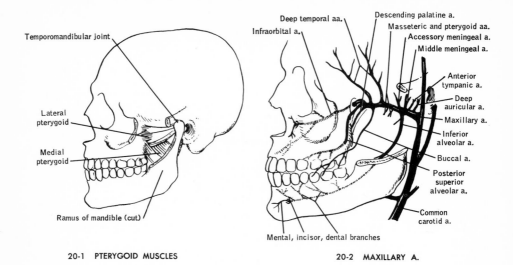

20-1 PTERYGOID MUSCLES

Temporomandibular joint

Lateral pterygoid

Medial pterygoid

Ramus of mandible (cut)

20-2 MAXILLARY A.

Deep temporal aa.

Infraorbital a.

Descending palatine a.

Masseteric and pterygoid aa.

Accessory meningeal a.

Middle meningeal a.

Anterior tympanic a.

Deep auricular a.

Maxillary a.

Inferior alveolar a.

Buccal a.

Posterior superior alveolar a.

Common carotid a.

Mental, incisor, dental branches

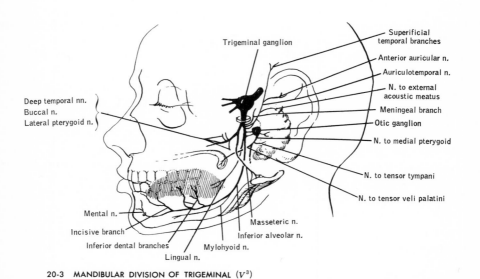

20-3 MANDIBULAR DIVISION OF TRIGEMINAL (V^3)

Trigeminal ganglion

Superificial temporal branches

Anterior auricular n.

Auriculotemporal n.

N. to external acoustic meatus

Meningeal branch

Otic ganglion

N. to medial pterygoid

N. to tensor tympani

N. to tensor veli palatini

Deep temporal nn.

Buccal n.

Lateral pterygoid n.

Mental n.

Incisive branch

Inferior dental branches

Lingual n.

Mylohyoid n.

Inferior alveolar n.

Masseteric n.

Plate 20

Table 21

Branch	Area innervated
Anterior auricular...............	Skin on upper part of auricle
To external acoustic meatus........	Skin on upper part of meatus and tympanic membrane
Articular......................	Posterior part of temporomandibular joint
Superficial temporal..............	Skin of temporal region

Table 22

Branch	Area innervated
Lingual............	Mucous membrane of anterior two-thirds of tongue, adjacent mouth, and gums
Special sensory.....	To taste buds of anterior two-thirds of tongue

LINGUAL N. Descending behind the lateral pterygoid muscle, it emerges at its lower border and receives the chorda tympani (see below). It passes between the medial pterygoid muscle and the ramus of the mandible, over the superior constrictor and styloglossus muscles, to the submandibular region. It continues between the hyoglossus muscle and the submandibular gland, over the duct, and on the undersurface, to the tip of the tongue. This nerve carries both sensory and secretory fibers and communicates with:

Chorda Tympani. This branch of the facial n. carries preganglionic parasympathetic fibers to the submandibular ganglion. These fibers leave the lingual n. to synapse in the ganglion and then continue to the submandibular and sublingual glands.

Hypoglossal N. (XII). This nerve forms a plexus at the anterior border of the hyoglossus muscle.

The branches of distribution of the lingual n. are shown in Table 22.

INFERIOR ALVEOLAR N. Descending behind and emerging at the lower border of the lateral pterygoid muscle, it continues between the sphenomandibular ligament and ramus of the mandible to pass through the mandibular foramen into the canal. Its branches are shown in Table 23.

OTIC GANGLION (Fig. 21-1). This is located just below the foramen ovale. Its roots and branches are shown in Table 24.

PTERYGOPALATINE FOSSA

1. Boundaries   *2. Contents*

The pterygopalatine fossa is a triangular interval.

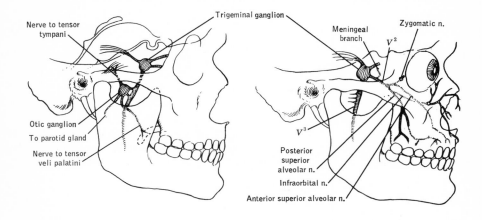

Nerve to tensor
tympani

Trigeminal ganglion

Meningeal
branch

Zygomatic n.

V^2

Otic ganglion

To parotid gland

Nerve to tensor
veli palatini

V^3

Posterior
superior
alveolar n.

Infraorbital n.

Anterior superior alveolar n.

21-1   OTIC GANGLION

21-2   MAXILLARY DIVISION OF TRIGEMINAL NERVE (V^2)

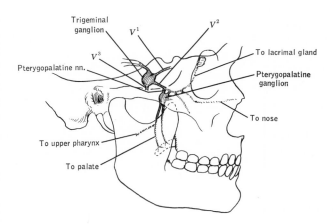

Trigeminal
ganglion

V^1

V^2

V^3

Pterygopalatine nn.

To lacrimal gland

Pterygopalatine
ganglion

To nose

To upper pharynx

To palate

21-3   PTERYGOPALATINE GANGLION

Plate 21

64

1. Boundaries (Fig. 19-3)

The pterygopalatine fossa presents the following five boundaries:

Anterior boundary: posterior surface of maxilla

Posterior boundary: lateral pterygoid plate and greater wing of sphenoid bone

Medial boundary: perpendicular plate of palatine bone

Lateral boundary: open (pterygomaxillary fissure)

Roof: body of sphenoid bone and orbital surface of palatine bone

2. Contents

MAXILLARY N. (V^2) (Fig. 21-2). This nerve is entirely sensory and arises from the middle stem of the trigeminal n. It leaves the middle cranial fossa through the foramen rotundum and enters the pterygopalatine fossa, from which its branches radiate. Its branches are:

Meningeal Branch. This small branch arises in the cranial cavity to supply the dura mater near the trigeminal ganglion.

Pterygopalatine Nn. Two communicating branches arise in the pterygopalatine fossa and descend to the pterygopalatine ganglion.

Posterior Superior Alveolar Branches. Arising just before the nerve enters the infraorbital groove, these branches enter the canals on the back of the maxilla to innervate the maxillary sinus, gums, and molar and premolar teeth.

Zygomatic N. Entering the orbit through the inferior orbital fissure, it divides into its zygomaticotemporal and zygomaticofacial nn.

Infraorbital N. The continuation of V^2 enters the orbit through the infraorbital fissure, passes along the infraorbital groove and canal, emerges on the face, and ramifies as palpebral, nasal, and labial branches. In the canal it provides the *middle superior alveolar n.*, which descends in the lateral wall of the sinus to innervate the upper bicuspid teeth; and the *anterior superior alveolar n.*, which descends in the anterior wall of the sinus to innervate the upper canine and incisor teeth.

PTERYGOPALATINE GANGLION (Fig. 21-3). This is located below V^2 in the upper part of the pterygopalatine fossa opposite the sphenopalatine foramen. Its roots and branches are shown in Table 25.

MANDIBLE AND TEMPOROMANDIBULAR JOINT

1. Mandible

The lower jaw, or mandible, is massively built to carry the lower teeth and the muscles of mastication and to provide attachment for the muscles of the tongue and

Table 23

Branch	Site of origin	Area innervated
Mylohyoid n................	Above mandibular foramen	Mylohyoid m. and anterior belly of digastric m.
Inferior dental n.............	In mandibular canal	Molar and premolar teeth
Incisive branch.............	In mandibular canal (terminal branch)	Canine and incisor teeth
Mental branch.............	Continuation of stem n.	Skin of chin, lower lip

Table 24

Roots	Synapse	Branches
Nerve to medial pterygoid (motor branch)	No	Tensor tympani and tensor veli palatini mm.
Preganglionic parasympathetic from IX	Yes	Postganglionic parasympathetic to parotid gland
Postganglionic sympathetic from plexus on medial meningeal a.	No	Postganglionic sympathetic to blood vessels of parotid gland

Table 25

Roots	Synapse	Branches
Ganglionic branch from V^2	No	Sensory fibers from branches of ganglion to nose (p. 43)
Preganglionic parasympathetic from VII	Yes	Postganglionic parasympathetic to lacrimal gland
Postganglionic sympathetic from internal carotid plexus	No	Postganglionic sympathetic to nose, palate, and pharynx

of the floor of the mouth. The mandible articulates with the skull at the temporomandibular joint. It consists of a body and a pair of rami; the body meets the ramus at the angle of the mandible. The body of the mandible is formed by fusion of the halves at the *symphysis menti.*

Lateral Surface of Body (Fig. 22-1)

mental protuberance. The triangular elevation which projects forward at the lower end of the symphysis.

mental tubercles. The projection at the basal angles of the protuberance.

oblique line. Extending from the mental tubercle to the anterior border of the ramus.

mental foramen. Above the oblique line and opposite the second premolar tooth.

incisive fossa. Below the alveolar processes of the incisor teeth.

Medial Surface of Body (Fig. 22-2)

genial tubercle. Projecting from behind the middle of the symphysis.

mylohyoid line. Extending obliquely backwards and upwards from below the tubercles.

sublingual fossa. Above the mylohyoid line.

submandibular fossa. Below the mylohyoid line.

digastric fossa. At the side of the symphysis menti.

Medial Surface of Ramus

mandibular foramen. The opening into the mandibular canal; located in the center of the ramus.

lingula. A spur projecting upward and forming the anterior boundary of the mandibular foramen.

mylohyoid groove. Extending from the mandibular foramen on the inner surface of the ramus.

Coronoid Process. This is the anterior, triangular, upward projection of the ramus. It is the site of insertion of the temporalis muscle.

Condyloid Process. The posterior projection is divided into a *head* and a *neck.* The head articulates with the disk of the temporomandibular joint. The neck is the constricted lower portion to which the joint capsule is attached.

mandibular notch. The depression between the processes.

2. Temporomandibular Joint (Fig. 22-3)

Type: The temporomandibular joint is of the ginglymoarthrodial type; the upper part glides, the lower part is a hinge.

Articulating elements: These consist of the mandibular fossa and the eminence of the temporal bone with the head of the mandible.

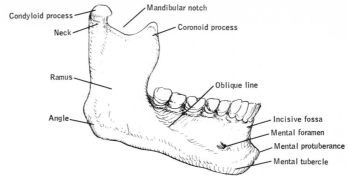

22-1 LATERAL SURFACE OF MANDIBLE

Condyloid process — Mandibular notch
Neck — Coronoid process
Ramus — Oblique line
Angle — Incisive fossa
Mental foramen
Mental protuberance
Mental tubercle

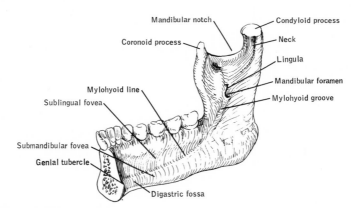

22-2 MEDIAL SURFACE OF MANDIBLE

Mandibular notch — Condyloid process
Coronoid process — Neck
Lingula
Mandibular foramen
Mylohyoid line
Mylohyoid groove
Sublingual fovea
Submandibular fovea
Genial tubercle
Digastric fossa

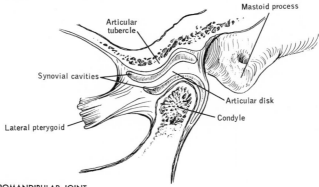

22-3 TEMPOROMANDIBULAR JOINT

Mastoid process
Articular tubercle
Synovial cavities
Articular disk
Lateral pterygoid
Condyle

Plate 22

Ligaments:

Articular capsule. This is thin, loose, and attached near the margins of the articular surfaces.

Temporomandibular ligament. A thickened part of the capsule extends from the zygoma and tubercle at its root to the lateral anterior and posterior surfaces of the neck of the mandible. This ligament is also known as the lateral ligament.

Articular disk. The circumference of this oval disk is fused with the articular capsule. Its lower surface is concave; its upper surface is concavoconvex.

Accessory ligaments:

Sphenomandibular ligament. It is thin and flat and descends from the spine of the sphenoid bond to the lingula of the mandible.

Stylomandibular ligament. This extends from about the apex of the styloid process to the posterior border of the ramus of the mandible near its angle.

Movements: Depression, elevation, protrusion, retraction, and grinding.

The superficial temporal branch of the external carotid a. supplies the temporomandibular joint. The nerve supply is provided by branches of the auriculotemporal and masseteric nn.

ORAL REGION

1. *Mouth*   4. *Gums*
2. *Lips*   5. *Teeth*
3. *Cheeks*   6. *Tongue*
              7. *Palate*

The oral region is the beginning of the alimentary canal.

1. Mouth

The mouth is divided into the vestibule and the oral cavity. The *vestibule* separates the lips and cheeks from the gums and teeth. The parotid duct opens into the vestibule opposite the second upper molar tooth. The *oral cavity* proper is bounded by:

Anterior and lateral boundaries: teeth and gums
Superior boundary (roof): hard and soft palate
Inferior boundary (floor): tongue and sublingual region
Posterior boundary: isthmus faucium and oropharynx

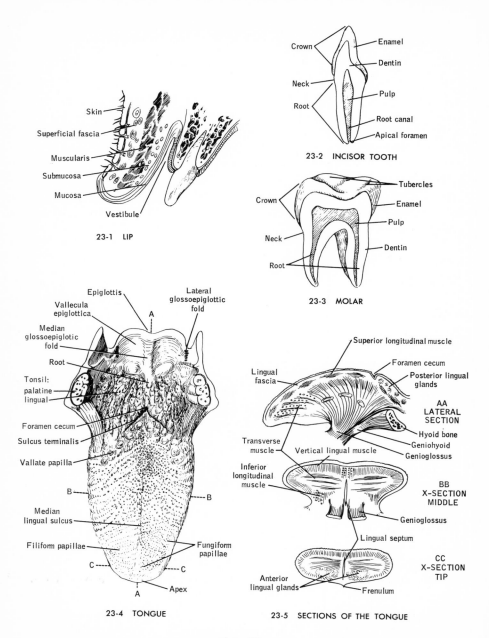

Skin
Superficial fascia
Muscularis
Submucosa
Mucosa
Vestibule

23-1   LIP

Crown
Neck
Root

Enamel
Dentin
Pulp
Root canal
Apical foramen

23-2   INCISOR TOOTH

Crown
Neck
Root

Tubercles
Enamel
Pulp
Dentin

23-3   MOLAR

Epiglottis
Vallecula epiglottica
Median glossoepiglotic fold
Root
Tonsil:
palatine
lingual
Foramen cecum
Sulcus terminalis
Vallate papilla
Median lingual sulcus
Filiform papillae

Lateral glossoepiglottic fold
A
B   B
C   C
A   Apex
Fungiform papillae

23-4   TONGUE

Lingual fascia

Superior longitudinal muscle
Foramen cecum
Posterior lingual glands
AA LATERAL SECTION
Hyoid bone
Geniohyoid
Genioglossus

Transverse muscle
Vertical lingual muscle
Inferior longitudinal muscle

BB X-SECTION MIDDLE
Genioglossus
Lingual septum

Anterior lingual glands
Frenulum

CC X-SECTION TIP

23-5   SECTIONS OF THE TONGUE

Plate 23

2. Lips (Fig. 23-1)

The lips are musculofibrous folds. The upper lip has a median shallow groove, the *philtrum*. Internally each lip is connected with its gum by a medial fold of mucous membrane, the *frenulum of the lip*. The five layers of the lip are shown in Table 26.

3. Cheeks

The cheeks resemble the lips in structure. The layers and characteristics of the cheek are shown in Table 27.

4. Gums

The gingivae, or gums, consist of vascular fibrous connective tissue mounted on the underlying alveolar margin of the maxilla and mandible. They are lined with mucous membrane continuous with that of the lips and cheeks.

5. Teeth (Figs. 23-2, 23-3)

Each tooth has a *crown* covered by enamel, a *neck* surrounded by the gingiva, and a *root* embedded in the alveolar socket. Inside the tooth is a pulp cavity, which contains fibrous tissue, and the vessels and nerves, which have entered via the *apical foramen*. The crown varies in shape; it is chisel-shaped in incisor (I) teeth, conical in canine (C) teeth, has two tubercles in bicuspid (premolar) (B) teeth, and three to four tubercles in molar (M) teeth. The dental formulas for the two sets of teeth (on one side and one jaw) are:

Deciduous				Permanent			
I	C	B		I	C	B	M
2	1	2		2	1	2	3

The arterial and nerve supply to the teeth is shown in Table 28.

6. Tongue

The tongue (Fig. 23-4) is the mobile, muscular organ of the floor of the mouth.

Parts

APEX. Like the margins of the tongue, it is free.

Table 26

Layer	Characteristics
Skin...............	Hair follicles and sebaceous and sweat glands
Superficial fascia.......	Loose connective tissue containing some fat
Muscularis...........	Orbicularis oris m.
Submucosa...........	Labial glands, blood vessels, nerves, and lymphatic
Mucosa..............	Mucous membrane covered with stratified epithelium

Table 27

Layer	Characteristics
Skin.............	Hair follicles and sebaceous and sweat glands
Superficial fascia...	Buccal fat pad and duct of parotid gland
Muscularis.......	Buccinator m. covered by buccopharyngeal fascia
Submucosa.......	Contains buccal glands and lymphatic vessels
Mucosa..........	Mucous membrane

Table 28

Teeth	Artery	Nerves	Branch of:
Maxillary......	Infraorbital	Superior alveolar	V^2
		Infraorbital	V^2
Mandibular....	Inferior alveolar branch of maxillary	Inferior alveolar	V^3

Table 29

Papilla	Shape	Number	Location
Filiform......	Conical	Most numerous	Throughout dorsum
Fungiform....	Mushroom	Numerous	Apex and margins
Vallate.......	Castle	About 10	Anterior and parallel with terminal sulcus
Foliate.......	Fold	Few	Margin near palatoglossal arch

DORSUM. The dorsum is convex and exhibits a V-shaped groove, the *sulcus terminalis,* the boundary between the anterior two-thirds, or oral part, and the posterior third, or pharyngeal part, of the dorsum of the tongue. At the apex of the sulcus terminalis is the *foramen cecum.* The pharyngeal part of the tongue is connected with the anterior surface of the epiglottis by folds of mucous membrane, the median and lateral *glossoepiglottic folds,* which bound two depressions, the *valleculae epiglotticae.*

INFERIOR SURFACE. The undersurface of the free part of the tongue is covered with mucous membrane and is connected with the floor of the mouth by means of a fold, the *frenulum of the tongue.* A fringed mucous membrane ridge, the *fimbriated fold,* passes on the lateral sides of this surface of the tongue.

ROOT. The fixed part of the tongue is connected by muscles to the mandible, in front, and to the hyoid bone, behind.

Components

Structurally the tongue is divided into two equal parts by a thin median fibrous septum and consists of:

MUCOUS MEMBRANE. This is rough on the oral surface because of the lingual papillae. The four types of lingual papillae are shown in Table 29.

The pharyngeal surface lacks papillae. It is covered with smooth mucous membrane that exhibits many nodules, the *lingual follicles,* produced by the underlying lymphoid masses. Collectively these nodules are known as the *lingual tonsil.* On the sides and back of the tongue are mucous glands; serous glands are found near the vallate papillae.

MUSCLES. These are divided into two groups, the extrinsic and intrinsic muscles. The *extrinsic muscles* consist of:

Styloglossus, Hyoglossus, and Genioglossus Muscles. These three muscles are described on p. 95.

Palatoglossus Muscle. See Soft Palate.

The *intrinsic muscles* (Fig. 23-5) are arranged in several planes within the tongue.

Superior Longitudinal Muscle. This lies under the mucous membrane of the dorsum and extends from the apex to the base.

Inferior Longitudinal Muscle. One on each side extends from the apex to the base in the lower part of the tongue.

Transverse Muscle. This extends from the median septum through the substance of the tongue to the sides and dorsum.

Vertical Muscle. This extends from the dorsum downward and laterally to the sides of the tongue.

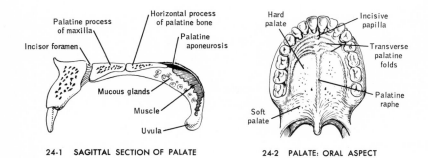

Palatine process
of maxilla

Horizontal process
of palatine bone

Palatine
aponeurosis

Incisor foramen

Mucous glands

Muscle

Uvula

24-1   SAGITTAL SECTION OF PALATE

Hard
palate

Incisive
papilla

Transverse
palatine
folds

Palatine
raphe

Soft
palate

24-2   PALATE: ORAL ASPECT

Sphenoid sinus

Tensor veli palatini

Cartilage of auditory tube

Levator veli palatini

Salpingopharyngeus

Palatoglossus

Uvula

Superior constrictor

Styloglossus

Glossopharyngeal n., IX

Tongue

Genioglossus

Stylohyoid ligament

Palatopharyngeus

Hyoid bone

Middle constrictor

24-3   MUSCLE OF ORAL PHARYNX

Plate 24

Table 30

Nerve	Type	Area innervated
Hypoglossal, XII.............	Motor	Intrinsic and extrinsic muscles
Lingual (from V³)............	Sensory	Mucous membrane of anterior two-thirds of tongue
Lingual via chorda tympani....	Taste	Mucous membrane of anterior two-thirds of tongue
Glossopharyngeal, IX.........	Sensory and taste	Mucous membrane of posterior one-third of tongue
Internal laryngeal............	Sensory and taste	Epiglottic region

Action: Alter the shape of the tongue.

Nerve supply: See Table 30.

7. Palate

The palate (Figs. 24-1, 24-2) forms the roof of the mouth and the floor of the nasal cavity. It consists of two parts.

Hard Palate

The hard palate is formed by the union of the palatine processes of the maxillae with the horizontal plates of the palatine (see Fig. 5-1). It is covered superiorly by the mucous membrane of the nasal cavity and inferiorly by the mucoperiosteum, which contains blood vessels, nerves, and the mucous palatine glands posteriorly. On the latter surface a median ridge, the *palatine raphe,* ends anteriorly in the incisive papilla. Extending sideways from the raphe are a number of *transverse palatine folds.*

Soft Palate

The soft palate is suspended from the posterior edge of the hard palate. It is continuous with the fauces laterally, and presents the *uvula* as an inferomedian projection. It consists of an aponeurosis, muscles, blood vessels, and nerves covered by mucous membrane.

PALATINE APONEUROSIS. This is attached to the posterior border of the hard palate and supports the muscles, all of which participate in swallowing.

LEVATOR VELI PALATINI. It is located lateral to the choanae.

Origin: Apex of petrous temporal bone and cartilage of auditory tube.

Insertion: Palatine aponeurosis.

Action: Elevates soft palate.

Nerve supply: Nerve to medial pterygoid muscle.

TENSOR VELI PALATINI. It passes under the pterygoid hamulus.

Origin: Scaphoid fossa, sphenoid spine, and cartilage of the auditory tube.

Insertion: Palatine aponeurosis.

Action: Elevates soft palate.

Nerve supply: Pharyngeal plexus.

MUSCULUS UVULAE

Origin: Posterior nasal spine and palatine aponeurosis.

Insertion: Uvula.

Action: Raises uvula.

Nerve supply: Pharyngeal plexus.

PALATOGLOSSUS. It forms the anterior arch of the tonsillar fossa.

Origin: Undersurface of palatine aponeurosis.

Insertion: Side of tongue.

Action: Approximates palatoglossal folds.

Nerve supply: Pharyngeal plexus.

PALATOPHARYNGEUS. It forms the posterior arch of the tonsillar fossa.

Origin: Posterior border of hard palate and palatine aponeurosis.

Insertion: Side of pharynx.

Action: Approximates palatopharyngeal folds.

Nerve supply: Pharyngeal plexus.

The neurovascular system of the palate is supplied by:

arteries: Ascending palatine branch of the maxillary a., the ascending palatine branch of the facial a., and the palatine branch of the ascending pharyngeal a.

veins: They consist of the pterygoid and tonsillar plexuses.

nerves: The sensory innervation is provided by branches of the palatine and nasopalatine nn. The motor innervation is provided by the pharyngeal plexus and the nerve to the medial pterygoid muscle.

PHARYNX

1. Structure of the pharyngeal wall   2. Divisions of the pharyngeal cavity

The pharynx is a fibromuscular tube that lies behind the nose, mouth, and larynx and communicates with them. Loose areolar tissue and fascia separate it from the prevertebral muscles. It extends from the skull base to the level of the sixth cervical vertebra, where it is continuous with the esophagus.

1. Structure of the Pharyngeal Wall (Fig. 25-1)

Mucous Membrane

This is continuous with the lining of the adjacent chambers.

Pharyngobasilar Fascia

The fibrous submucosal layer is exposed in the interval between the superior constrictor muscle and the base of the skull.

Muscular Layer (Figs. 25-1, 25-2)

This is divided into two groups:

CIRCULAR COAT. The circular coat consists of the three constrictor muscles. These are fan-shaped and incomplete anteriorly. Each overlaps its neighbor from below upwards.

Inferior Constrictor

Origin: Oblique line of thyroid cartilage; side of cricoid cartilage.

Middle Constrictor

Origin: Lesser and greater horns of hyoid bone; stylohyoid ligament.

Superior Constrictor

Origin: Pterygoid hamulus, pterygomandibular raphe, mylohyoid line, side of root of the tongue.

Insertion: Each muscle meets its fellow in the posterior median plane at the fibrous *pharyngeal raphe* which extends up to attach to the pharyngeal tubercle of the occipital bone.

Action: Participate in act of swallowing.

Nerve supply: From pharyngeal plexus. The inferior constrictor muscle is also innervated by branches of the external and recurrent laryngeal nn.

LONGITUDINAL COAT. The longitudinal coat also consists of three muscles which originate separately and blend at their insertions.

Stylopharyngeus

Origin: Styloid process near its root.

Insertion: Posterior border of thyroid cartilage and wall of pharynx.

Action: Elevates larynx and pharynx.

Nerve supply: Glossopharyngeal n., IX.

Palatopharyngeus. See p. 76.

Salpingopharyngeus. It lies in the salpingopharyngeal fold.

Origin: Lower part of auditory tube.

Insertion: Joins fibers of palatopharyngeus muscle.

Action: Same as that of the palatopharyngeus muscle.

Nerve supply: Pharyngeal plexus.

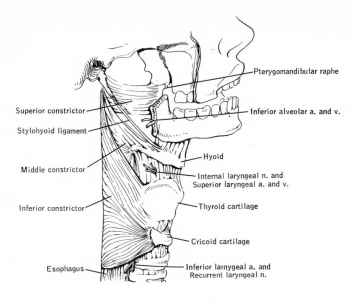

Pterygomandibular raphe

Superior constrictor

Inferior alveolar a. and v.

Stylohyoid ligament

Hyoid

Internal laryngeal n. and
Superior laryngeal a. and v.

Middle constrictor

Thyroid cartilage

Inferior constrictor

Cricoid cartilage

Esophagus

Inferior laryngeal a. and
Recurrent laryngeal n.

25-1   MUSCLES OF THE PHARYNX

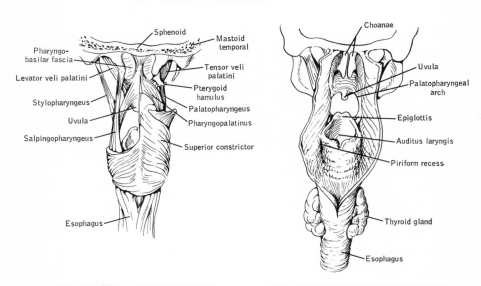

Sphenoid

Mastoid
temporal

Pharyngo-
basilar fascia

Tensor veli
palatini

Levator veli palatini

Pterygoid
hamulus

Stylopharyngeus

Palatopharyngeus

Uvula

Pharyngopalatinus

Salpingopharyngeus

Superior constrictor

Esophagus

25-2   POSTERIOR ASPECT OF PHARYNX

Choanae

Uvula

Palatopharyngeal
arch

Epiglottis

Auditus laryngis

Piriform recess

Thyroid gland

Esophagus

25-3   POSTERIOR VIEW THROUGH PHARYNX

Plate 25

BUCCOPHARYNGEAL FASCIA. The areolar coat covers the muscles, is continuous with the buccinator fascia, and contains pharyngeal venous and nerve plexuses.

2. Divisions of the Pharyngeal Cavity (Figs. 25-3, 26-1)

Having no anterior wall, the pharynx communicates directly with the nasal, oral, and laryngeal cavities; it is subdivided accordingly.

NASOPHARYNX. This part of the pharynx extends from the base of the skull to the level of the soft palate.

choanae. The two posterior nasal apertures.

pharyngeal ostium of auditory tube. Lying on the lateral wall.

torus tubarius. The elevation behind the ostium; produced by the medial end of the auditory tube.

salpingopharyngeal fold. Produced by the muscle of the same name. It extends from the lower part of the torus to the lateral wall of the pharynx.

pharyngeal recess. The space behind the torus.

pharyngeal tonsil. The mass of lymphatic tissue lying on the roof of the pharynx.

pharyngeal isthmus. The interval between the soft palate and the back of the pharynx, marking the junction of naso- and oropharynx.

OROPHARYNX. This part extends from the soft palate to the hyoid bone.

fauces. The space surrounded by the palate, tonsils, and uvula.

faucial isthmus. The aperture through which the mouth communicates with the oropharynx.

palatoglossal arch. Produced by the muscle of the same name. It extends from the side of the root of the tongue to the soft palate in front of the tonsil.

palatopharyngeal arch. Produced by the muscle of the same name. It extends from the end of the soft palate to the pharyngeal wall.

palatine tonsil. The mass of lymphatic tissue between the two folds. The space above the tonsil between the two folds is devoid of lymphatic tissue and is known as the *supratonsillar fossa.* The front of the tonsil is covered with mucous membrane which bounds the supratonsillar fossa superiorly as the *semilunar fold.* The fold continues down in front of the tonsil as the triangular fold, which is separated from the tonsil by the *tonsillar sinus.* The lateral surface of the tonsil is embedded in a fibrous capsule. The arrangement of lymphatic tissue around the fauces is known as *tonsillar ring.* It consists of the lingual tonsil, anteriorly; the palatine tonsils, laterally; and the pharyngeal tonsil, posteriorly.

LARYNGOPHARYNX. This part of the pharynx extends from the level of the hyoid bone to the lower border of the cricoid cartilage. It is continuous with the esophagus.

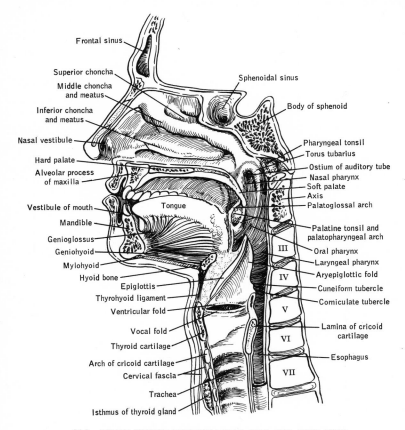

Frontal sinus

Superior choncha

Middle choncha
and meatus

Inferior choncha
and meatus

Nasal vestibule

Hard palate

Alveolar process
of maxilla

Vestibule of mouth

Mandible

Genioglossus

Geniohyoid

Mylohyoid

Hyoid bone

Epiglottis

Thyrohyoid ligament

Ventricular fold

Vocal fold

Thyroid cartilage

Arch of cricoid cartilage

Cervical fascia

Trachea

Isthmus of thyroid gland

Sphenoidal sinus

Body of sphenoid

Pharyngeal tonsil

Torus tubarius

Ostium of auditory tube

Nasal pharynx

Soft palate

Axis

Palatoglossal arch

Palatine tonsil and
palatopharyngeal arch

Oral pharynx

Laryngeal pharynx

Aryepiglottic fold

Cuneiform tubercle

Corniculate tubercle

Lamina of cricoid
cartilage

Esophagus

Tongue

III

IV

V

VI

VII

26-1   MEDIAN SECTION THROUGH LOWER HEAD AND UPPER NECK

Plate 26

aditus laryngis. The end of the anterior part of the laryngopharynx.

piriform recess. On each side of the aditus.

The neurovascular system of the pharynx is supplied by:

arteries: These arise from the external carotid a., the ascending pharyngeal and ascending palatine branches of the facial a., and the greater palatine branch of the maxillary a.

veins: An extensive pharyngeal venous plexus is formed on the posterior and lateral walls. It drains into the internal jugular v. and communicates with the pterygoid plexus.

nerves: Pharyngeal branches from the IX and X and from the superior cervical sympathetic ganglion form the *pharyngeal plexus* on the middle constrictor muscle.

LARYNX

1. Cartilages	3. Ligaments and membranes
2. Joints	4. Interior
	5. Intrinsic muscles

The larynx is a specialized upper portion of the respiratory system. It is a musculo-membranous-cartilaginous box lined by mucous membrane which acts as a vocal organ, as a valve controlling the exchange of air, and as a sphincter during swallowing.

1. Cartilages

There are nine laryngeal cartilages: three single—thyroid, cricoid, and epiglottic; three paired—arytenoid, cuneiform, and corniculate.

THYROID CARTILAGE (Figs. 27-1, 27-2). This cartilage consists of a pair of quadrilateral *laminae,* the anterior borders of which are fused below at the *thyroid angle* and separated above by the V-shaped *thyroid notch.* Below the notch, the anterior border projects outward as the *laryngeal prominence.* Posteriorly the laminae diverge widely. Each has a free border which projects upward and downward as the *superior* and *inferior horns;* the latter have articular facets at their lower ends. An *oblique line* extends downward and forward on the lateral surfaces. It begins at the *superior thyroid tubercle* in front of the root of the superior horn, and terminates at the *inferior thyroid tubercle* located in the middle of the inferior border of the cartilage.

CRICOID CARTILAGE (Figs. 27-3, 27-4). Located below the thyroid cartilage, the cricoid cartilage has the shape of a signet ring. It is divided into a wider *lamina,* representing the seal-like part which lies posteriorly, and the *arch,* the narrower

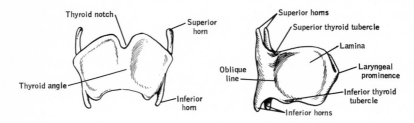

27-1 ANTERIOR ASPECT OF THYROID CARTILAGE   27-2 LATERAL ASPECT OF THYROID CARTILAGE

27-3 POSTERIOR ASPECT OF CRICOID CARTILAGE   27-4 LATERAL ASPECT OF CRICOID CARTILAGE

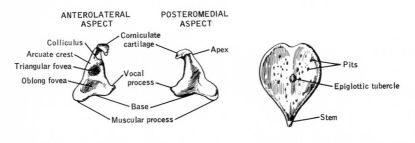

27-5 RIGHT ARYTENOID CARTILAGE   27-6 LARYNGEAL ASPECT OF EPIGLOTTIS

Plate 27

anterior and lateral hoop of the ring. Two facets are located on each side of the lamina where it meets the arch. The superior oval facet articulates with the base of the arytenoid cartilage; the middle circular facet articulates with the inferior horn of the thyroid cartilage.

ARYTENOID CARTILAGES (Fig. 27-5). Each is a three-sided pyramid, with a sharp anterior border, beginning above as a blunt protuberance, the *colliculus,* and ending at the base in the forward-projecting *vocal process.* The posterolateral border begins at the apex and descends to the backward-projecting *muscular process.* These two borders bound the anterolateral surface, which contains a deep depression, the *triangular fovea,* above, and a more shallow depression, the *oblong fovea,* below. The two depressions are separated from each other by part of the *arcuate crest.* This crest extends downward from the colliculus, backward to the posterior border, and then forward to the vocal process. The medial and posterior surfaces are smooth.

EPIGLOTTIC CARTILAGE (Fig. 27-6). This leaf-shaped structure serves as the skeleton of the epiglottis. It is located behind the base of the tongue and in front of the upper aperture of the larynx. The stem is attached by the *thyroepiglottic ligament* to the angle between the thyroid laminae a little below the thyroid notch. The upper round, free end is curved from side to side. The posterior surface has an elevation, the *epiglottic tubercle,* and contains numerous foramens for nerves and vessels, and pits for glands. Mucous membrane covers the upper third of the anterior surface and the entire posterior surface of the epiglottic cartilage.

CORNICULATE CARTILAGES. These are small nodules at the apices of the arytenoid cartilages.

CUNEIFORM CARTILAGES. These are rod-shaped and located in front of the corniculate cartilages within the aryepiglottic folds. They may be absent.

2. Joints

CRICOTHYROID JOINT

Type: Synovial.

Articulating elements: Inferior horn of the thyroid cartilage with the lower facet on the cricoid cartilage.

Ligament:

Articular Capsule. This is reinforced by the ceratocricoid ligament, which is divided into anterior, lateral, and posterior parts.

Movement: Rotation around a horizontal axis, and gliding.

CRICOARYTENOID JOINT

Type: Synovial.

Articulating elements: Base of arytenoid cartilage with the upper facet of the cricoid cartilage.

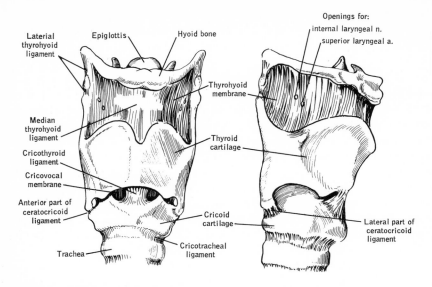

28-1 ANTERIOR ASPECT OF LARYNX

28-2 LATERAL ASPECT OF LARYNX

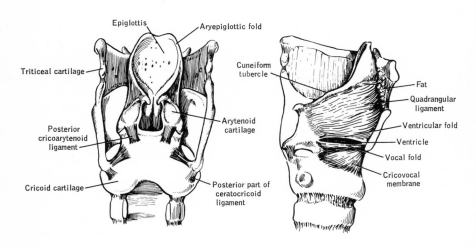

28-3 POSTERIOR ASPECT OF LARYNX

28-4 LATERAL ASPECT (thyroid cartilage removed)

Plate 28

Ligament:

Articular Capsule. This is reinforced by the posterior cricoarytenoid ligament.
Movement: Rotation around a vertical axis, and gliding.

3. Ligaments and Membranes

THYROHYOID MEMBRANE (Fig. 28-1). This is attached above to the upper part of the posterior surface of the body and greater horns of the hyoid bone. It extends down to the upper margin of the thyroid cartilage and to the front of the superior horns. The fibroelastic membrane is separated by a bursa from the posterior surface of the hyoid bone and by a fat pad from the anterior surface of the epiglottis. The middle part of the membrane is strengthened by elastic fibers, the *median thyrohyoid ligament,* which extends from the body of the hyoid bone to the thyroid notch. Similar fibers thicken the lateral margins of the membrane and convert them to cords, the *lateral thyrohyoid ligaments;* these connect the tips of the greater horns of the hyoid bone with the superior horns of the thyroid cartilage. Embedded in this ligament is a fibrocartilaginous nodule, the *triticeal cartilage.*

CRICOTHYROID LIGAMENT (Fig. 28-2). This is triangular and composed of elastic fibers. Its apex is attached to the middle of the inferior border of the thyroid cartilage and its base to the arch of the cricoid cartilage below. This ligament is also referred to as the anterior part of the conus elasticus.

CRICOVOCAL MEMBRANE (Conus Elasticus, Lateral Parts of the Cricothyroid Ligament) (Fig. 28-3). Each triangular membrane has three margins and two surfaces. The medial surface of the cricovocal membrane is covered by mucous membrane. Laterally the thyroarytenoid and lateral cricoarytenoid muscles separate it from the thyroid cartilage. The anterior margins are partly attached to the thyroid cartilage and are partly continuous with the cricothyroid ligament. Inferiorly the membrane it attached to the upper border of the cricoid cartilage. The posterior third of the superior margin is attached to the undersurface of the vocal processes; the anterior two-thirds has a free margin, the *vocal ligament.* This band, composed of yellow elastic tissue, extends from the tip of the vocal process to the thyroid angle.

QUADRANGULAR MEMBRANE (Fig. 28-4). This ligament has two free margins and two surfaces. The medial surface is covered by mucous membrane and the lateral surface by the aryepiglottic muscle. The membrane extends from the lateral margin of the epiglottic cartilage to the corniculate cartilage and the medial margin of the arytenoid cartilage. The inferior free border of this fascial membrane is the *ventricular ligament.* This is a band of fibrous tissue attached anteriorly to the thyroid angle just below the insertion of the thyroepiglottic ligament. Posteriorly the attachment is to the anterolateral surface of the arytenoid cartilage a little above the vocal ligament. The superior free margin is thickened and forms the *aryepiglottic ligament.*

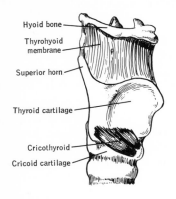

Hyoid bone

Thyrohyoid membrane

Superior horn

Thyroid cartilage

Cricothyroid

Cricoid cartilage

29-1   LATERAL SURFACE OF LARYNX

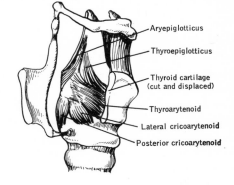

Aryepiglotticus

Thyroepiglotticus

Thyroid cartilage (cut and displaced)

Thyroarytenoid

Lateral cricoarytenoid

Posterior cricoarytenoid

29-2   LATERAL VIEW (cricothyroid removed)

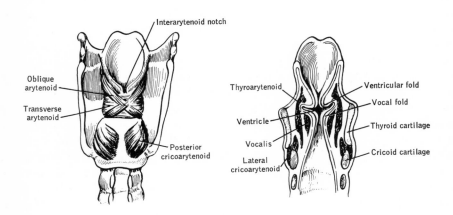

Interarytenoid notch

Oblique arytenoid

Transverse arytenoid

Posterior cricoarytenoid

29-3   POSTERIOR ASPECT OF LARYNX

Thyroarytenoid

Ventricle

Vocalis

Lateral cricoarytenoid

Ventricular fold

Vocal fold

Thyroid cartilage

Cricoid cartilage

29-4   CORONAL SECTION THROUGH LARYNX

Plate 29

CRICOTRACHEAL LIGAMENT. This fibrous ring connects the lower border of the cricoid with the upper end of the trachea.

4. Interior

INLET. The entrance into the larynx is triangular, wide in front and narrow behind; it slopes downward and backward. It is bounded anteriorly by the epiglottis and laterally by the *epiglottic folds*. These consist of the aryepiglottic ligaments and muscles covered by mucous membrane. A cuneiform cartilage located within each fold produces an elevation, the *cuneiform tubercle,* near its posterior end. The posterior boundary of the inlet is formed by the apices of the arytenoid cartilages, the corniculate cartilages, and the *interarytenoid notch.*

CAVITY. May be divided into three areas: vestibule, ventricle, and infraglottic compartment (Figs. 26-1, 28-4).

Vestibule. The vestibule extends from the laryngeal inlet to the *ventricular folds.* Each fold is a ridge of mucous membrane of no functional significance produced by the underlying ventricular ligaments. The interval between the folds is the *rima vestibuli.* The walls of the vestibule are the epiglottic (and thyroepiglottic) ligament, aryepiglottic folds, and the *interarytenoid fold,* a fold of mucous membrane extending between the arytenoid cartilages.

Ventricle. This is a depression on the sides of the wall of the cavity of the larynx between the ventricular and *vocal folds* (true vocal cords). The vocal fold is a sharp prominent ridge of mucous membrane produced by the underlying vocal ligaments. The interval between the vocal folds, vocal processes, and bases of the arytenoid cartilages is the *rima glottidis.* The *laryngeal saccule* is a diverticulum of mucous membrane extending upwards from the sinus between the ventricular folds and the inner surface of the thyroid cartilage.

Infraglottic Compartment. This region extends from the vocal folds to the lower border of the cricoid cartilage. It is bounded by the thyroid and cricoid cartilages and cricovocal membrane.

The muscles of the larynx are divided into two groups. The *extrinsic* (infrahyoid) *muscles* (p. 95) suspend the larynx from the surrounding bony structures. The *intrinsic muscles* are limited to the larynx and act upon it as sphincters or adjusters of the tension of the rima glottidis.

5. Intrinsic Muscles (Figs. 29-1 to 29-4)

CRICOTHYROID. This muscle is triangular in shape.

Origin: Anterior and lateral surfaces of the cricoid cartilage.

Insertion: Inferior horn and inferior border of the thyroid cartilage.

LATERAL CRICOARYTENOID. Lying lateral and parallel to the vocal cord, it supports the wall of the ventricle.

Table 31

Muscle	Action
Narrowing and widening of the glottis	
Posterior cricoarytenoids.....	Separate the vocal folds by rotating the arytenoid cartilages laterally
Lateral cricoarytenoids.......	Approximate vocal folds by rotating arytenoid cartilages medially
Arytenoids................	Draw the arytenoid cartilages together, thus tending to close the laryngeal inlet
Regulating tension of vocal folds	
Cricothyroid...............	Produces tension by tilting the thyroid cartilage of the chords downwards
Thyroarytenoid............	Produces relaxation of the cords by tilting the arytenoid cartilages forward

Origin: Lower half of thyroid angle and cricothyroid ligament.

Insertion: Base of arytenoid cartilage.

TRANSVERSE ARYTENOID. This is the only unpaired laryngeal muscle.

Origin and insertion: Extends from the back of one arytenoid cartilage to the other.

OBLIQUE ARYTENOID. It consists of muscle bands on the transverse arytenoid.

Origin: Muscular process of the arytenoid cartilages.

Insertion: Apex of the other arytenoid muscle, continuing to the edge of the epiglottis as the *aryepiglotticus* in the aryepiglottic fold.

POSTERIOR CRICOARYTENOID

Origin: Depression on the dorsum of the lamina of the cricoid cartilage.

Insertion: Back of the muscular process of the arytenoid cartilage.

THYROARYTENOID

Origin: Inner surface of the thyroid lamina near the laryngeal prominence.

Insertion: Lateral border of the arytenoid cartilage.

Fibers from the superior border of the thyroarytenoid muscle continue upward as the *thyroepiglotticus.* The part of the thyroarytenoid muscle adjacent to the vocal fold is known as the *vocalis.*

The action of the intrinsic laryngeal muscles is given in Table 31.

The neurovascular system of the larynx is supplied by:

arteries: They are the laryngeal branches of the superior and inferior thyroid aa.

veins: They are the superior and inferior laryngeal vv.

nerves: The internal laryngeal n. innervates the mucous membrane on the back of the larynx and on its interior as far as the vocal folds. The external laryngeal n. innervates the cricothyroid muscle while the recurrent laryngeal n. innervates all the other laryngeal muscles.

NECK

1. Bony-cartilaginous framework   *2. Fascia*

The neck supports the head by means of its cervical vertebrae and muscles. The various structures of the neck are mostly long, running between the head above and the trunk below. The shorter structures either are the component parts of the longer ones or are separate organs. The upper limits of the neck extend along the lower border of the mandible to its angle, and by a line to the mastoid process and superior nuchal line of the occipital bone. The lower limits are the sternal notch, the clavicles, and a line from the acromioclavicular joint to the spinous process of Cv 7.

1. Bony-cartilaginous Framework

HYOID BONE (Figs. 28-1, 28-2). This U-shaped bone is located between the mandible and the larynx at the level of Cv 3. It is suspended from the stylohyoid processes by the stylohyoid ligament. The *greater horns* project backwards from the *body*. The *lesser horns* project backwards and upwards from the junction of the body and the greater horns.

THYROID CARTILAGE, CRICOID CARTILAGE, TRACHEAL RINGS. See Larynx.

Fascial membranes extend between the components of the bony-cartilaginous framework (e.g., thyrohyoid membrane, p. 85).

2. Fascia (Fig. 30-1)

Superficial

The superficial fascia is continuous below with the superficial fascia of the deltoid and pectoral regions and backward with the same layer of the dorsum of the neck. It envelops the platysma and is separated from the deep cervical fascia by a fascial cleft.

Deep Cervical

The deep cervical fascia consists of four layers, investing, muscular, visceral, and prevertebral, which are separated by fascial clefts.

INVESTING LAYER. This layer forms a complete collar around the neck. It covers the posterior triangle and splits to envelop the sternocleidomastoid and trapezius muscles and the submandibular and parotid glands. The attachments of the investing layer are:

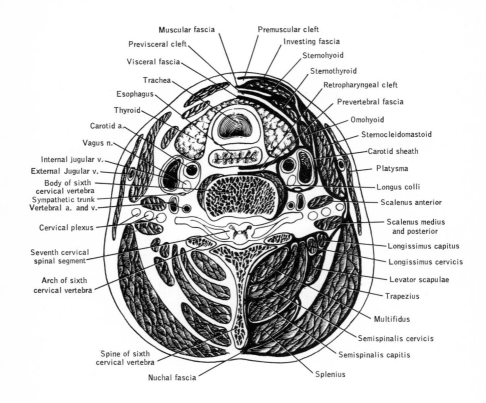

Muscular fascia   Premuscular cleft

Previsceral cleft   Investing fascia

Visceral fascia   Sternohyoid

Sternothyroid

Trachea   Retropharyngeal cleft

Esophagus   Prevertebral fascia

Thyroid

Carotid a.   Omohyoid

Vagus n.   Sternocleidomastoid

Carotid sheath

Internal jugular v.   Platysma

External Jugular v.

Body of sixth   Longus colli
cervical vertebra

Sympathetic trunk   Scalenus anterior

Vertebral a. and v.

Scalenus medius
and posterior

Cervical plexus

Longissimus capitus

Longissimus cervicis

Seventh cervical   Levator scapulae
spinal segment

Arch of sixth   Trapezius
cervical vertebra

Multifidus

Semispinalis cervicis

Spine of sixth   Semispinalis capitis
cervical vertebra

Nuchal fascia   Splenius

30-1   TRANSVERSE SECTION OF THE NECK INTERSECTING THE SIXTH CERVICAL VERTEBRA

Plate 30

Anterior attachment: body and greater horn of the hyoid bone

Posterior attachment: nuchal ligament

Superior attachment: lower border of the mandible, zygomatic arch, cartilage of the ear, mastoid bone, superior nuchal line

Inferior attachment: clavicle, acromion, posterior border of the spine of the scapula, manubrium sterni

MUSCULAR LAYER. It envelops the infrahyoid muscles, forming separate lamellae. Its attachments are, superiorly, the hyoid bone; inferiorly, the posterior surface of the sternum; laterally, the investing layer on the deep surface of the sternocleidomastoid muscle.

VISCERAL LAYER. This tubular prolongation of the visceral fascia of the mediastinum encloses the trachea and esophagus. It is called the *pretracheal fascia* at a higher level, where it encloses the pharynx, larynx, and thyroid gland. This layer is continuous above with the buccopharyngeal fascia, which covers the posterior and lateral aspects of the constrictor muscles and extends forward over the buccinator muscle. It is attached to the base of the skull at the pharyngeal tubercle and to the pterygoid hamulus.

PREVERTEBRAL LAYER. Clothing the prevertebral muscles, it serves as the anterior lamella of the fascia that envelops the muscles of the back. It extends over the longus colli and across the anterior vertebral muscles. The prevertebral layer is continuous with the fascial envelope of the scalenus anterior muscle. The attachments of the prevertebral layer are, superiorly, to the base of the skull; inferiorly, to the anterior longitudinal ligament; and laterally to the tips of the transverse processes.

Carotid Sheath. The carotid sheath is the tubular fascial envelope containing the common and internal carotid aa., internal jugular v., and the vagus n. It is a condensation of fascia that is connected with the other layers of cervical fascia. The sympathetic trunk is embedded in its posterior wall.

FASCIAL CLEFTS. These are the potential spaces that exist between the layers of fascia. The major fascial clefts of the neck are:

Premuscular Cleft. Between the investing layer and the middle layer.

Previsceral Cleft. Between the visceral layer and the muscular layer anterolaterally, and the carotid sheath laterally.

Retropharyngeal Cleft. Between the visceral layer and the prevertebral layer.

ANTERIOR CERVICAL TRIANGLE

1. Boundaries
2. Submental triangle
3. Digastric triangle
4. Muscular triangle
5. Carotid triangle

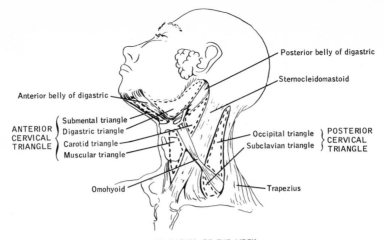

ANTERIOR CERVICAL TRIANGLE
{ Submental triangle
Digastric triangle
Carotid triangle
Muscular triangle }

Anterior belly of digastric

Posterior belly of digastric

Sternocleidomastoid

Occipital triangle
Subclavian triangle } POSTERIOR CERVICAL TRIANGLE

Omohyoid

Trapezius

31-1 TRIANGLES OF THE NECK

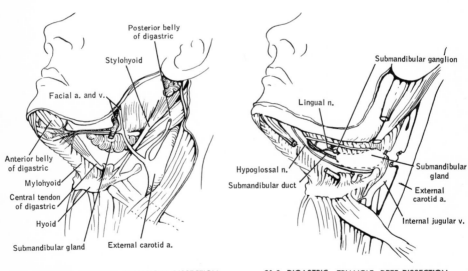

Posterior belly of digastric

Stylohyoid

Facial a. and v.

Anterior belly of digastric

Mylohyoid

Central tendon of digastric

Hyoid

Submandibular gland

External carotid a.

31-2 DIGASTRIC TRIANGLE: SUPERFICIAL DISSECTION

Submandibular ganglion

Lingual n.

Hypoglossal n.

Submandibular duct

Submandibular gland

External carotid a.

Internal jugular v.

31-3 DIGASTRIC TRIANGLE: DEEP DISSECTION

Plate 31

The sternocleidomastoid muscle (p. 118) serves to divide the side of the neck into the anterior and posterior cervical triangles.

1. Boundaries (Fig. 31-1)

The anterior cervical triangle has the following boundaries:

Anterior boundary: midline—from the chin to the jugular notch

Lateral boundary: anterior border of the sternocleidomastoid muscle

Superior boundary: lower margin of the body of the mandible extended to the mastoid process

The anterior triangle is subdivided into four triangles: submental, digastric, submandibular, and muscular.

2. Submental Triangle

The boundaries (Fig. 31-1) of the submental triangle are as follows:

Lateral boundary: anterior belly of digastric muscle

Medial boundary: midline from symphysis menti to hyoid bone

Inferior boundary: body of hyoid bone

Floor: medial portion of mylohyoid muscle

The submental triangle contains the submental lymph nodes.

3. Digastric Triangle

The boundaries (Fig. 31-1) of the digastric triangle are as follows:

Superior boundary: lower margin of the body of mandible extended to the mastoid process

Medial boundary: anterior belly of digastric muscle

Lateral boundary: posterior belly of digastric muscle

Floor: mylohyoid muscle in front and hyoglossus muscle behind

The digastric triangle (Figs. 31-2, 31-3) contains:

SUBMANDIBULAR GLAND. This almost fills the triangle.

FACIAL V. Piercing the deep fascia at the lower border of the mandible, it descends behind the submandibular gland to join the retromandibular v.

SUBMANDIBULAR LYMPH GLANDS. About five glands lie between the submandibular gland and the mandible.

FACIAL A. Appearing in front of the facial v., it provides submental branches and passes up into the face.

MYLOHYOID N. Proceeding from the mylohyoid groove of the mandible on to the mylohyoid muscle beneath the gland, it passes forwards to innervate the mylohyoid muscle and the anterior belly of the digastric muscle.

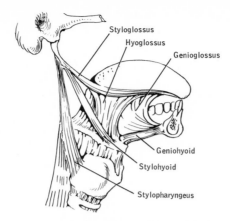

32-1   EXTRINSIC MUSCLES OF THE TONGUE

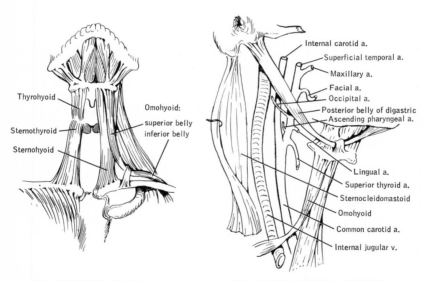

32-2   INFRAHYOID MUSCLES

32-3   CAROTID TRIANGLE: CONTENTS

Plate 32

TENDON OF DIGASTRIC MUSCLE. It lies on the hyoglossus muscle just above the hyoid bone, with its pulley (i.e., the fascial sling) binding the tendon to the hyoid bone.

HYPOGLOSSAL N. (XII). This passes forward on the hyoglossus muscle beneath the submandibular gland.

Extrinsic Muscles of the Tongue (Fig. 32-1)

These muscles lie deep to the digastric triangle and thus are also related to the contents of the submandibular and oral regions. They all are innervated by the hypoglossal n. (XII).

GENIOGLOSSUS. This muscle is fan-shaped, with its apex at the origin.
Origin: Upper genial tubercle.
Insertion: Radiates into the tongue from the back to its tip.
Action: Anterior fibers depress, posterior fibers protrude the tongue.
STYLOGLOSSUS. This is the shortest of the three styloid muscles.
Origin: Anterolateral surface of the styloid process.
Insertion: Side of the tongue along its entire length.
Action: Draws the tongue up and back during swallowing.
HYOGLOSSUS. This muscle is quadrilateral in shape.
Origin: Part of body and entire greater horn of the hyoid bone.
Insertion: Posterior half of the tongue.
Action: Depresses the tongue to produce a trough, as in sucking.
PALATOGLOSSUS. See Soft Palate.

4. Muscular Triangle

The boundaries (Fig. 31-1) of the muscular triangle are as follows:
Medial boundary: midline from hyoid bone to jugular notch
Lateral boundary: superior belly of omohyoid muscle and anterior margin of lower part of sternocleidomastoid muscle
Floor: sternohyoid, sternothyroid, and thyrohyoid muscles
Its contents are the following (Fig. 32-2):

Infrahyoid Muscles

STERNOHYOID. This is a thin, narrow muscle.
Origin: Back of manubrium and sternal end of clavicle.
Insertion: Medial half of lower border of body of hyoid bone.
Action: Draws hyoid bone down.
Nerve supply: Ansa cervicalis.

Table 32

Branches	*Relation*
Ascending pharyngeal a............	Ascends between internal carotid a. and pharynx
Superior thyroid a................	Descends beside pharynx and under the omohyoid m.
Infrahyoid a....................	On thyrohyoid membrane
Superior laryngeal a............	Pierces thyrohyoid membrane
Sternocleidomastoid branch......	Upper border of omohyoid m.
Lingual a........................	Over middle constrictor m. and under hyoglossus m.
Superior hyoid a................	On upper border of hyoid bone
Facial a........................	Passes deep to the posterior belly of digastric m.
Occipital a......................	Ascends behind posterior belly of digastric m.
Sternomastoid branch..........	Descends over hypoglossal n. to its muscle
Meningeal branch..............	Ascends beside internal jugular v. to jugular foramen

STERNOTHYROID. It lies beneath the sternohyoid muscle.

Origin: Back of manubrium and first costal cartilage.

Insertion: Oblique line of thyroid cartilage.

Action: Draws thyroid cartilage down.

Nerve supply: Ansa cervicalis.

THYROHYOID. It is small and quadrilateral.

Origin: Oblique line of thyroid cartilage.

Insertion: Lower border of body and greater horn of hyoid bone.

Action: Draws hyoid bone down and thyroid cartilage up.

Nerve supply: Nerve to thyrohyoid muscle (Cn 1).

OMOHYOID. Its two bellies are united by a common tendon.

Origin: Inferior belly—upper border of scapula near notch.

Insertion: Superior belly—lower border of body of hyoid bone.

Action: Draws hyoid bone down.

Nerve supply: Ansa cervicalis.

5. Carotid Triangle

The boundaries (Fig. 31-1) of the carotid triangle are as follows:

Superior boundary: posterior belly of digastric muscle

Medial boundary: superior belly of omohyoid muscle

Lateral boundary: anterior margin of upper part of sternocleidomastoid muscle

It contains (Fig. 32-3):

Arteries (Fig. 33-1)

COMMON CAROTID A. Lying in the lower part of the triangle along the medial side of the internal jugular v., it has two terminal branches, the external and internal carotid aa., formed by the division of the common carotid a. at the level of the upper border of the thyroid cartilage.

External Carotid A. Ascending behind the angle of the mandible, it leaves the carotid triangle under the posterior belly of the digastric and stylohyoid muscles, to continue on to the face, where it terminates. It gives off five branches in the neck (Table 32), some of which provide rami in the carotid triangle.

Internal Carotid A. Ascending beside the pharynx to the base of the skull, it enters the foramen lacerum. It has no branches in the neck.

The oval *carotid body* is a specialized cell mass embedded at the bifurcation angle of the common carotid a. Sympathetic external and internal carotid plexuses, derived from the superior cervical ganglion, envelop the respective arteries. The *carotid sinus* is the dilated junction of the common carotid and internal carotid aa.

Veins (Fig. 33-2)

INTERNAL JUGULAR V. (Fig. 33-2). The largest structure in the carotid triangle, it descends vertically and receives four tributaries.

Pharyngeal V. Originating in the pharyngeal plexus on the outer surface of the pharynx, it descends to join the internal jugular v.

Common Facial V. Beginning in the carotid triangle below the angle of the mandible by the union of the facial and the anterior division of the retromandibular vv., it descends to join the internal jugular v.

Lingual V. Formed by the convergence of four veins at the posterior border of the hyoglossus muscle, it crosses the carotid aa. to form the upper part of the internal jugular v.

Superior Thyroid V. Emerging from the thyroid gland, it ascends to join the upper part of the internal jugular v.

Nerves

VAGUS N. (X). This nerve lies between the back parts of the internal jugular v. and the carotid aa.

Superior Laryngeal N. Arising from the vagus near the base of the skull, it descends medial to the carotid where, at a variable point, it divides into the internal and external laryngeal nn.

ACCESSORY N. (XI). Descending backward across the internal jugular v. to the upper part of the triangle, it is accompanied by lymph glands and the upper sternocleidomastoid branch of the occipital a.

HYPOGLOSSAL N. (XII). It emerges from the short hypoglossal canal, where it gives off a meningeal branch to the dura of the posterior cranial fossa. It de-

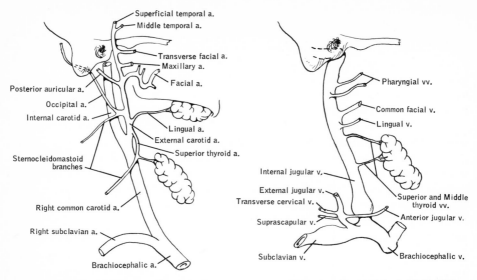

33-1 BRANCHES OF EXTERNAL CAROTID ARTERY

Superficial temporal a.
Middle temporal a.
Transverse facial a.
Maxillary a.
Facial a.
Posterior auricular a.
Occipital a.
Internal carotid a.
Lingual a.
External carotid a.
Superior thyroid a.
Sternocleidomastoid branches
Right common carotid a.
Right subclavian a.
Brachiocephalic a.

33-2 TRIBUTARIES OF INTERNAL JUGULAR VEIN

Pharyngial vv.
Common facial v.
Lingual v.
Internal jugular v.
External jugular v.
Transverse cervical v.
Superior and Middle thyroid vv.
Suprascapular v.
Anterior jugular v.
Subclavian v.
Brachiocephalic v.

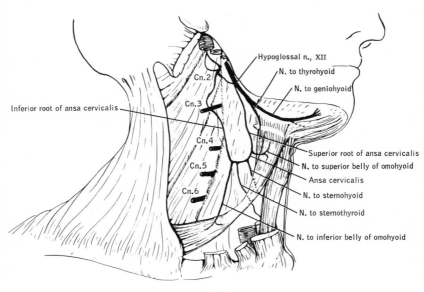

Hypoglossal n., XII
N. to thyrohyoid
Cn.2
N. to geniohyoid
Cn.3
Inferior root of ansa cervicalis
Cn.4
Cn.5
Superior root of ansa cervicalis
N. to superior belly of omohyoid
Ansa cervicalis
Cn.6
N. to sternohyoid
N. to sternothyroid
N. to inferior belly of omohyoid

33-3 ANSA CERVICALIS

Plate 33

scends to appear in the carotid triangle, at the lower border of the posterior belly of the digastric muscle, between the internal carotid a. and the internal jugular v. It curves forward across the carotid aa. and passes deep to the posterior belly of the digastric muscle again, to enter the digastric triangle. In the carotid triangle it gives off two branches.

Nerve to Thyrohyoid Muscle. It consists of fibers from Cn 1 which descend to its muscle.

Superior Root of Ansa Cervicalis. It consists of fibers from Cn 1 descending to terminate in the ansa cervicalis.

INFERIOR ROOT OF ANSA CERVICALIS. It consists of fibers from the ventral rami of Cn 2 and 3. The fibers unite on the lateral side of the internal jugular v., on which it descends to join the ansa cervicalis. It provides no branches.

ANSA CERVICALIS (Fig. 33-3). This loop is formed by the union of its two roots; thus it contains fibers from Cn 1, 2, and 3. It lies on the common carotid a. at the level of the cricoid cartilage. It provides branches which innervate the sternothyroid and sternohyoid muscles and both bellies of the omohyoid muscle.

SUBMANDIBULAR REGION

1. *Muscles*   3. *Arteries*
2. *Salivary glands*   4. *Veins*
5. *Nerves*

The submandibular region lies under cover of the body of the mandible and above the hyoid bone. Superficially it includes the submental and digastric triangles and the deeper structures related to the mylohyoid and hyoglossus muscles.

1. Muscles (Fig. 34-1)

DIGASTRIC. Its two bellies are united by a tendon.

Anterior Belly

Origin: Lower border of mandible near symphysis.

Insertion: Common tendon.

Nerve supply: Mylohyoid n. (from inferior alveolar branch of V^3).

Posterior Belly

Origin: Mastoid notch.

Insertion: Common tendon.

Action: Anterior belly tilts head back; posterior belly pulls down the mandible; both bellies raise hyoid bone during swallowing.

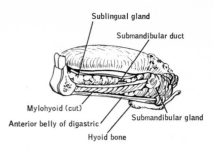

34-2   LATERAL VIEW OF SUBMANDIBULAR REGION

Sublingual gland
Submandibular duct
Mylohyoid (cut)
Anterior belly of digastric
Hyoid bone
Submandibular gland

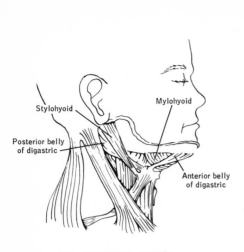

Stylohyoid
Mylohyoid
Posterior belly of digastric
Anterior belly of digastric

34-1   SUPRAHYOID MUSCLES

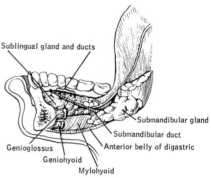

Sublingual gland and ducts
Submandibular gland
Submandibular duct
Anterior belly of digastric
Genioglossus
Geniohyoid
Mylohyoid

34-3   MEDIAL VIEW OF SUBMANDIBULAR REGION

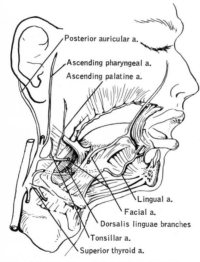

Posterior auricular a.
Ascending pharyngeal a.
Ascending palatine a.
Lingual a.
Facial a.
Dorsalis linguae branches
Tonsillar a.
Superior thyroid a.

34-4   ARTERIES OF SUBMANDIBULAR REGION

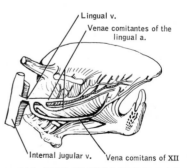

Lingual v.
Venae comitantes of the lingual a.
Internal jugular v.
Vena comitans of XII

34-5   VEINS OF SUBMANDIBULAR REGION

Plate 34

Nerve supply: Facial n. (VII).

STYLOHYOID. It courses along the posterior belly of the digastric muscle, the tendon of which perforates the muscle.

Origin: Styloid process near its root.

Insertion: Hyoid bone at the junction of body with greater horn.

Action: Draws hyoid bone up and back during swallowing.

Nerve supply: Facial n. (VII).

MYLOHYOID. It forms the diaphragm across the floor of the mouth.

Origin: Mylohyoid line of mandible.

Insertion: Body of hyoid bone and mylohyoid raphe.

Action: Raises hyoid bone and tongue during swallowing.

Nerve supply: Mylohyoid n.

GENIOHYOID. It is narrow and located above the medial border of the mylohyoid.

Origin: Lower genial tubercle.

Insertion: Body of hyoid bone.

Action: Draws hyoid bone forwards and upwards.

Nerve supply: Hypoglossal n. (XII) carrying Cn 1 fibers.

2. Salivary Glands (Figs. 34-2, 34-3)

SUBMANDIBULAR GLAND. Lying partly under cover of the mandible and partly between the mandible and the hyoid bone, it overlaps the bellies of the digastric muscle. The gland has three surfaces, shown in Table 33.

The submandibular gland has a *deep process* which is prolonged forward from its medial surface between the mylohyoid and hyoglossus muscles.

The neurovascular system of the submandibular gland is supplied by:

arteries: Branches of the facial and lingual aa.

veins: Drain into the external jugular v.

nerves: The sympathetic nerves are derived from the plexus around the facial a. The parasympathetic nerves pass via the chorda tympani to the lingual n. and then to the submandibular ganglion. Postganglionic fibers then go to the gland.

Submandibular Duct. Together with the deep process, it emerges from the medial surface of the gland. It passes between the mylohyoid and hyoglossus muscles and then between the sublingual gland and the genioglossus muscle. It opens into the mouth on the sublingual papilla, at the side of the frenulum of the tongue. It has thin walls and a narrow orifice.

SUBLINGUAL GLAND. This small, flattened gland presents four borders and two surfaces, as shown in Table 34.

Table 33

Surface	*Relations*
Lateral	Medial surface of mandible and medial pterygoid m.
Inferior	Covered by platysma and deep fascia
Medial	Mylohyoid, hyoglossus, middle constrictor mm.

Table 34

Border or surface	*Relations*
Border:	
Upper	Mucous membrane of floor of mouth
Lower	Mylohyoid m.
Front	Gland of opposite side
Back	Deep process of submandibular gland
Surface:	
Lateral	Sublingual fossa
Medial	Genioglossus m.

Table 35

Branches	Relation	Area supplied
Ascending palatine a.	Styloglossus and superior constrictor mm., pierces pharyngobasilar fascia	Soft palate
Tonsillar a.	Styloglossus m., pierces superior constrictor m.	Tonsil
Glandular branches	Mylohyoid m.	Submandibular gland
Submental a.	Mylohyoid m.	Adjacent muscles

Table 36

Branches	Origin	Relation	Area supplied
Suprahyoid a.	First part	Upper border of hyoid bone	Adjacent muscles
Dorsalis linguae branches	Second part	Medial to hyoglossus m.	Dorsum of tongue
Sublingual a.	Third part	Anterior margin of hyoglossus m.	Sublingual gland
Deep lingual a.	Terminal	Under lower surface of tongue	Front of tongue

The neurovascular system of the sublingual gland is supplied by:

arteries: Sublingual a. (from lingual a.) and submental a. (from facial a.).

nerves: Parasympathetic, postganglionic fibers from the submandibular ganglion.

Sublingual Ducts. From 10 to 20 open separately into the mouth on the sublingual fold.

3. Arteries (Fig. 34-4)

FACIAL A. Represented by its S-shaped cervical part and its branches, it arises from the external carotid a., ascends beneath the posterior belly of the digastric and stylohyoid muscles, and reaches the back of the submandibular gland. Then it descends forward to the lower border of the mandible, from where it ascends at the anterior border of the masseter muscle to continue as the proper facial portion of this artery (p. 23). Its branches in the neck are shown in Table 35.

LINGUAL A. This arises from the external carotid a. about the level of the hyoid bone. Its course is divided into three parts:

First Part. Lying in the carotid triangle, it is S-shaped and ends at the posterior border of the hyoglossus muscle.

Second Part. Lying beneath the hyoglossus muscle, it courses on the upper border of the hyoid bone on the middle constrictor muscle.

Third Part. It courses on the genioglossus muscle to the tongue.

The branches of the lingual a. are shown in Table 36.

4. Veins (Fig. 34-4)

LINGUAL V. Draining into the internal jugular v., it is formed at the posterior border of the hyoglossus muscle from the venae comitantes of the lingual a. and the hypoglossal n. It also receives the vena comitans of XII from the deep part of the tongue.

5. Nerves (Fig. 35-1)

MYLOHYOID N. A branch of the inferior alveolar n. that passes into this region from the infratemporal fossa, passes beneath the submandibular gland on the mylohyoid muscle, and supplies this muscle as well as the anterior belly of the digastric muscle.

LINGUAL N. The nerve originates from V^3, enters this region from the infratemporal fossa, and passes over the styloglossus and hyoglossus muscles and the deep part of the submandibular gland. It spirals around the duct to ramify and innervate the anterior two-thirds of the tongue. The branches of this nerve have already been described (p. 63).

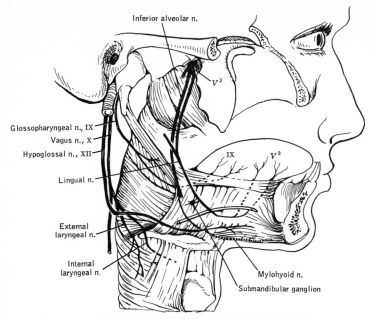

Inferior alveolar n.

V^3

Glossopharyngeal n., IX

Vagus n., X

Hypoglossal n., XII

Lingual n.

External
laryngeal n.

Internal
laryngeal n.

IX V^3

Mylohyoid n.

Submandibular ganglion

35-1   INNERVATION OF THE SUBMANDIBULAR REGION

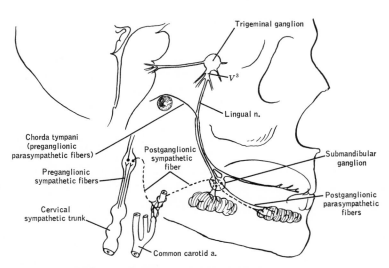

Trigeminal ganglion

V^3

Lingual n.

Chorda tympani
(preganglionic
parasympathetic fibers)

Postganglionic
sympathetic
fiber

Submandibular
ganglion

Preganglionic
sympathetic fibers

Cervical
sympathetic trunk

Postganglionic
parasympathetic
fibers

Common carotid a.

35-2   AUTONOMIC INNERVATION OF SUBMANDIBULAR REGION

Plate 35

Table 37

Roots	Synapse	Branches
Sympathetic from facial plexus...........	No	Both salivary glands
Parasympathetic preganglionic via chorda tympani...............................	Yes	Postganglionic secretory to both glands
Sensory from lingual n.	No	Mucous membrane of mouth

Table 38

Branches	*Area supplied*
Nerve to stylopharyngeus muscle....	Innervates this muscle
Pharyngeal branches..............	Contributes to pharyngeal plexus
Nerve to carotid sinus.............	Contributes to internal carotid plexus
Tonsillar branches................	Innervates palatine tonsil and soft palate
Lingual branches.................	Terminal; for posterior third of tongue and front of epiglottis

Submandibular Ganglion (Fig. 35-2). This is located on the lateral surface of the hyoglossal muscle below the lingual n. The roots and branches of the submandibular ganglion are shown in Table 37.

HYPOGLOSSAL N. (XII). The nerve enters this region from the carotid triangle. It passes beneath the posterior belly of the digastric and stylohyoid muscles on the hyoglossus muscle and continues forward on this muscle beneath the submandibular gland and mylohyoid muscle to terminate in the genioglossus muscle. This supplies all the extrinsic (except palatoglossus) and intrinsic muscles of the tongue.

GLOSSOPHARYNGEAL N. (IX). Originating from the medulla oblongata, it presents superior and inferior ganglions as it emerges through the jugular foramen. It descends between the interior jugular v. and internal carotid a. on the superior constrictor muscle. It curves forward to pass between the carotid aa. and passes deep to the hyoglossus muscle, where it ramifies to supply the tonsil and mucous membrane of the posterior third of the tongue. Its first branch is the:

Tympanic N. Carrying preganglionic parasympathetic fibers, it arises in the jugular foramen from the inferior ganglion of IX. It enters the tympanic canaliculus to reach the tympanic cavity, where it ramifies on the promontory to contribute to the formation of the *tympanic plexus* (see Fig. 16-2). Some fibers of the tympanic plexus reunite to form the *lesser petrosal n.,* which passes forward through the petrous temporal bone, emerging into the middle cranial fossa just lateral to the hiatus of VII. It leaves the cranial cavity usually through the foramen ovale to reach the otic ganglion.

Other Branches of the Glossopharyngeal N. See Table 38.

POSTERIOR CERVICAL TRIANGLE

1. Boundaries	*3. Contents*
2. Fascia	*4. Muscles*

The posterior cervical triangle is the second of the two large triangles of the neck (p. 93).

1. Boundaries (Fig. 31-1)

The posterior cervical triangle presents the following five boundaries:
Anterior boundary: posterior border of sternocleidomastoid muscle
Posterior boundary: anterior border of trapezius muscle
Base boundary: middle third of clavicle
Roof boundary: superficial fascia
Floor boundary: deep fascia, muscles (see below)
The inferior belly of the omohyoid muscle divides the posterior triangle into the larger *occipital* and smaller *subclavian triangles.*

2. Fascia (Fig. 30-1)

SUPERFICIAL. The superficial fascia contains a part of the platysma, some small blood vessels and lymphatic vessels, and the supraclavicular nn. It is represented by that part of the investing layer extending between the sternocleidomastoid and trapezius muscles.

DEEP. Covering the muscles of the floor of the triangle, it is represented by their prevertebral fascia.

3. Contents

Superficial Structures (Fig. 36-1)

OCCIPITAL A. The occipital artery crosses the apex of the triangle.

EXTERNAL JUGULAR V. It descends from the face to enter the anterior lower corner of the triangle before it joins the subclavian v.

TRANSVERSE CERVICAL V. It passes a little above the clavicle to join the external jugular v.

SUPRASCAPULAR V. It courses with its corresponding artery to empty into the external jugular v.

CUTANEOUS BRANCHES OF CERVICAL PLEXUS. The plexus is formed by the union of ventral rami of Cn 2 to 4, and lies on the scalenus medius muscle under cover of the upper half of the sternocleidomastoid muscle. Its four cutaneous branches become evident above the middle of the posterior border of this muscle.

Lesser Occipital N. (**Cn 2**). Ascending along the posterior border of the sterno-cleidomastoid muscle, it ramifies to supply the scalp above and behind the ear; another branch supplies the skin of the upper third of the cranial surface of the auricle. This nerve communicates with the other nerves located in the same area.

Great Auricular N. (**Cn 2, 3**). Curving around to ascend the superficial surface of the sternocleidomastoid muscle parallel with the external jugular v., it divides near the auricle into:

auricular branch. Supplying the skin of the lower cranial surface of the auricle.

mastoid branch. Supplying the scalp behind the ear.

parotid branches. Supplying the gland and the overlying skin.

Transverse N. of Neck (**Cn 2, 3**). This nerve hooks around the posterior border of the sternocleidomastoid muscle, crosses its superficial surface, pierces the deep fascia, and divides into:

ascending branch. Supplying the skin of the upper anterior part of the neck.

descending branch. Supplying the skin of the side and front of the neck.

Supraclavicular Nn. (**Cn 3, 4**). These nerves arise from a common trunk, which divides into three groups.

medial supraclavicular nn. Crossing the sternocleidomastoid muscle and the sternal third of the clavicle, they supply the skin and sternoclavicular joint.

intermediate supraclavicular nn. Crossing over the middle of the clavicle, they supply the skin over the pectoralis major and deltoid muscles.

lateral supraclavicular nn. Passing onto the trapezius muscle and across the lateral third of the clavicle, they supply the skin of this region.

ACCESSORY N. (XI). Passing from the cranial cavity through the jugular foramen, it descends along the internal jugular v. to a little below the mastoid process, where it curves laterally to pierce (and supply) the sternocleidomastoid muscle. It emerges into the posterior triangle at the junction of the upper and middle thirds of the muscle. The XI nerve then continues down across the triangle, passes deep to the trapezius muscle a little above the clavicle, and ramifies.

Deep Structures (Fig. 36-2)

TRANSVERSE CERVICAL A. Arising from the thyrocervical trunk, it ascends and crosses the lower third of the triangle, passing over the scalenus anterior muscle and the brachial plexus. At the levator scapulae muscle it divides into:

ascending branch. To the levator scapulae and adjacent deep cervical muscles.

descending branch. Beneath the levator scapulae to the scapula.

SUPRASCAPULAR A. Also arising from the thyrocervical trunk, it descends laterally along the root of the neck, passing behind the sternocleidomastoid muscle and the clavicle. It then passes deep to the trapezius muscle to the scapula.

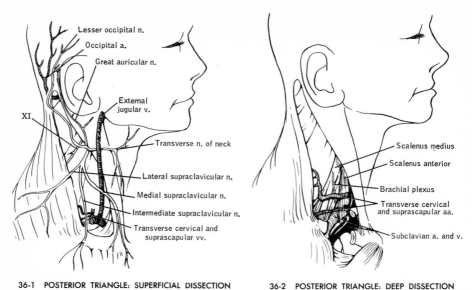

36-1 POSTERIOR TRIANGLE: SUPERFICIAL DISSECTION

36-2 POSTERIOR TRIANGLE: DEEP DISSECTION

Lesser occipital n.

Occipital a.

Great auricular n.

External jugular v.

XI

Transverse n. of neck

Lateral supraclavicular n.

Medial supraclavicular n.

Intermediate supraclavicular n.

Transverse cervical and suprascapular vv.

Scalenus medius

Scalenus anterior

Brachial plexus

Transverse cervical and suprascapular aa.

Subclavian a. and v.

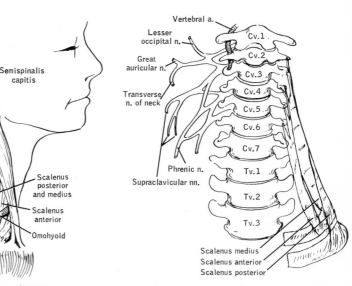

36-3 POSTERIOR TRIANGLE: MUSCLES

36-4 CERVICAL PLEXUS AND SCALENE MUSCLES

Semispinalis capitis

Splenius capitis

Levator scapulae

Scalenus posterior and medius

Scalenus anterior

Omohyoid

Vertebral a.

Lesser occipital n.

Great auricular n.

Transverse n. of neck

Phrenic n.

Supraclavicular nn.

Cv.1
Cv.2
Cv.3
Cv.4
Cv.5
Cv.6
Cv.7
Tv.1
Tv.2
Tv.3

Scalenus medius
Scalenus anterior
Scalenus posterior

Plate 36

SUBCLAVIAN A. (THIRD PART). Entering the triangle at the lateral border of the scalenus anterior muscle a little above the clavicle, it descends laterally, leaves the triangle at the outer margin of the first rib (apex of the axilla), and becomes the axillary a. It has no branches in the triangle.

SUBCLAVIAN V. The continuation of the axillary v. enters the triangle behind the middle of the clavicle, ascends medially on the scalenus anterior muscle (which separates it from the subclavian a.), and joins the internal jugular v. to form the brachiocephalic v. behind the sternocleidomastoid muscle.

BRACHIAL PLEXUS. Emerging into the triangle at the lateral border of the scalenus anterior muscle above the third part of the subclavian a., it descends on the scalenus medius, passes behind the transverse cervical and suprascapular aa., and leaves the triangle behind the middle third of the clavicle to enter the axilla. In the triangle the branches of the brachial plexus are those from its roots (p. 135).

4. Muscles of the Floor of the Triangle (Fig. 36-3)

SEMISPINALIS CAPITIS. This lies only in the triangle at its apex. (See back muscles, p. 354).

SPLENIUS CAPITIS. (p. 353)

LEVATOR SCAPULAE. (p. 122)

Lateral Vertebral Muscles (Fig. 36-4)

SCALENUS ANTERIOR. It lies behind the sternocleidomastoid muscle.

Origin: Anterior tubercles of the transverse processes of Cv 3 to 6.

Insertion: Scalene tubercle of first rib.

Action: Elevates first rib and bends neck to the side.

Nerve supply: Ventral rami of Cn 4 to 7.

SCALENUS MEDIUS. Longest and largest muscle of this group.

Origin: Posterior tubercles of the transverse processes of Cv 1 to 7.

Insertion: First rib, between its tubercle and the subclavian groove.

Action: Elevates first rib and bends neck to the side.

Nerve supply: Ventral rami of Cn 3 to 7.

SCALENUS POSTERIOR. Smallest muscle of the group, it lies behind and may be blended with the medius muscle.

Origin: Posterior tubercles of the transverse processes of Cv 4 to 6.

Insertion: Lateral surface of second rib.

Action: Elevates second rib, bends neck to side.

Nerve supply: Ventral rami of Cn 5 to 7.

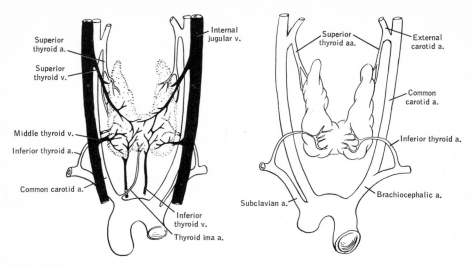

37-1 BLOOD SUPPLY OF THYROID: ANTERIOR VIEW

Superior thyroid a.
Superior thyroid v.
Middle thyroid v.
Inferior thyroid a.
Common carotid a.
Internal jugular v.
Inferior thyroid v.
Thyroid ima a.

37-2 BLOOD SUPPLY OF THYROID: POSTERIOR VIEW

Superior thyroid aa.
External carotid a.
Common carotid a.
Inferior thyroid a.
Subclavian a.
Brachiocephalic a.

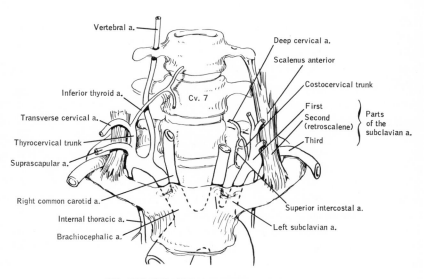

37-3 BRANCHES OF THE SUBCLAVIAN ARTERY

Vertebral a.
Deep cervical a.
Scalenus anterior
Costocervical trunk
Inferior thyroid a.
Cv. 7
First
Second (retroscalene)
Parts of the subclavian a.
Transverse cervical a.
Thyrocervical trunk
Third
Suprascapular a.
Right common carotid a.
Internal thoracic a.
Brachiocephalic a.
Superior intercostal a.
Left subclavian a.

Plate 37

ROOT OF THE NECK

1. *Thymus*
2. *Thyroid and parathyroid glands*
3. *Trachea and esophagus* (cervical part)
4. *Deep arteries*
5. *Deep veins*
6. *Deep nerves: vagus n. and sympathetic trunk*
7. *Prevertebral muscles*

This region is occupied by the structures that enter or leave the thoracic cavity. In the neck they lie largely behind the sternocleidomastoid muscle, which must be displaced when this area is examined.

1. Thymus

This ductless gland is functional in the child. In the adult it consists of fibrous and fatty tissue. It is usually composed of two lobes, which lie on the trachea, behind the infrahyoid muscles, and extends into the thorax over the great vessels and pericardium.

2. Thyroid Gland (Figs. 37-1, 37-2) and Parathyroid Glands

The thyroid gland, also a ductless gland, is enclosed in a fibrous capsule. It consists of two *lobes* united across the front of the trachea by an *isthmus*. Each piriform lobe extends from the oblique line of the thyroid cartilage to the level of the sixth tracheal ring. The isthmus lies on the second to fourth tracheal rings. A *pyramidal lobe* extends up from the left side of the isthmus and is connected with the hyoid bone by a fibrous or muscular band.

The neurovascular system of the thyroid gland is supplied by:

arteries: The superior thyroid from the external carotid a.; the inferior thyroid from the thyrocervical trunk of the first part of the subclavian a. and the thyroidea ima a., an occasional branch from the brachiocephalic a.

veins: These are derived from the plexus on the surface of the gland. The superior thyroid v. empties into the upper part of the internal jugular v. The middle thyroid v. empties into the lower part of the internal jugular v. and the inferior thyroid v. empties into the brachiocephalic v.

nerves: Vasoconstrictors, derived from the cervical sympathetic ganglions.

The parathyroid glands are two pairs of lens-shaped ductless glands embedded in the back of the capsule of the thyroid gland. A branch of the inferior thyroid a. supplies each gland.

3. Trachea and Esophagus (Cervical Part)

The trachea is continuous with the larynx. It begins opposite Cv 6, just below the cricoid cartilage, to which it is attached by the cricotracheal ligament. It terminates opposite the sternal angle (Tv 5) by dividing into the right and left *bronchi*. The structural frame of the trachea consists of about 15 horseshoe-shaped cartilaginous bars which round out the front and sides of the trachea. The back is flat and closed by the *trachealis* muscle. The cervical part of the trachea lies behind the infrahyoid muscles and in front of the esophagus.

The esophagus, a flattened muscular tube, is continuous with the pharynx (also at the level of Cv 6) and with the stomach. It lies behind the trachea and in front of the cervical vertebrae. The lower part of the esophagus lies in the thorax and abdomen.

4. Deep Arteries (Fig. 37-3)

Brachiocephalic A.

Arising from the arch of the aorta opposite the center of the manubrium on the front of the trachea, it ascends laterally behind the right sternoclavicular joint and divides into the right common carotid and the right subclavian aa.

RIGHT COMMON CAROTID A. The other terminal branch of the brachiocephalic a. ascends through the lower part of the neck and provides no branches until it enters the carotid triangle, where it divides into the external and internal carotid aa. The left common carotid a. arises from the aortic arch and takes the same course as the right common carotid a.

RIGHT SUBCLAVIAN A. This artery extends as an arch from the joint to the outer border of the first rib, where it becomes the axillary a. The left subclavian a. arises directly from the arch of the aorta on the left side of the trachea. It takes the same course in the neck as the right subclavian a.

The subclavian a. is divided into three parts by the scalenus anterior muscle.

First Part. The first, or prescalene, portion extends from behind the sternoclavicular joint to the medial border of the scalenus anterior muscle. Its branches are:

Vertebral a.: Arising from the upper surface of the subclavian a., it ascends behind the carotid sheath to pass into the foramen transversarium of Cv 6. It continues through the foramens of the upper cervical vertebrae and winds around the lateral mass of the atlas in the suboccipital triangle. It enters the cranial cavity through the foramen magnum and unites with its counterpart to form the basilar a. This artery can be divided into cervical, vertebral, suboccipital, and intracranial parts.

Table 39

Branch	Areas supplied
Ascending cervical a................	Muscular branches: to scalenus anterior and longus colli mm.
	Spinal branches: to vertebrae and spinal cord
Inferior laryngeal a..................	Mucous membrane and muscles of larynx
Tracheal and esophageal branches....	Trachea and esophagus

Thyrocervical trunk: This trunk also arises from the upper surface of the subclavian a., but closer to the scalenus anterior muscle than does the vertebral a. It ascends for a short distance, then divides into (1) the *transverse cervical a.* and (2) the *suprascapular a.*, which course laterally across the scalenus medius muscle behind the sternocleidomastoid muscle to enter the posterior triangle.

Inferior thyroid a.: This ascends along the medial border of the scalenus anterior muscle to the level of Cv 6, where it curves medially to the middle of the back of the lobe of the thyroid gland. Its branches are given in Table 39.

Second Part. The second, or retroscalene, portion represents the highest part of the arch. Its sole branch is:

Costocervical trunk: Arising from the back of the subclavian a., it arches over the cupola of the pleura to the neck of the first rib, where it divides into:

deep cervical a. Coursing backward between Cv 7 and the neck of the first rib, it ascends in the back of the neck and supplies the muscles of this region.

superior intercostal a. Descending behind the pleura, it divides into the first two posterior intercostal aa.

Third Part. The third, or postscalene, portion is located in the posterior triangle and extends from the lateral border of the scalenus muscle to the outer border of the first rib. No branches arise from this part.

5. Deep Veins (Fig. 38-1)

VERTEBRAL V. Descending through the foramina transversaria of the upper six cervical vertebrae, it terminates in the brachiocephalic v. It receives the anterior vertebral v. and the deep cervical v., which correspond to the ascending cervical a. and deep cervical a., respectively.

INTERNAL JUGULAR V. The largest vein in the neck begins as the dilated superior bulb at the jugular foramen, as a continuation of the sigmoid sinus. It descends on the lateral side of the internal and common carotid aa. and joins the subclavian v. to form the brachiocephalic v. Near its lower end it is dilated as the inferior bulb.

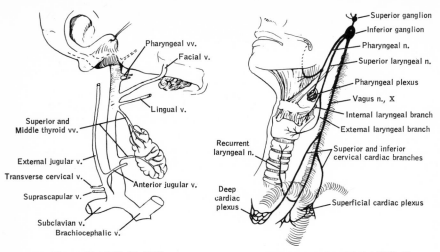

Pharyngeal vv.

Facial v.

Lingual v.

Superior and
Middle thyroid vv.

External jugular v.

Transverse cervical v.

Suprascapular v.

Subclavian v.

Brachiocephalic v.

38-1   DEEP VEINS OF NECK

Superior ganglion

Inferior ganglion

Pharyngeal n.

Superior laryngeal n.

Pharyngeal plexus

Vagus n., X

Internal laryngeal branch

External laryngeal branch

Recurrent
laryngeal n.

Superior and inferior
cervical cardiac branches

Deep
cardiac
plexus

Superficial cardiac plexus

38-2   CERVICAL PART OF VAGUS NERVE (X)

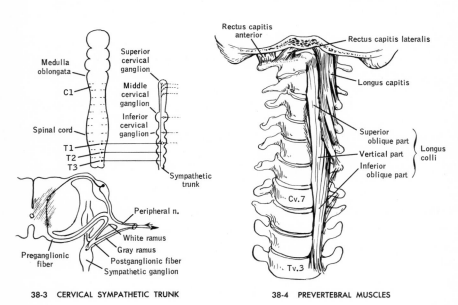

Medulla
oblongata

C1

Spinal cord

T1
T2
T3

Superior
cervical
ganglion

Middle
cervical
ganglion

Inferior
cervical
ganglion

Sympathetic
trunk

Peripheral n.

White ramus

Gray ramus

Postganglionic fiber

Sympathetic ganglion

Preganglionic
fiber

38-3   CERVICAL SYMPATHETIC TRUNK

Rectus capitis
anterior

Rectus capitis lateralis

Longus capitis

Superior
oblique part

Vertical part

Inferior
oblique part

Longus
colli

Cv. 7

Tv. 3

38-4   PREVERTEBRAL MUSCLES

Plate 38

Table 40

Region	Tributary
At jugular foramen....	Inferior petrosal sinus
In carotid triangle.....	Lingual vv., pharyngeal vv., common facial v., superior thyroid v.
In root of neck........	Middle thyroid v.

The tributaries of the internal jugular v. are shown in Table 40.

INFERIOR THYROID V. This arises from the venous plexus on the isthmus and medial parts of the lobes and terminates in the brachiocephalic v.

SUBCLAVIAN V. This short vein begins as a continuation of the axillary v. at the outer border of the first rib. It terminates by joining the internal jugular v. to form the brachiocephalic v. Its sole tributary is the external jugular v.

BRACHIOCEPHALIC VV. Beginning behind the clavicle by the union of the subclavian and internal jugular vv., they terminate by joining each other to form the superior vena cava behind the junction of the first right costal cartilage and the manubrium. The left vein is longer than the right, and both lack valves. Tributaries are the vertebral, inferior thyroid, and highest intercostal vv.

6. Deep Nerves

VAGUS N. (X) (Fig. 38-2). Containing sensory, motor, and secretory fibers, it originates at the side of the medulla and emerges from the jugular foramen, where it exhibits its superior and inferior ganglions. It descends in the carotid sheath, between the back parts of the internal jugular v. and carotid aa. to the root of the neck. The right vagus passes between the internal jugular v. and the first part of the subclavian a.; the left vagus passes between the left common carotid a. and the first part of the left subclavian a. Both continue into the thorax.

The branches of the vagus n. in the head and neck are summarized in Table 41.

Branches in the Head. Two branches arise in the jugular fossa:

Meningeal branch: A recurrent branch to the dura mater.

Auricular branch: Passing into the mastoid canaliculus starting in the lateral wall of the jugular fossa, it emerges again through the tympanomastoid fissure on the side of the skull just behind the external acoustic meatus.

Branches in the Neck

Pharyngeal branches: These branches descend between the external and internal carotid aa. to the side of the pharynx, where they ramify and, together with branches from IX and the sympathetic n., form the pharyngeal plexus. They also contribute branches to the internal carotid plexus, which innervates the carotid body.

Table 41

Site of origin	Branch	Area supplied
Superior ganglion.....	Meningeal	Dura mater and posterior cranial fossa
	Auricular	Back of external ear; lower part of meatus and tympanic membrane
Inferior ganglion.....	Pharyngeal branches	Muscles of pharynx and soft palate
	Superior laryngeal n.	
	Internal laryngeal branch	Mucous membrane of larynx from epiglottis to the vocal cords
	External laryngeal branch	Inferior constrictor and cricothyroid mm.
Trunk..............	Cervical cardiac branches	Cardiac plexuses
	Recurrent laryngeal n.	Muscles of larynx and mucous membranes below vocal cords

Table 42

Branches	*Course*
Gray rami communicantes...............	Join ventral rami of Cv 1–4
Pharyngeal branches....................	Join pharyngeal plexus
Internal carotid n......................	Forms internal carotid plexus
External carotid n......................	Forms external carotid plexus
Nerve to internal carotid plexus...........	Forms with branches of IX and X to carotid body
Superior cervical cardiac n...............	Right—deep; left—superficial, cardiac plexuses

Table 43

Branches	*Course*
Gray rami communicantes...............	Join ventral rami of Cn 5 and 6
Thyroid branches.......................	Accompany the inferior thyroid a. to the gland
Middle cervical cardiac n................	Joins the deep cardiac plexus
Ansa subclavia.........................	Loops around subclavian a. and joins inferior ganglion

Table 44

Branches	*Course*
Gray rami communicantes.................	Join ventral rami of Cn 5 and 6
Vertebral branches.......................	Form a plexus around vertebral a.
Inferior cervical cardiac n.................	Accompanies middle n. to deep cardiac plexus
Subclavian branches.....................	Join ansa subclavia

Superior laryngeal n.: It descends medial to the internal carotid a. along the side of the pharynx, where it divides into:

internal laryngeal branch. Piercing the thyrohyoid membrane, it descends to reach the larynx.

external laryngeal branch. It courses deep to the sternothyroid muscle and thyroid gland to the cricothyroid muscle.

Cervical cardiac branches: Arising from the trunk of X at two different levels, they are named accordingly:

superior cardiac branch. Descending behind the carotid plexus and major vessels to the deep cardiac plexus.

inferior cardiac branch. Arising at the root of the neck and on the right side, it passes into the thorax at the side of the trachea to the deep cardiac plexus. On the left side this branch descends over the arch of the aorta and curves medially to end in the superficial cardiac plexus.

Recurrent laryngeal n.: Arising on the right side from the vagus n., it crosses the subclavian a., hooks around the artery, and ascends on the side of the esophagus and trachea. On the left side it arises as the vagus n. crosses the aortic arch, and hooks around it. In the neck each nerve ascends on the side of the trachea, passes under the lower border of the inferior constrictor muscle, and reaches the larynx. The branches of this nerve are:

cardiac branches. To the deep cardiac plexus.

tracheal and esophageal branches. To the muscles and mucosa of the trachea and esophagus.

pharyngeal branches. To the inferior constrictor muscle.

laryngeal branches. To intrinsic muscles of the larynx (except the cricothyroid).

SYMPATHETIC TRUNK (Fig. 38-3). This is embedded in the posterior wall of the carotid sheath. In the neck it consists of three interconnected ganglions and their branches. It has no white rami communicantes but consists of ascending preganglionic axons that have entered the trunk from Tn 2 and 3.

Superior Cervical Ganglion. This spindle-shaped ganglion is the largest of the three comprising the sympathetic trunk; it is located in front of the transverse process of Cv 2. Its branches are shown in Table 42.

Middle Cervical Ganglion. The smallest of the ganglions is opposite Cv 6. Its branches are given in Table 43.

Inferior Cervical Ganglion. This generally lies at the level of Cn 6. Its branches are listed in Table 44.

Stellate Ganglion. This ganglion is formed by fusion of the inferior cervical and first thoracic ganglions and is present most of the time. It has branches to Cn 6 to Tn 2 and forms a vertebral plexus. It is also known as the *cervicothoracic ganglion.*

7. Prevertebral Muscles (Fig. 38-4)

The prevertebral, or anterior vertebral, muscles are four in number:

LONGUS CAPITIS. This is broad and thick above, narrow below.

Origin: Anterior tubercles of transverse processes of Cv 3 to 6.

Insertion: Basilar part of occipital bone.

Action: Flexes head.

Nerve supply: Branches from ventral rami of Cn 1 to 3.

LONGUS COLLI. This consists of three parts:

Superior Oblique Part

Origin: Anterior tubercles of transverse processes of Cv 3 to 5.

Insertion: Tubercle on anterior arch of atlas.

Vertical Part

Origin: Anterior surface of bodies of Cv 5 to 7 and Tv 1 to 3.

Insertion: Anterior surface of bodies of Cv 2 to 4.

Inferior Oblique Part

Origin: Anterior surface of bodies of Tv 1 to 2.

Insertion: Anterior tubercles of transverse processes of Cv 5 to 6.

Action: Flexes neck and slightly rotates the cervical part of the vertebral column.

Nerve supply: Branches from ventral rami of Cn 2 to 7.

RECTUS CAPITIS ANTERIOR. It is short and flat.

Origin: Transverse process and lateral mass of atlas.

Insertion: Inferior surface of basilar part of occipital bone.

Action: Flexes head.

Nerve supply: Branches of ventral rami of Cn 1 and 2.

RECTUS CAPITIS LATERALIS. It is short and flat.

Origin: Transverse process of atlas.

Insertion: Inferior surface of jugular process of occipital bone.

Action: Bends head laterally.

Nerve supply: Branch of ventral rami of Cn 1 and 2.

The sternocleidomastoid muscle covers the structures at the root of the neck.

STERNOCLEIDOMASTOID. Extends obliquely up the neck (Fig. 31-1).

Origin:

Sternal head: front of the manubrium. It is rounded and tendinous.

Clavicular head: medial third of the clavicle. It is of variable width.

Insertion: The lateral surface of the mastoid process and the lateral third of the superior nuchal line on the occipital bone.

Action: Acting together they flex the neck and extend the head. Acting alone each flexes the head and bends it to that side.

Nerve supply: Accessory n. (XI) and ventral rami of Cn 2 and 3.

UPPER EXTREMITY

The upper limb consists of the shoulder, arm, forearm, and hand.

Table 45

Shoulder	Arm	Forearm	Hand
Superficies of back Deltoid and scapula regions Pectoral region Axilla	Front Back Cubital fossa	Front Back	Dorsum Palm

SHOULDER

The upper limbs are connected to the trunk by the bones of the shoulder, the *pectoral girdle*. This girdle consists of the scapulae, the clavicles, and the manubrium of the sternum, which articulates with the medial ends of the clavicles. The scapula and clavicle on each side articulate at the acromioclavicular joint. The upper limb is characterized by its wide range of mobility, which it owes to bony contact between the limb and the trunk at only one point, the small sternoclavicular joint.

SUPERFICIES OF THE BACK

1. Superficial fascia   *2. Superficial muscles of the back*

The superficial muscles of the back provide support during many movements of the upper limb and are thus discussed at this point.

1. Superficial Fascia

The superficial fascia of the back varies in thickness and fat content.

Cutaneous Nerves (Figs. 39-1, 39-2). Originating from the dorsal ramus (posterior primary division) of the spinal nerves, each of these rami divides into a medial and a lateral branch; these branches innervate the deep muscles of the back. Only one branch appears on the surface as a cutaneous nerve. Above the midthorax, the terminal cutaneous nerves arise from the medial branches; below this level, they arise from the lateral branches. Table 46 shows the cutaneous distribution of the dorsal rami of the spinal nerves.

119

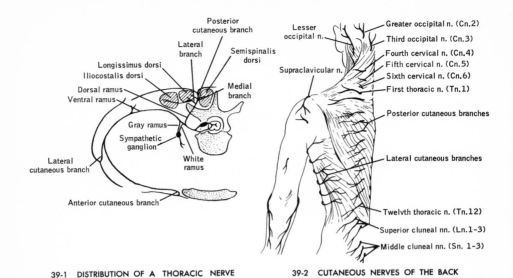

Posterior
cutaneous branch

Lateral
branch

Semispinalis
dorsi

Longissimus dorsi
Iliocostalis dorsi

Dorsal ramus
Ventral ramus

Medial
branch

Gray ramus

Sympathetic
ganglion

White
ramus

Lateral
cutaneous branch

Anterior cutaneous branch

Lesser
occipital n.

Supraclavicular n.

Greater occipital n. (Cn.2)

Third occipital n. (Cn.3)

Fourth cervical n. (Cn.4)

Fifth cervical n. (Cn.5)

Sixth cervical n. (Cn.6)

First thoracic n. (Tn.1)

Posterior cutaneous branches

Lateral cutaneous branches

Twelvth thoracic n. (Tn.12)

Superior cluneal nn. (Ln.1-3)

Middle cluneal nn. (Sn. 1-3)

39-1 DISTRIBUTION OF A THORACIC NERVE   39-2 CUTANEOUS NERVES OF THE BACK

Levator scapulae

Rhomboideus minor

Rhomboideus major

Trapezius

Deltoid

Teres major

Teres minor

Latissimus dorsi

Thoracolumbar fascia

39-3 SUPERFICIAL BACK MUSCLES

Plate 39

Table 46

Origin	Nerve	Cutaneous distribution
Cervical region:		
Cn 1...............		No sensory branches
Cn 2...............	Greater occipital n.	Back of head
Cn 3...............	Third occipital n.	Upper back of neck
Cn 4–6............		Lower back of neck
Cn 5...............		No sensory branches
Thoracic region:		
Tn 1–6.............		Scapular region
Tn 7–12............		Lower chest and loin
Lumbar region:		
Ln 1–3.............	Superior cluneal nn.	Gluteal region
Ln 4–5.............		No sensory branches
Sacral region:		
Sn 1–3.............	Middle cluneal nn.	Back of sacrum

Cutaneous Blood Vessels. The cutaneous blood vessels accompany the cutaneous nerves, and they arise from the ascending branch of the transverse cervical a. in the neck, the intercostal aa. in the thorax, and the lumbar aa. in the loin.

2. Superficial Muscles of the Back (Fig. 39-3)

The five superficial muscles of the back connect the upper limb to the vertebral column. Because they originate from a ventrolateral sheet of trunk musculature that migrated backward, they are innervated by the ventral rami of the spinal nerves. The muscles are arranged in two layers. The trapezius and latissimus dorsi are superficial, and the levator scapulae and the two rhomboideae lie deep to the trapezius and have a continuous insertion on the vertebral border of the scapula.

TRAPEZIUS. Large and triangular, the trapezius is located on the back of the neck and thorax.

Origin: External occipital protuberance, medial third of superior nuchal line, nuchal ligament, spinous processes of Cv 7 and Tv 1 to 12, and supraspinous ligaments.

Insertion:

Occipital part: Posterior border of the lateral third of the clavicle.

Cervical part: Medial border of the acromion and crest of the scapular spine.

Thoracic part: Tubercle of the crest of the scapular spine.

Action:

Entire muscle: Rotates scapula and elevates its lateral angle.

Occipital part: Elevates scapula.

Cervical part: Draws scapula toward vertebral column.

Thoracic part: Depresses scapula.

Nerve supply: Accessory n. (IX).

LATISSIMUS DORSI. The latissimus dorsi muscle is large, triangular, and located over the lower part of the back.

Origin: Aponeurosis from the posterior layer of the thoracolumbar fascia (p. 351). It provides attachment to the spinous processes of the lower six thoracic vertebrae, all the lumbar and sacral vertebrae, the supraspinous ligaments, and the posterior third of the iliac crest.

Insertion: Floor of the intertubercular groove.

Action:

Trunk fixed: Adducts, extends, and rotates the humerus medialward.

Humerus fixed: Elevates the trunk and the pelvis.

Nerve supply: Middle subscapular (thoracodorsal) n.

LEVATOR SCAPULAE. Thick and straplike, the levator scapulae muscle is located on the back and side of the neck.

Origin: Posterior tubercles of the transverse processes of Cv 1 to 4.

Insertion: Vertebral border of the scapula from the superior angle to the root of the spine.

Action: Raises the scapula and tends to rotate it so as to lower its lateral angle; with the scapula fixed, it rotates the neck to the same side.

Nerve supply: Cn 3 and 4 direct from the cervical plexus; Cn 5 via the dorsal scapular n.

RHOMBOIDEUS MINOR. A slender band, this muscle parallels the rhomboideus major muscle and is poorly separated from it.

Origin: Lower part of nuchal ligament and the spinous processes of Cv 7 and Tv 1 and associated supraspinal ligaments.

Insertion: Vertebral border of the scapula at the root of the spine.

Action: Elevates and draws the scapula towards the vertebral column.

Nerve supply: Dorsal scapular n.

RHOMBOIDEUS MAJOR. The rhomboideus major muscle is thin and flat.

Origin: Spinous processes of Tv 2 to 5 and supraspinous ligaments.

Insertion: Vertebral border of the scapula from the root of the scapular spine to its inferior angle.

Action: Elevates and draws the scapula towards the vertebral column.

Nerve supply: Dorsal scapular n.

DELTOID AND SCAPULAR REGIONS

1. *Fascia*   3. *Deep arteries*

2. *Muscles*   4. *Deep nerves*

The deltoid and scapular regions provide the general form of the shoulder. This form is determined primarily by the skeleton, but the details are provided by the muscles and tendons.

1. Fascia

SUPERFICIAL. The superficial fascia of the deltoid and scapular regions contains a moderate quantity of fat and the lateral part of the platysma.

Cutaneous Nerves (Fig. 41-1)

cutaneous branches of dorsal rami. From the upper thoracic nerves.

lateral supraclavicular nn. Extending over the upper half of the deltoid.

lateral brachial cutaneous n. A branch of the axillary n.

Cutaneous Vessels. They consist of unnamed branches of the circumflex humeral and thoracoacromial aa.

DEEP. The deltoid muscle is invested by fascia which passes between the fasciculi. The fascia covering the pectoralis major muscle is continous with the fascia covering the infraspinatus muscle via the deep fascia of the deltoid muscle. It is attached above to the clavicle, acromion, and scapular spine and is continuous with the deep fascia of the arm. Over the supraspinatus muscle, it is thin; over the infraspinatus and teres major and minor muscles, it is dense.

2. Muscles (Figs. 40-1, 40-2)

DELTOID. The deltoid muscle is thick, triangular, and coarse-textured.

Origin:

Clavicular part: Front of lateral third of the clavicle.

Acromial part: Lateral border of the acromion.

Spinous part: Lower lip of the crest of the scapular spine.

Insertion: Deltoid tuberosity of the humerus.

Action:

Clavicular part: Flexor and medial rotator.

Acromial part: Abducts arm.

Spinous part: Extensor and lateral rotator.

Nerve supply: Axillary n.

SUPRASPINATUS. The triangular supraspinatus muscle fills the supraspinatus fossa.

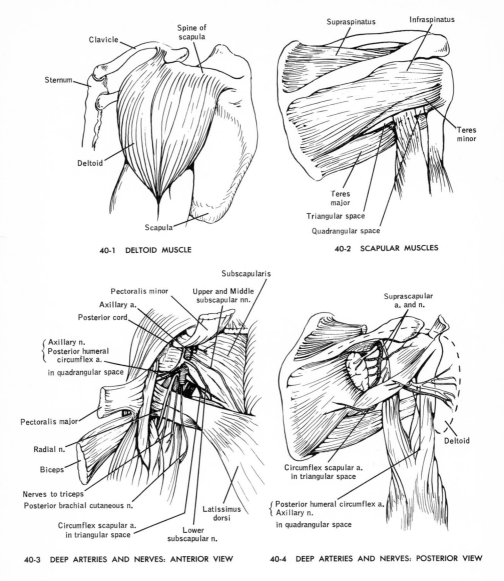

40-1 DELTOID MUSCLE

40-2 SCAPULAR MUSCLES

40-3 DEEP ARTERIES AND NERVES: ANTERIOR VIEW

40-4 DEEP ARTERIES AND NERVES: POSTERIOR VIEW

Plate 40

Origin: Medial three-fourths of the walls of the infraspinous fossa and from the fascia that covers the muscle.

Insertion: Superior facet on the greater tuberosity of the humerus.

Action: Abductor.

Nerve supply: Suprascapular n.

INFRASPINATUS. The infraspinatus muscle is also triangular; it fills most of the infraspinatus fossa.

Origin: Medial three-fourths of the walls of the infraspinous fossa and from the fascia that covers the muscle.

Insertion: Middle facet on the greater tuberosity of the humerus.

Action: Extends arm and rotates it laterally.

Nerve supply: Suprascapular n.

TERES MAJOR

Origin: Dorsal surface of the inferior angle of the scapula.

Insertion: Medial lip of intertubercular groove of the humerus.

Action: Adductor and medial rotator of the arm.

Nerve supply: Lower subscapular n.

SUBSCAPULARIS. The large, triangular subscapularis muscle fills the sub-scapular fossa.

Origin: Medial two-thirds of the subscapular fossa.

Insertion: Lesser tuberosity of the humerus.

Action: Adductor and medial rotator of the arm.

Nerve supply: Upper and lower subscapular nn.

Quadrangular Space (Figs. 40-3, 40-4). It transmits the axillary n. and posterior humeral circumflex vessels. Its boundaries are:

Superior boundary: subscapularis and teres minor muscles

Inferior boundary: teres major muscle

Lateral boundary: surgical neck of humerus

Medial boundary: long head of triceps muscle

Triangular Space (Figs. 40-3, 40-4). It transmits the scapular circumflex vessels and has the following boundaries:

Superior boundary: subscapularis and teres minor muscles

Inferior boundary: teres major muscle

Lateral boundary: long head of triceps muscle

3. Deep Arteries (Figs. 40-3, 40-4)

ANTERIOR HUMERAL CIRCUMFLEX A. A branch of the axillary a., it curves around the surgical neck of the humerus and anastomoses with the posterior humeral circumflex a. Its branches are:

muscular branches. To the coracobrachialis, short head of the biceps, and a descending branch to the pectoralis major muscle.

ascending branch. Courses in the intertubercular groove to the shoulder joint.

POSTERIOR HUMERAL CIRCUMFLEX A. Arising from the third part of the axillary a., it accompanies the axillary n. and its anterior branch. It terminates by anastomosing with the anterior humeral circumflex a. Its branches are:

articular branch. To the shoulder joint.

muscular branch. To the deltoid muscle.

nutrient branch. To the greater tuberosity.

descending branch. Follows the lateral head of the triceps to supply it and the long head, and to anastomose with the ascending branch of the deep brachial a.

CIRCUMFLEX SCAPULAR A. A branch of the subscapular a., it arises in the axilla. It curves backward at the lower border of the subscapularis muscle into the triangular space and leaves the space by turning medially deep to the teres minor muscle onto the dorsum of the scapula, which it grooves. Its branches in the infraspinous fossa are:

anterior branch. Runs deep to the subscapularis muscle and supplies it.

descending branch. Runs toward the inferior angle of the scapula, between the teres major and minor muscles, supplying them both.

SUPRASCAPULAR A. Arising in the neck from the thyrocervical trunk, it takes a course downwards, sidewards, and backwards along the root of the neck, descending under the trapezius muscle to the scapula. It passes over the suprascapular ligament to reach the supraspinous fossa and terminates in the infraspinous fossa, where it joins the circumscapular anastomoses. Its branches are:

muscular branches. To the supraspinatus and infraspinatus muscles.

articular branches. To the acromioclavicular and shoulder joints.

acromial branches. Piercing the trapezius muscle, they supply the skin over the acromion.

subscapular branches. They pass into the subscapular fossa, ramifying there and supplying the subscapularis muscle.

The corresponding veins are superficial and end in the external jugular v.

Circumscapular Anastomosis. This anastomosis establishes a link between the first part of the subclavian a. and the third part of the axillary a. It is derived from the four sources shown in Table 47.

4. Deep Nerves (Fig. 40-4)

AXILLARY N. This is a branch of the posterior cord of the brachial plexus which leaves the axilla at the lower border of the subscapularis muscle by passing back-

Table 47

Scapular border	*Arterial branch*
Superior........	Suprascapular
Lateral.........	Subscapular
Medial.........	Deep branch of transverse cervical a.
Dorsum........	Scapular circumflex

ward through the quadrangular space. It provides an articular branch to the shoulder joint and divides into two branches. Its branches are:

anterior branch. Winds around beneath the deltoid muscle, supplying it and the overlying skin.

posterior branch. Provides rami to the teres minor and deltoid muscles and curves around the lower border of the deltoid muscle. It pierces the deep fascia and, as the lateral brachial cutaneous n., supplies the skin on the upper posterior part of the arm. This encompasses the skin over the long head of the triceps and part of the deltoid.

SUPRASCAPULAR N. A branch of the brachial plexus, it crosses the posterior cervical triangle and passes deep to the trapezius muscle just above the clavicle. It descends to the suprascapular notch, where it courses under the ligament and into the supraspinous fossa, continuing on to terminate in the infraspinous fossa. Its branches are:

articular branches. To the shoulder joint.

muscular branches. To the supraspinatus and infraspinatus muscles.

PECTORAL REGION

1. Superficial fascia   *3. Deep fascia*

2. Breast   *4. Muscles*

The breast situated on the front of the thorax, is intimately related to the pectoral region and thus is included in this section.

1. Superficial Fascia

Fat is particularly abundant in the region of the mammary gland. The fascia also contains:

Cutaneous Nerves (Fig. 41-1)

supraclavicular nn. The ends of these three nerves pass over the clavicle onto the pectoral region (p. 107).

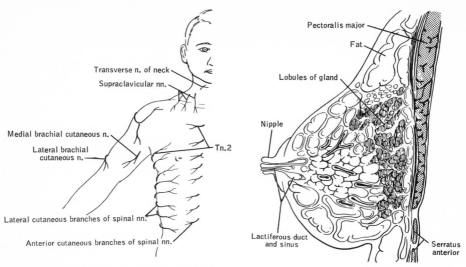

41-1 PECTORAL REGION: CUTANEOUS NERVES

Transverse n. of neck
Supraclavicular nn.
Medial brachial cutaneous n.
Lateral brachial cutaneous n.
Tn. 2
Lateral cutaneous branches of spinal nn.
Anterior cutaneous branches of spinal nn.

41-2 BREAST: LONGITUDINAL SECTION

Pectoralis major
Fat
Lobules of gland
Nipple
Lactiferous duct and sinus
Serratus anterior

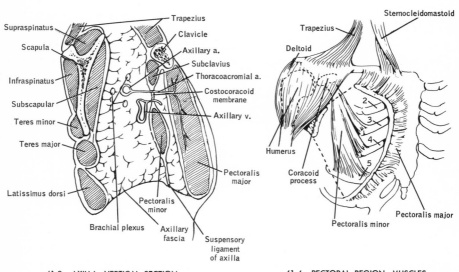

41-3 AXILLA: VERTICAL SECTION

Supraspinatus
Scapula
Infraspinatus
Subscapular
Teres minor
Teres major
Latissimus dorsi
Brachial plexus
Axillary fascia
Trapezius
Clavicle
Axillary a.
Subclavius
Thoracoacromial a.
Costocoracoid membrane
Axillary v.
Pectoralis major
Pectoralis minor
Suspensory ligament of axilla

41-4 PECTORAL REGION: MUSCLES

Sternocleidomastoid
Trapezius
Deltoid
Humerus
Coracoid process
Pectoralis minor
Pectoralis major

Plate 41

128

anterior cutaneous nn. The upper six terminal branches of the intercostal nn. emerge through the intercostal spaces to pierce the pectoralis major muscle and deep fascia at the border of the sternum. Each nerve divides into a short medial branch, which passes to the midline, and a longer lateral branch. The lateral branch passes sideways over the pectoral musculature to innervate the skin and fascia. In the female it provides medial mammary branches to the breast. Collectively, the anterior cutaneous nn. supply the medial part of the anterior thoracic wall. Their distribution meets that of the anterior branches of the lateral cutaneous nn.

lateral cutaneous nn. The third to sixth intercostal nn. provide branches that pierce the musculature covering the ribs at the midaxillary line and then divide into anterior and posterior branches. The anterior branches curve forward, out of the axilla, and around the lateral margin of the pectoralis major muscle. They supply the lateral part of the anterior thoracic wall.

Cutaneous Arteries. Small perforating branches of the internal thoracic a. accompany the anterior cutaneous nn. In the female, branches in the second to fourth intercostal spaces are large because they supply the mammary gland.

2. Breast (Fig. 41-2)

The mammary gland is rudimentary in the male, in the aged female, and in children. Each breast extends from the second to the sixth rib and from the sternum to the axilla. The breast consists of the mammary gland, stroma, and skin.

MAMMARY GLAND. This exocrine, compound alveolar gland consists of from 15 to 20 lobes that radiate from the nipple and occupy the central portion of the breast. Each lobe has a single *lactiferous duct.* The ducts converge towards the areola (see p. 130), beneath which each is dilated to form a secretory reservoir, the *lactiferous sinus.* The ducts then narrow and directly traverse the nipple to its summit, where they open in very constricted individual orifices. Distally each duct branches and rebranches and finally terminates in an *alveolus.* The alveoli and their ducts are lined with the secretory cells that are activated during pregnancy. A group of alveoli, which have a common duct, constitute a *lobule.* This is the basic structural unit of the mammary gland. All lobules that drain through the same excretory lactiferous duct comprise a *lobe.*

STROMA. Fibrous connective tissue loosely envelops the entire gland and extends into its substance to enclose the parenchymal units, the lobes, lobules, and alveoli. In addition bundles of collagenous fibers, the *suspensory ligaments,* traverse the breast; they extend from the skin to the pectoral fascia. The areolar tissue that lies in the stroma predominates in the periphery of the breast. It invests the surface of the mammary gland, fills the intervals between the lobes, and is absent beneath the nipple and the areola.

SKIN. At the level of the fourth intercostal space, a papilla-like projection, the *nipple*, contains the openings of the lactiferous ducts. There is no hair on the nipple, but there are numerous sebaceous glands and end organs of varying types. In the deeper parts of the dermis, smooth-muscle fibers, generally circularly arranged, are present and account for the erectile capacity of the nipple. The circular area of skin that surrounds the nipple is the *areola*. Its pigmentation accounts for its pink color in the nullipara. During pregnancy the areola darkens and increases in diameter. The small elevations of its surface are produced by the numerous, large, underlying sebaceous areolar glands. These glands also enlarge during pregnancy and produce a lipoid material which lubricates and protects the nipple during nursing. A layer of circular smooth-muscle fibers, continuous with that in the nipple, is also present in the deep dermis of the areola.

The neurovascular system of the breast is supplied by:

arteries: The medial mammary rami of the second to fourth perforating branches of the internal thoracic a. and the lateral mammary rami of the third to fifth lateral cutaneous branches of the posterior intercostal aa.

veins: The superficial vv. drain into the perforating branches of the internal thoracic vv. The deep vv. drain into the perforating branches of the internal thoracic, axillary, and intercostal vv.

nerves: Mammary rami from the branches of the cutaneous nerves of the anterior thoracic region.

Lymphatic Drainage. The skin contains a dense cutaneous plexus which drains into the subareolar plexus beneath the skin. The converging perilobular and interlobular vessels drain the substance of the gland to the medial and lateral axillary lymph trunks. Both trunks terminate in the pectoral group of axillary nodes. Accessory axillary lymph paths are also present.

3. Deep Fascia (Fig. 41-3)

The *pectoral fascia* is thin and encloses the pectoralis major muscle. It is attached above the clavicle. Below, it is continuous with the deep fascia over the abdominal muscles; laterally, with fascia over the deltoid muscle. The sternum is its medial attachment. The deeper *clavipectoral fascia* envelops the subclavius and pectoralis minor muscles. The part of this fascia between the muscles is known as the *costo-coracoid membrane*. It descends from the lower border of the pectoralis minor muscle to the axillary fascia as the *suspensory ligament of the axilla*.

4. Muscles (Fig. 41-4)

PECTORALIS MAJOR. This is the flat, large, superficial muscle of the chest.

Origin:

Clavicular head: Anterior surface of the sternal half of the clavicle.

Sternocostal head: Anterior surface of the sternum and costal cartilages.

Abdominal head: Aponeurosis of the external abdominal oblique muscle.

Insertion: Lateral lip of the intertubercular groove.

Action: Flexes and adducts the arm and rotates it medially.

Nerve supply: Lateral and medial pectoral nn.

PECTORALIS MINOR. This flat, triangular muscle lies beneath the pectoralis major muscle.

Origin: Sternal ends of the second to fifth ribs.

Insertion: Coracoid process of the scapula.

Action: Draws the shoulder downwards and forwards; raises the ribs when the shoulder is fixed.

Nerve supply: Medial pectoral thoracic n.

SUBCLAVIUS. This small, elongated muscle is located between the clavicle and the first rib.

Origin: Junction of the first rib and its cartilage.

Insertion: Groove on the lower surface of the clavicle.

Action: Draws the clavicle downwards and backwards.

Nerve supply: Nerve to the subclavius muscle.

SERRATUS ANTERIOR. This broad, flat muscle forms the medial wall of the axilla.

Origin: Digitations from the lateral surfaces of the upper eight ribs.

Insertion: First digitation into the superior angle of the scapula, second to fourth digitation into the medial border of the scapula, fifth to eighth digitation into the inferior angle of the scapula.

Action: Draws the scapula forward and rotates its inferior angle laterally.

Nerve supply: Long thoracic n.

AXILLA

1. Boundaries   *3. Axillary v.*

2. Axillary a.   *4. Brachial plexus*

5. Axillary lymph nodes

The axilla or armpit, lies between the upper part of the arm and the chest wall (Fig. 42-1). It is a pyramid-shaped area.

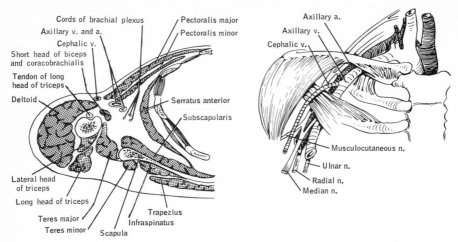

42-1 AXILLA: TRANSVERSE SECTION

Cords of brachial plexus
Axillary v. and a.
Cephalic v.
Short head of biceps
and coracobrachialis
Tendon of long
head of triceps
Deltoid
Pectoralis major
Pectoralis minor
Serratus anterior
Subscapularis
Lateral head
of triceps
Long head of triceps
Teres major
Teres minor
Scapula
Trapezius
Infraspinatus

42-2 AXILLA: CONTENTS

Axillary a.
Axillary v.
Cephalic v.
Musculocutaneous n.
Ulnar n.
Radial n.
Median n.

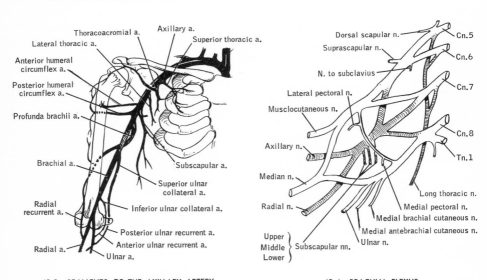

42-3 BRANCHES OF THE AXILLARY ARTERY

Thoracoacromial a.
Lateral thoracic a.
Anterior humeral
circumflex a.
Posterior humeral
circumflex a.
Profunda brachii a.
Brachial a.
Radial
recurrent a.
Radial a.
Axillary a.
Superior thoracic a.
Subscapular a.
Superior ulnar
collateral a.
Inferior ulnar collateral a.
Posterior ulnar recurrent a.
Anterior ulnar recurrent a.
Ulnar a.

42-4 BRACHIAL PLEXUS

Dorsal scapular n.
Suprascapular n.
N. to subclavius
Lateral pectoral n.
Musclocutaneous n.
Axillary n.
Median n.
Radial n.
Upper
Middle } Subscapular nn.
Lower
Cn.5
Cn.6
Cn.7
Cn.8
Tn.1
Long thoracic n.
Medial pectoral n.
Medial brachial cutaneous n.
Medial antebrachial cutaneous n.
Ulnar n.

Plate 42

1. Boundaries

The four walls, or boundaries, of the axilla and its apex and base are composed as follows:

Anterior wall: pectoralis major and minor muscles, clavipectoral fascia

Posterior wall: subscapularis, teres major, latissimus dorsi muscles

Medial wall: serratus anterior muscle, first to fifth ribs and intercostal muscles

Lateral wall: intertubercular groove of humerus

Apex (truncated):

Anterior: posterior border of clavicle

Medial: lateral border of first rib

Posterior: superior border of scapula

Base: axillary fascia

The axillary a. and v. and brachial plexus pass from the neck and thorax through the axilla to the arm (Fig. 42-2). They are enclosed within the *axillary sheath,* a fascial extension of the prevertebral layer of cervical fascia covering the scalene muscles. The axillary lymph nodes are located within the fat and loose areolar tissue of the axilla. The axilla also contains the tendon of the long head of the biceps, the short head of the biceps, and the coracobrachialis muscle.

2. Axillary A. (Fig. 42-3)

This continuation of the subclavian a. is defined by the limits of the axilla and extends from the lateral border of the first rib to the lower border of the teres major muscle. It continues down the arm as the brachial a. The artery may be considered as consisting of three parts, located (1) above, (2) behind, and (3) below the pectoralis minor muscle, respectively. Each part provides the same number of branches as its name indicates.

First Part

The first part of the axillary a. extends from the first rib to the upper border of the pectoralis major muscle and gives off a single branch.

SUPERIOR THORACIC A. Arising at the lower border of the subclavius muscle, the superior thoracic a. courses inferomedially, behind the axillary v., to supply the first intercostal muscle and the upper part of the serratus anterior muscle.

Second Part

The second part of the axillary a. lies behind the tendon of the pectoralis minor muscle and provides two branches.

THORACOACROMIAL A. Arising beneath the upper border of the pectoralis minor muscle, from the anterior aspect of the axillary a., the thoracoacromial a. curves around the muscle border to pierce the clavipectoral fascia where it, in turn, divides into four branches.

Acromial Branch. The acromial branch runs superolaterally over the coracoid process to reach the acromion, on which it ramifies.

Deltoid Branch. The deltoid branch descends, beside the cephalic v., in the deltopectoral triangle and gives branches to both the deltoid and the pectoralis muscles.

Pectoral Branch. A large branch that descends between and supplies the pectoral muscles, in the female the pectoral branch also supplies the deep aspect of the mammary gland.

Clavicular Branch. A slender vessel, the clavicular branch runs superomedially to supply the subclavius muscle and the sternoclavicular joint.

LATERAL THORACIC A. Arising near and descending along the lower border of the pectoralis minor muscle to the thoracic wall, the lateral thoracic a. provides branches to the pectoral and serratus anterior muscles and to the breast in the female.

Third Part

The third part of the axillary a. extends between the lower borders of the pectoralis minor and teres major muscles and provides three branches.

SUBSCAPULAR A. The largest branch of the axillary a., the subscapular a. arises opposite the lower border of the subscapularis muscle. It provides the *circumflex scapular* a. and continues along the axillary border of the subscapularis to the inferior angle of the scapula as the *thoracodorsal a.* The circumflex scapular a. passes posteriorly through the triangular space and enters the scapular region (Fig. 40-4). There it ramifies and supplies the muscles on the dorsum of the scapula.

ANTERIOR HUMERAL CIRCUMFLEX A. See Scapular Region.

POSTERIOR HUMERAL CIRCUMFLEX A. See Scapular Region.

3. Axillary V.

This continuation of the basilic v. is large and is defined by the upper and lower limits of the axilla. It ascends medial to the axillary a. and becomes the subclavian v.

Tributaries. The tributaries of the axillary v. correspond to the branches of the axillary a. except for the thoracoacromial a., whose respective venae comitantes end in the cephalic v. It also receives thoracoepigastric vv. from the subcutaneous parts of the lower thoracic and upper abdominal regions.

4. Brachial Plexus (Fig. 42-4)

Each of the peripheral nerves of both the upper and lower limbs innervates a distinct region with muscular, sensory, and sympathetic fibers. Structures such as the brachial and lumbosacral plexuses permit the intermingling of nerve components from several segments of the spinal cord, to form composite nerves which supply individual territories.

The brachial plexus lies partly in the neck, partly behind the clavicle, and partly in the axilla. It consists of roots, trunks, divisions, cords, and terminal branches.

ROOTS. The roots are formed from the ventral rami (anterior primary divisions) of Cn 5 to 8 and Tn 1 which are sometimes joined by contributions from Cn 4 and Tn 2. The roots emerge between the scalenus anterior and medius muscles in line with similar roots constituting the cervical plexus.

TRUNKS. The roots unite to form three trunks:

Upper Trunk. The ventral rami of Cn 5 and 6 unite.

Middle Trunk. The ventral ramus of Cn 7 continues directly.

Lower Trunk. The ventral rami of Cn 8 and Tn 1 unite.

DIVISIONS. Each trunk bifurcates, forming an anterior and a posterior division.

CORDS. The divisions join to form three cords, named with respect to the second part of the axillary a.

Posterior Cord. The three posterior divisions constitute the posterior cord.

Lateral Cord. The lateral cord is made up of the anterior divisions of the upper and middle trunks.

Medial Cord. The medial cord consists of the anterior division of the lower trunk.

TERMINAL BRANCHES. At the inferolateral border of the pectoralis minor muscle, the cords provide four terminal branches. The lateral and medial cords bifurcate.

Radial N. Terminal branch of the posterior cord.

Musculocutaneous N. Terminal branch of the lateral cord.

Ulnar N. Terminal branch of the medial cord.

Median N. Formed by union of the remaining branches of the lateral and medial cords.

BRANCHES. These branches arise from the various components of the plexus, as shown in Table 48.

Branches of the Roots

DORSAL SCAPULAR N. (Cn 5). Piercing the scalenus medius muscle, it passes deep to the levator scapulae muscle, to which it gives a branch. It enters the deep surface of the rhomboidei muscles.

Table 48

Component	Branch	Area supplied
Roots...............	Dorsal scapular n. * Long thoracic n.	Rhomboidei mm. Serratus anterior m.
Trunks..............	Nerve to subclavius m. * Suprascapular n. *	Subclavius m. Supra- and infraspinatus mm.
Cords: Lateral............	Lateral pectoral n. Musculocutaneous n. Lateral origin of median n.	Pectoralis major m. Flexors of the arm Skin of lateral forearm Flexors of forearm Muscles of thumb
Medial............	Medial origin of median n. Medial pectoral n. Medial brachial cutaneous n. Medial anterior brachial cutaneous n. Ulnar n. Upper subscapular n. Middle subscapular n. Lower subscapular n.	Skin on lateral hand Pectoralis mm. Skin on medial arm Skin on medial forearm Muscles of hand Skin on medial hand Subscapularis m. Latissimus dorsi m. Subscapularis m. Teres major m.
Posterior..........	Axillary n. Radial n.	Deltoid and teres minor mm. Extensors of arm and fore- arm Skin on back of entire limb

* These nerves do not enter the axilla and are discussed only for the sake of completeness

LONG THORACIC N. (Cn 5 to 7). It descends behind the brachial plexus and the first part of the axillary a. to ramify on the external surface of the serratus anterior muscle.

Branches of the Trunks

NERVE TO THE SUBCLAVIUS MUSCLE (Cn 5, 6). It descends behind the clavicle and in front of the brachial plexus to reach the subclavius muscle.

SUPRASCAPULAR N. (Cn 5, 6). See Scapular Region, p. 127.

Branches of the Cords

LATERAL PECTORAL N. Arising from the lateral cord, it provides a communicating branch to the medial pectoral n. It pierces the clavipectoral fascia to innervate the clavicular and upper sternocostal portions of the pectoralis major muscle.

MUSCULOCUTANEOUS N. (Cn 5 to 7). It pierces the coracobrachialis muscle and is ultimately distributed to the flexor muscles on the front of the arm, to the skin on the lateral side of the forearm, and to the elbow joint.

MEDIAN N. (Cn 6 to 8, Tn 1). It descends along the anterolateral side of the axillary a. to innervate most of the flexors of the forearm, most of the short muscles of the thumb, the skin on the front and lateral sides of the hand, and the joints of the elbow and hand.

MEDIAL PECTORAL N. (Cn 6 to 8). Passing forward between the axillary a. and its vein, it provides a branch which joins with the communicating branch from the lateral pectoral n., forming a loop around the artery. The nerve then enters the deep surface of the pectoralis minor muscle, which it supplies, and sends terminal branches to the lower part of the pectoralis major muscle.

MEDIAL BRACHIAL CUTANEOUS N. (Cn 8, Tn 1). It passes behind the axillary v. to descend along the medial side. It pierces the deep fascia at about the middle of the arm to supply the skin of the medial and posterior aspects of the lower third of the arm.

MEDIAL ANTEBRACHIAL CUTANEOUS N. (Cn 8, Tn 1). A branch of the medial cord descends on the medial side of the axillary and brachial aa. to pierce the deep fascia about the middle of the arm. It divides into two branches which supply the skin on the anterior and posterior surfaces of the medial side of the forearm.

ULNAR N. The terminal branch of the medial cord descends along the medial side of the axillary a. It is distributed to some of the flexors of the forearm, to the short muscles of the hand, to the skin on the front and back of the medial side of the hand, and to the joints of the elbow and the hand.

SUBSCAPULAR NN. (Cn 5, 6). Three nerves supply the muscles of the posterior wall of the axilla.

Upper Subscapular N. After a short course downwards and backwards, it enters the upper part of the subscapularis muscle.

Middle Subscapular (Thoracodorsal) N. After passing behind the axillary a. and descending across the subscapularis and teres major muscles to the inferior angle of the scapula, it terminates in the latissimus dorsi muscle.

Lower Subscapular N. After descending laterally across the subscapularis muscle, the lower part of which it supplies, it terminates in the teres major muscle.

AXILLARY N. A branch of the posterior cord descends between the axillary a. and the subscapularis muscle lateral to the radial n. At the lower border of the subscapularis muscle it curves posteriorly to leave the axilla by passing through the quadrangular space. It innervates the shoulder joint, the deltoid and teres minor muscles, as well as the skin of the back of the shoulder.

Table 49

Group	Location	Region drained	Draining nodes
Lateral......	Behind axillary v.	Upper limb	Central and apical
Pectoral	Along lower border of pectoralis minor m.	Anterior thoracic wall; breast	Central and apical
Subscapular .	Along subscapular vessels	Posterior thoracic wall	Central
Central.....	Near base of axilla	Lateral, pectoral, and subscapular groups	Apical
Apical......	Behind clavipectoral fascia	Subscapular group	Subclavian lymph trunk

RADIAL N. (Cn 5 to 8, Tn 1). The terminal branch of the posterior cord descends behind the axillary a. anterior to the subscapularis, teres major, and latissimus dorsi muscles. It innervates the extensors of the arm and forearm, as well as the skin on the back of the arm, forearm, and hand.

5. Axillary Lymph Nodes

There are five groups of axillary nodes (shown in Table 49):

ARM

The arm extends from the shoulder to the elbow. Its bone, the humerus, articulates with the scapula at the shoulder joint.

FRONT OF ARM

> 1. *Fascia*   3. *Deep artery*
> 2. *Muscles*   4. *Deep veins*
>   5. *Deep nerves*

The front of the arm extends down from the deltoid region to the cubital fossa.

1. Fascia

SUPERFICIAL. The superficial fascia of the front of the arm contains blood vessels, nerves, and a variable amount of fat.

Unnamed Arteries. They are derived from the deep arteries.

Superficial Veins. See Fig. 43-1.

cephalic v. Ascending from the cubital fossa in the lateral bicipital groove, it pierces the brachial fascia and continues up in the interval between the deltoid and pectoralis major muscles. At the deltopectoral triangle the cephalic v. pierces the costocoracoid membrane and terminates in the axillary v.

basilic v. Ascending from the front of the medial epicondyle in the medial bicipital groove, it pierces the brachial fascia in the middle of the arm, and ascends to the axilla, where it joins the brachial v. or venae comitantes to form the axillary v. Its major tributary is the median cubital v.

median cubital v. This communicating v. arises from the cephalic v. a little below the elbow and ascends obliquely to join the basilic v. a little above the medial epicondyle.

CUTANEOUS NERVES (Fig. 43-1)

lateral brachial cutaneous n. The termination of the posterior branch of the axillary n., it curves around the posterior border of the deltoid muscle, pierces the brachial fascia, and branches to supply the skin over the lower half of the deltoid muscle.

posterior brachial cutaneous n. Arising in the axilla, it passes to the medial side of the arm to supply the skin on the dorsal surface almost to the olecranon.

intercostobrachial n. The lateral cutaneous branch of the second intercostal n. does not divide into anterior and posterior branches. It pierces the intercostal and serratus anterior muscles, crosses the axilla to the medial side of the arm, and pierces the brachial fascia. It innervates the skin of the medial and posterior surfaces of the arm as far as the elbow.

medial brachial cutaneous n. Arising from the medial cord, it descends on the medial side of the brachial a. to the middle of the arm, where it pierces the deep fascia. It innervates the skin of the medial and adjoining posterior parts of the lower half of the arm.

DEEP. The brachial fascia completely envelops the arm. It is continuous above with the fascia of the shoulder and axilla and below with the fascia of the forearm, where it is also attached to the olecranon and epicondyles. The fascia gives off intermuscular septums, two of which are especially prominent.

Medial Intermuscular Septum. Attached to the medial supracondylar ridge and epicondyle, it extends to the insertion of the coracobrachialis muscle.

Lateral Intermuscular Septum. Attached to the lateral supracondylar ridge and epicondyle, it extends to the deltoid tuberosity.

This fascial arrangement divides the arm into anterior and posterior compartments.

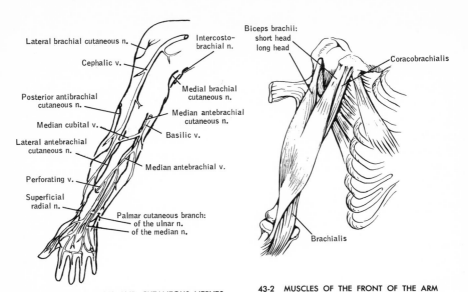

43-1 SUPERFICIAL VEINS AND CUTANEOUS NERVES

Lateral brachial cutaneous n.

Cephalic v.

Posterior antibrachial cutaneous n.

Median cubital v.

Lateral antebrachial cutaneous n.

Perforating v.

Superficial radial n.

Intercosto-brachial n.

Medial brachial cutaneous n.

Median antebrachial cutaneous n.

Basilic v.

Median antebrachial v.

Palmar cutaneous branch:
of the ulnar n.
of the median n.

43-2 MUSCLES OF THE FRONT OF THE ARM

Biceps brachii:
short head
long head

Coracobrachialis

Brachialis

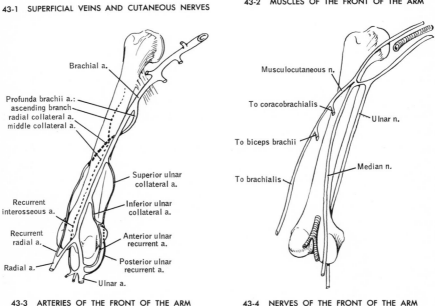

43-3 ARTERIES OF THE FRONT OF THE ARM

Brachial a.

Profunda brachii a.:
ascending branch
radial collateral a.
middle collateral a.

Recurrent interosseous a.

Recurrent radial a.

Radial a.

Superior ulnar collateral a.

Inferior ulnar collateral a.

Anterior ulnar recurrent a.

Posterior ulnar recurrent a.

Ulnar a.

43-4 NERVES OF THE FRONT OF THE ARM

Musculocutaneous n.

To coracobrachialis

To biceps brachii

To brachialis

Ulnar n.

Median n.

Plate 43

2. Muscles (Fig. 43-2)

CORACOBRACHIALIS. This bandlike muscle lies in the upper, medial part of the arm.

Origin: Tip of the coracoid process.

Insertion: Middle third of the medial surface of the shaft of the humerus.

Action: Flexes and adducts the arm.

Nerve supply: Musculocutaneous n.

BICEPS BRACHII. It is a long, large, spindle-shaped muscle.

Origin:

Short head: Tip of the coracoid process.

Long head: Supraglenoid tubercle of the scapula.

Insertion: Tuberosity of the radius and by the *bicipital aponeurosis,* a tendinous expansion, onto the fascia of the forearm.

Action: Flexor and supinator of the forearm.

Nerve supply: Musculocutaneous n.

BRACHIALIS. It lies deep to the biceps.

Origin: Anterior surface of the lower two-thirds of the shaft of the humerus.

Insertion: Tuberosity of the ulna and the coronoid process.

Nerve supply: Musculocutaneous and radial nn.

3. Deep Artery (Fig. 43-3)

BRACHIAL A. This continuation of the axillary a. extends from the lower border of the teres major muscle to the cubital fossa opposite the neck of the radius. Its inferolateral course is superficial and crosses the long-head of the triceps, the coracobrachialis, and the brachialis muscles. Its branches are shown in Table 50.

4. Deep Veins

BRACHIAL VV. Two veins accompany the brachial a. They arise at the elbow by the union of the venae comitantes of the radial and ulnar aa. Tributaries of these veins correspond to the branches of the brachial a. The lateral brachial v. crosses the artery near the lower border of the subscapularis muscle to join the basilic v. and forms the axillary v. Near the point of union, the medial brachial v. also joins the basilic v.

5. Deep Nerves (Fig. 43-4)

MEDIAN N. It descends on the anterolateral side of the brachial a. to the middle of the arm, where it gradually crosses to the medial side of the artery. It usually provides no branches in the arm.

Table 50

Branches	Course	Area supplied or artery joined
Profunda brachii a.....	Descends in spiral groove	Neighboring muscles
Ascending branch....	Between lateral and long head of triceps m.	Posterior humeral circumflex a.
Middle collateral a.	Through medial head of triceps m.	Interosseous recurrent a.
Radial collateral a....	Accompanies radial n.	Radial recurrent a.
Nutrient a............	To nutrient foramen of humerus	Humerus
Superior ulnar collateral a..........	Accompanies ulnar n.	Posterior ulnar recurrent a.
Inferior ulnar collateral a........	Above medial epicondyle	Divides on brachialis m.
Anterior branch.....	Between brachialis and teres mm.	Anterior ulnar recurrent a.
Posterior branch.....	Across humerus deep to triceps m.	Posterior ulnar recurrent a.

ULNAR N. The terminal branch of the medial cord, it descends on the medial side of the axillary and upper half of the brachial aa. At the middle of the arm it pierces the medial intermuscular septum, descends on the medial head of the triceps muscle, and crosses behind the medial epicondyle into the forearm. It provides no branches in the arm.

MUSCULOCUTANEOUS N. This terminal branch of the lateral cord turns laterally to pierce the coracobrachialis muscle and then descends obliquely between the biceps and brachialis muscles to the lateral side of the arm. A little above the elbow and lateral to the biceps tendon the nerve pierces the brachial fascia and becomes the *lateral antebrachial cutaneous n.* (p. 147). Its branches are:

muscular branches. To the coracobrachialis, brachialis, and biceps brachii muscles.

articular branch. To the elbow joint (derived from the ramus that supplies the brachialis muscle).

humeral branch. Coursing with the nutrient artery.

BACK OF ARM

1. *Fascia*   2. *Muscles*
3. *Deep nerve: radial*

The back of the arm extends from the deltoid region to the back of the elbow joint.

1. Fascia

SUPERFICIAL. The superficial fascia of the back of the arm contains nerve branches from the front of the arm which are supplemented by the posterior brachial cutaneous n. It arises in the axilla as a branch of the radial n. and passes posteromedially to pierce the brachial fascia, where it innervates the skin of the middle of the back of the arm.

DEEP. See p. 139.

2. Muscles (Fig. 44-1)

TRICEPS. It covers the back of the humerus.

Origin:

Long head: Infraglenoid tubercle of the scapula.

Lateral head: Posterolateral surface of the humerus above the spiral groove.

Medial head: Posteromedial surface of the humerus below the spiral groove and the medial and lateral intermuscular septums.

Insertion: Posterior surface of the upper part of the olecranon.

Action: Extensor of the forearm. The long head is also an adductor of the forearm.

Nerve supply: Radial (a distinct branch innervates each head).

ANCONEUS. It represents a small, triangular continuation of the triceps muscle.

Origin: Lateral epicondyle.

Insertion: Lateral surface of the olecranon.

Action: Extensor of the forearm.

Nerve supply: Radial n.

3. Deep Nerves (Fig. 44-2)

RADIAL N. This terminal branch of the posterior cord of the brachial plexus descends behind the third part of the axillary a. and the proximal part of the brachial a. to curve obliquely across the back of the humerus. It pierces the intramuscular septum at the lateral border of the humerus to enter the anterior compartment of the arm. The radial n. descends between the brachialis and brachioradialis muscles to the front of the lateral epicondyle, where it divides into *superficial* and *deep branches.* The branches are primarily cutaneous and muscular; they are shown in Table 51.

CUBITAL FOSSA

     1. Boundaries   *2. Contents*

The cubital fossa is the triangular hollow on the front of the elbow.

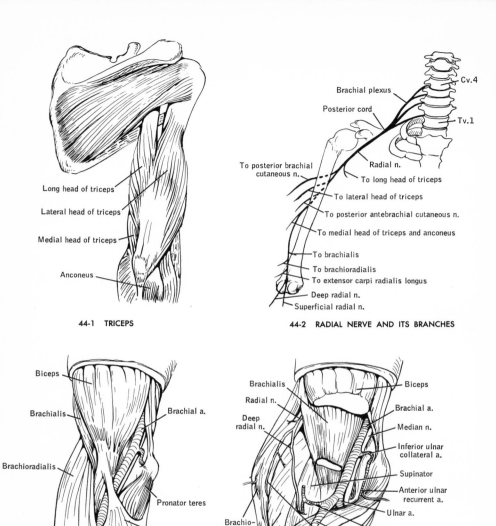

44-1 TRICEPS

Long head of triceps

Lateral head of triceps

Medial head of triceps

Anconeus

44-2 RADIAL NERVE AND ITS BRANCHES

Brachial plexus

Posterior cord

Cv. 4

Tv. 1

Radial n.

To posterior brachial cutaneous n.

To long head of triceps

To lateral head of triceps

To posterior antebrachial cutaneous n.

To medial head of triceps and anconeus

To brachialis

To brachioradialis

To extensor carpi radialis longus

Deep radial n.

Superficial radial n.

44-3 CUBITAL FOSSA: BOUNDARIES

Biceps

Brachialis

Brachioradialis

Brachial a.

Pronator teres

Bicipital aponeurosis

44-4 CUBITAL FOSSA: DEEP DISSECTION

Brachialis

Radial n.

Deep radial n.

Brachio-radialis

Extensor carpi radialis brevis

Biceps

Brachial a.

Median n.

Inferior ulnar collateral a.

Supinator

Anterior ulnar recurrent a.

Ulnar a.

Radial recurrent a.

Radial a.

Superficial branch of radial n.

Plate 44

Table 51

Branches	*Area innervated*

Arising in axilla

Posterior brachial cutaneous n.............. Skin on back of arm
Median muscular branch:
    Nerve to long head of triceps m........... Long head of triceps m.

Arising in spiral groove

Posterior muscular branches:
    Nerve to lateral head of triceps m......... Lateral head of triceps m.
    Nerve to medial head of triceps and
        anconeus mm...................... Medial head of triceps and anconeus mm.
    Posterior antebrachial cutaneous n........ Skin on back of forearm

Arising in anterior compartment

Lateral muscular branches:
    Nerve to brachialis m................... Brachialis m.
    Nerve to brachioradialis m.............. Brachioradialis m.
    Nerve to extensor carpi radialis longus m.... External carpi radialis longus m.
Articular branches....................... Elbow joint

1. Boundaries (Fig. 44-3)

Lateral boundary: brachioradialis muscle
Medial boundary: pronator teres muscle
Apex: medial and lateral intersection
Base: line between epicondyles
Roof: skin, superficial and deep fascia
Floor: brachialis and supinator muscles

2. Contents (Fig. 44-4)

Tendon of Biceps. The central structure in the fossa, the tendon of the biceps descends to its insertion on the tuberosity of the radius.

Brachial A. This artery bifurcates, forming the radial and ulnar aa. medial to the tendon. The ulnar a. passes out of the fossa under the pronator teres muscle; the radial a. descends to exit at the apex.

Median N. Coursing medial to the brachial a., it leaves the fossa between the heads of the pronator teres muscle.

The following structures are not within the fossa but lie beneath its boundaries:

radial n. Located beneath the brachioradialis muscle above the elbow it gives rise to the posterior interosseous n.

radial recurrent a. Ascending on the supinator muscle, it anastomoses with the anterior branch of the profunda brachii a.

anterior ulnar recurrent a. Ascending over the brachialis muscle beneath the pronator teres muscle, it anastomoses with the inferior ulnar collateral a.

FOREARM

The forearm extends from the elbow to the wrist. The radius and ulna articulate with the humerus at the elbow joint and with each other at their upper and lower ends, forming the proximal and distal radioulnar joints.

FRONT OF FOREARM

1. Fascia	*3. Deep arteries*
2. Muscles	*4. Deep nerves*

The front of the forearm extends from the elbow to the distal crease at the wrist. It contains two bones, the ulna and radius (p. 178).

1. Fascia

SUPERFICIAL. The superficial fascia of the front of the forearm contains vessels, nerves, and a variable amount of fat.

Unnamed Arteries. They are derived from the deep arteries.

Superficial Veins (Fig. 43-1)

cephalic v. The lateral end of the dorsal venous arch gives rise to this vein, which passes obliquely to the front of the forearm. It ascends in front of the elbow to the upper arm.

basilic v. The medial end of the dorsal venous arch gives rise to this vein, which ascends along the medial side of the forearm. It passes gradually forward to ascend into the upper arm in front of the medial epicondyle.

median antebrachial v. The volar venous plexus frequently gives rise to this vein, which ascends the middle of the forearm. It terminates in the basilic v. or the median cubital v.

Cutaneous Nerves (Fig. 43-1)

medial antebrachial cutaneous n. The medial cord of the brachial plexus provides a branch that descends along the anteromedial side of the axillary and brachial aa. to the middle of the arm. It pierces the brachial fascia and divides into an anterior branch, which descends to innervate the skin of the anteromedial surface of the forearm, and a posterior branch, which descends to innervate the posteromedial surface of the forearm.

lateral antebrachial cutaneous n. This continuation of the musculocutaneous n. descends from a little above the elbow to pierce the brachial fascia lateral to the biceps tendon. It passes behind the cephalic v. to divide into an anterior branch, which innervates the skin on the anterolateral side of the forearm, and a posterior branch, which passes backward to innervate the skin on the posterolateral side of the forearm.

DEEP FASCIA. The antebrachial fascia is a continuation of the brachial fascia. It is dense except on the front of the distal part of the forearm and is especially strong near the elbow, where it gives partial origin to the muscles that arise from the epicondyles. Septums extend from the fascia between the fleshy bellies of the muscles. Because the intermuscular septums do not run directly outward to the antebrachial fascia, complete separation of the muscles into two compartments, as in the arm, does not occur.

2. Muscles

The muscles of the front of the forearm are arranged in three layers: superficial, middle, and deep (Fig. 45-1).

Superficial Layer

From lateral to medial, the muscles of the superficial layer are:

PRONATOR TERES. It is on the upper part of the forearm.

Origin:
   Humeral head: Medial epicondyle.
   Ulnar head: Medial side of the coronoid process.
Insertion: Rough impression on the middle of the lateral surface of the radius.
Action: Flexor and pronator of the forearm.
Nerve supply: Median n.

FLEXOR CARPI RADIALIS. It is in the middle of the front of the forearm. It is located between the pronator teres and the palmaris longus.

Origin: Medial epicondyle by means of the common tendon.
Insertion: Base of the second metacarpal.
Action: Flexor and abductor of the hand.
Nerve supply: Median n.

PALMARIS LONGUS. It parallels the flexor carpi radialis muscle.

Origin: Medial epicondyle by means of the common tendon.
Insertion: Palmar aponeuroses and flexor retinaculum.
Action: Flexes the hand.
Nerve supply: Median n.

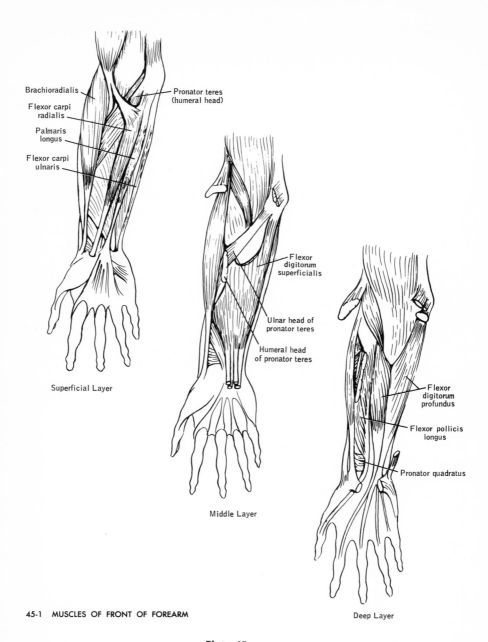

Brachioradialis

Flexor carpi radialis

Palmaris longus

Flexor carpi ulnaris

Pronator teres (humeral head)

Superficial Layer

Flexor digitorum superficialis

Ulnar head of pronator teres

Humeral head of pronator teres

Middle Layer

Flexor digitorum profundus

Flexor pollicis longus

Pronator quadratus

Deep Layer

45-1 MUSCLES OF FRONT OF FOREARM

Plate 45

FLEXOR CARPI ULNARIS. It is the most medial muscle of the forearm.
Origin:

Humeral head: Medial epicondyle by means of the common tendon.

Ulnar head: Medial side of the olecranon and upper two-thirds of the posterior border of the ulna.

Insertion: Pisiform bone and via two ligaments from the pisiform to the hamulus of the hamate and the base of the fifth metacarpal.

Action: Flexor and adductor muscles of the hand.

Nerve supply: Ulnar n.

Middle Layer

FLEXOR DIGITORUM SUPERFICIALIS
Origin:

Humeroulnar head: Medial epicondyle by means of the common tendon, the ulnar collateral ligament, and the medial surface of the coronoid process.

Radial head: Upper two-thirds of the anterior border of the radius.
The two heads are connected by a fibrous bridge which forms the *superficialis arch.* In the wrist, the tendons for the third and fourth digits are superficial to the tendons for the second and fifth digits. These tendons diverge in the palm.

Insertion: Margins of the shafts of the middle phalanges of the second to fifth digits.

Action: Flexes the middle phalanges and the wrist.

Nerve supply: Median n.

Deep Layer

FLEXOR DIGITORUM PROFUNDUS. It lies over the ulna.

Origin: Upper two-thirds of the anterior and medial surface of the ulna, the medial surface of the coronoid process, and the interosseous membrane.

Insertion: Bases of the distal phalanges of the second to fifth digits by four tendons.

Action: Flexes the terminal phalanges of the second to fifth digits and the wrist.

Nerve supply: Anterior interosseous n. of the median to lateral half; ulnar n. to the medial half.

FLEXOR POLLICIS LONGUS. It lies over the radius.

Origin: Upper three-fourths of the anterior surface of the radius and the adjacent interosseous membrane.

Insertion: Base of the distal phalanx of the thumb.

Action: Flexor of the distal phalanx of the thumb.

Nerve supply: Anterior interosseous n.

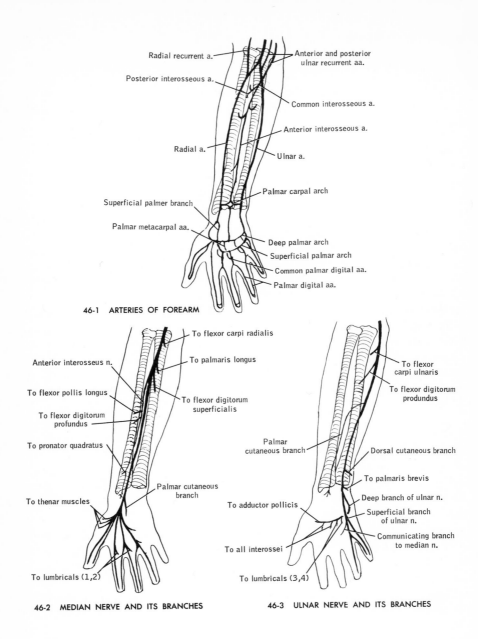

46-1 ARTERIES OF FOREARM

Radial recurrent a.

Posterior interosseous a.

Radial a.

Superficial palmer branch

Palmar metacarpal aa.

Anterior and posterior ulnar recurrent aa.

Common interosseous a.

Anterior interosseous a.

Ulnar a.

Palmar carpal arch

Deep palmar arch

Superficial palmar arch

Common palmar digital aa.

Palmar digital aa.

46-2 MEDIAN NERVE AND ITS BRANCHES

Anterior interosseus n.

To flexor pollis longus

To flexor digitorum profundus

To pronator quadratus

To thenar muscles

To lumbricals (1,2)

To flexor carpi radialis

To palmaris longus

To flexor digitorum superficialis

Palmar cutaneous branch

46-3 ULNAR NERVE AND ITS BRANCHES

To flexor carpi ulnaris

To flexor digitorum produndus

Palmar cutaneous branch

Dorsal cutaneous branch

To palmaris brevis

To adductor pollicis

Deep branch of ulnar n.

Superficial branch of ulnar n.

Communicating branch to median n.

To all interossei

To lumbricals (3,4)

Plate 46

PRONATOR QUADRATUS. It is located at the distal end of the forearm deep to the flexor tendons.

Origin: Pronator ridge on the distal fourth of the anterior surface of the ulna.

Insertion: Distal fourth of the anterior surface of the radius and a triangular area above the ulnar notch.

Action: Pronator of the forearm.

Nerve supply: Anterior interosseous n.

3. Deep Arteries (Fig. 46-1)

RADIAL A. A terminal branch of the brachial a., it begins in the cubital fossa opposite the neck of the radius. It continues in a direct line to the distal end of the radius, where it curves around the lateral border of the wrist. In the upper third of the forearm it courses between the brachioradialis and pronator teres muscles. In the lower two-thirds it lies directly under the deep fascia. It is accompanied by two venae comitantes. It has several branches in the forearm.

Radial Recurrent A. Arising in the cubital fossa, it ascends on the supinator muscle. It anastomoses with the radial collateral branch of the profunda brachii a. in front of the lateral epicondyle. It supplies the adjacent muscles and the elbow joint.

Muscular Branches. It supplies the muscles on the radial side of the forearm.

Palmar Carpal Branch. This small vessel arises at the upper border of the flexor retinaculum. It crosses the wrist to unite with the corresponding branch of the ulnar a. forming the palmar carpal arch.

Superficial Palmar Branch. This arises just before the radial a. curves around the wrist. It ascends through the thenar muscles, supplying them, and joins the superficial volar arch by anastomosing with the terminal part of the ulnar a.

For the branches at the wrist, see p. 161 and for the branches in the hand, see p. 170.

ULNAR A. This larger terminal branch of the brachial a. also begins in the cubital fossa opposite the neck of the radius. It descends, curving medially, beneath the superficialis arch to reach the ulnar border at the middle of the forearm. It joins the ulnar n. and descends straight to the wrist, on the flexor digitorum profundus muscle under cover of the flexor carpi radialis muscle. It pierces the deep fascia immediately above the flexor retinaculum and terminates by giving off the deep volar branch and forming the superficial volar arch. The ulnar a. is accompanied by two venae comitantes.

The branches of the ulnar a. in the forearm are shown in Table 52.

For the branches at the wrist, see p. 167 and for the branches in the palm, see p. 170.

Table 52

Branches	Course	Area supplied or artery joined
Anterior ulnar recurrent a..	Between brachioradialis and pronator teres mm.	Superior and inferior ulnar collateral a.
Posterior ulnar recurrent a.	Between flexor digitorum superficialis and profundus mm.	Superior and inferior ulnar collateral a.
Common interosseous a....	To upper border of interosseous membrane and divides	
Anterior interosseous a....	Descends on front of interosseous membrane	
Muscular branches.....	To adjacent muscles	Adjacent muscles
Nutrient branches......	To nutrient foramens	Radius and ulna
Median branch.........	Accompanies median n.	Median n.
Communicating branch.	Behind pronator quadratus m. to palm	Volar carpal network
Posterior interosseous a....	Passes over interosseous membrane to back of forearm (p. 157)	

4. Deep Nerves

MEDIAN N. (Fig. 46-2). Passing between the two heads of the pronator teres muscle, it leaves the cubital fossa. Under the superficialis arch it crosses the ulnar a. and descends straight down the middle of the forearm. At the wrist it lies at the radial side of the tendon of the palmaris longus muscle. It has branches in the cubital fossa and forearm.

Articular Branches. To the elbow joint.

Muscular Branches. They innervate all the superficial flexor muscles except the flexor carpi ulnaris.

Anterior Interosseous Branch. Arising from the back of the median n. in the cubital fossa, it descends on the front of the interosseous membrane accompanied by its corresponding artery. It supplies the three muscles of the deep layer and then passes deep to the pronator quadratus muscle to supply the joints of the wrist.

ULNAR N. (Fig. 46-3). Passing behind the medial epicondyle, it enters the forearm between the two heads of the flexor carpi ulnaris muscle. It descends under cover of this muscle, on the flexor digitorum profundus muscle, to the wrist at the radial side of the pisiform bone, where it terminates by dividing into superficial and deep branches. Proximal to the middle of the forearm the nerve meets the ulnar a. It has branches in the forearm.

Articular Branches. To the elbow joint.

Muscular Branches. To the flexor carpi ulnaris muscle and then the medial half of the flexor digitorum profundus muscle.

Palmar Cutaneous Branch. Arising in the middle of the forearm, it descends into the palm and supplies the medial side of the palm.

Dorsal Cutaneous Branch. Arising just above the wrist, it passes to the dorsum of the hand.

SUPERFICIAL (BRANCH OF) RADIAL N. The smaller of the two terminal branches of the radial n. is purely sensory. It arises in front of the lateral epicondyles and descends along the lateral border of the forearm deep to the brachioradialis muscle. It approaches the radial a. in the upper arm. They course together in the middle third of the arm and diverge distally. The superficial branch of the radial n. provides some articular branches to the elbow joint and none to the forearm. It curves under the tendon of the brachioradialis muscle to ramify on as digital nn. (p. 160) of the dorsum of the hand.

DEEP (BRANCH OF) RADIAL N. The larger of the terminal branches of the radial n. is also known as the *posterior interosseous n.* It provides muscular and articular branches. It courses to the back of the forearm beneath the brachioradialis muscle.

BACK OF FOREARM

1. *Fascia*   3. *Deep arteries*
2. *Muscles*   4. *Deep nerves*

The back of the forearm extends from the back of the elbow to the back of the wrist.

1. Fascia

SUPERFICIAL. The superficial fascia of the back of the forearm contains a variable amount of fat and vessels and nerves.

Unnamed Arteries. They are derived from the deep arteries.

Superficial Veins

accessory cephalic v. Arising in a venous plexus on the dorsum of the forearm, it ascends diagonally to join the cephalic v. near the elbow.

Cutaneous Nerves (Fig. 39-2)

posterior antebrachial cutaneous n. Arising from the radial n. as it passes through the spiral groove, it pierces the lateral head of the triceps muscle below the deltoid

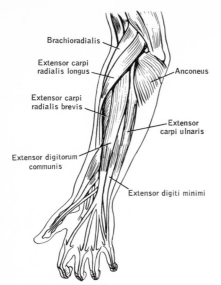

Brachioradialis

Extensor carpi
radialis longus

Extensor carpi
radialis brevis

Anconeus

Extensor
carpi ulnaris

Extensor digitorum
communis

Extensor digiti minimi

47-1 SUPERFICIAL MUSCLES OF BACK OF FOREARM

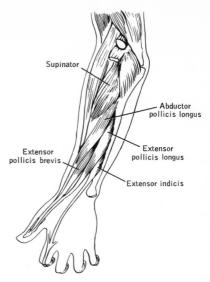

Supinator

Abductor
pollicis longus

Extensor
pollicis brevis

Extensor
pollicis longus

Extensor indicis

47-2 DEEP MUSCLES OF BACK OF FOREARM

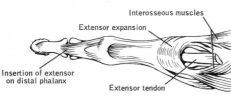

Interosseous muscles

Extensor expansion

Insertion of extensor
on distal phalanx

Extensor tendon

47-3 EXTENSOR EXPANSION: DORSAL VIEW

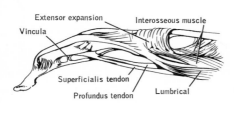

Extensor expansion

Interosseous muscle

Vincula

Superficialis tendon

Profundus tendon

Lumbrical

47-4 EXTENSOR EXPANSION: LATERAL VIEW

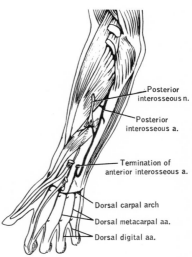

Posterior
interosseous n.

Posterior
interosseous a.

Termination of
anterior interosseous a.

Dorsal carpal arch

Dorsal metacarpal aa.

Dorsal digital aa.

47-5 DEEP AA. AND NN. OF BACK OF FOREARM

Plate 47

154

tuberosity and descends to innervate the skin on the lower third of the lateral part of the arm and the middle of the back of the forearm as far as the wrist.

ulnar branch of the medial antebrachial cutaneous n. It innervates the skin on the posteromedial surface of the forearm.

posterior branch of the lateral antebrachial cutaneous n. It innervates the skin on the posterolateral surface of the forearm.

DEEP. See p. 147.

2. Muscles

The muscles of the back of the forearm divide on the basis of their position into superficial and deep groups.

Superficial Group (Fig. 47-1)

From lateral to medial, the muscles of this group are:

BRACHIORADIALIS. It lies on the radial side of the forearm.

Origin: Upper two-thirds of the lateral supracondylar ridge, and the lateral intermuscular septum.

Insertion: Lateral surface of the distal end of the radius just above the styloid process.

Action: Flexes the forearm.

Nerve supply: Radial n.

EXTENSOR CARPI RADIALIS LONGUS. It lies behind the brachioradialis muscle.

Origin: Lower third of the lateral supracondylar ridge and the lateral intermuscular septum.

Insertion: Base of the second metacarpal.

Action: Extends and abducts the hand.

Nerve supply: Radial n.

EXTENSOR CARPI RADIALIS BREVIS. This muscle lies on the posterolateral side of the forearm.

Origin: Lateral epicondyle by means of the common tendon.

Insertion: Base of the third metacarpal.

Action: Extends the hand.

Nerve supply: deep radial n.

EXTENSOR DIGITORUM COMMUNIS. It lies on the back of the forearm.

Origin: Lateral epicondyle by means of the common tendon.

Above the wrist the muscle ramifies into four tendons which diverge on the back of the hand but remain connected by bands.

Insertion: Extensor expansion to the second to fifth digits.

Action: Extends the phalanges and hand.

Nerve supply: Deep radial n.

Extensor Expansion (Figs. 47-3, 47-4). On the dorsum of the proximal phalanx, each tendon broadens out to form an expansion, which also receives the insertions of the tendons of the lumbrical and interossei muscles on the sides. At the distal end of the phalanx it splits into three parts: the central part inserts into the base of the middle phalanx; the two collateral parts unite and are inserted into the base of the terminal phalanx.

EXTENSOR DIGITI MINIMI. It appears to be part of the extensor digitorum communis.

Origin: Lateral epicondyle by means of the common tendon.

Insertion: Tendon of the extensor digitorum communis to the fifth digit, thus helping to form its extensor expansion.

Action: Extends the phalanges.

Nerve supply: Posterior interosseous n.

EXTENSOR CARPI ULNARIS. It lies on the posterolateral side of the ulna.

Origin: Lateral epicondyle by means of the common tendon.

Insertion: Base of the fifth metacarpal.

Action: Extends and adducts the hand.

Nerve supply: deep radial n.

Deep Group (Fig. 47-2)

SUPINATOR. It surrounds the upper third of the radius.

Origin: Lateral epicondyle of the humerus, radial collateral and annular ligaments, supinator crest, and fossa of the ulna.

Insertion: Anterior, lateral, and posterior surfaces of the upper third of the radius, from the radial tuberosity above to the insertion of the pronator teres muscle below.

Action: Supinates the forearm and hand.

Nerve supply: Deep radial n. (Divides the supinator muscle into two lamellae.)

ABDUCTOR POLLICIS LONGUS. This muscle lies deep in the middle third of the forearm and superficial on the back and radial side of the lower third.

Origin: Lateral part of the posterior surface of the ulna, adjacent interosseous membrane, middle third of the posterior surface of the radius.

Its tendon runs obliquely across those of the extensor carpi radialis longus and brevis muscles.

Insertion: Base of the first metacarpal.

Action: Abducts the thumb.

Nerve supply: Deep radial n.

EXTENSOR POLLICIS BREVIS. This lies on the dorsal and lateral surfaces of the lower third of the forearm.

Origin: Medial part of the lower third of the posterior surface of the radius and adjacent interosseous membrane. Its tendon courses with that of the extensor pollicis longus muscle.

Insertion: Dorsum of the base of the proximal phalanx of the thumb.

Action: Extends the thumb and abducts the hand.

Nerve supply: Deep radial n.

EXTENSOR POLLICIS LONGUS. This lies deep in the back of the middle third of the forearm and superficial on the back of the wrist and thumb.

Origin: Lateral part of the middle third of the posterior surface of the ulna and the adjacent interosseous membrane.

Its tendon also runs obliquely across those of both radial extensors of the wrist.

Insertion: Base of the distal phalanx.

Action: Extends the distal phalanx and abducts the hand.

Nerve supply: Deep radial n.

EXTENSOR INDICIS. It lies deep in the lower third of the forearm and superficial on the dorsum of the wrist and hand.

Origin: Distal part of the posterior surface of the ulna and the adjacent interosseous membrane.

Insertion: Joins the ulnar side of the tendon of the digital extensor for the index finger to form the extensor expansion.

Action: Extends the index finger.

Nerve supply: Deep radial n.

3. Deep Arteries (Fig. 47-5)

POSTERIOR INTEROSSEOUS A. This branch of the common interosseous a. reaches the back of the forearm by passing over the interosseous membrane (p. 185). It emerges between the supinator and abductor pollicis muscles and descends between the superficial and deep groups of extensor muscles, accompanied by its corresponding nerve and venae comitantes. It ends in anastomoses with the anterior interosseous a.

Interosseous Recurrent A. Arising just after the parent artery enters the back of the forearm, it ascends over the supinator muscle and deep to the anconeus to the back of the lateral epicondyle, where it anastomoses with the posterior branch of the profunda brachii.

Muscular Branches. To the superficial and deep groups of extensor muscles.

ANTERIOR INTEROSSEOUS A. Perforating the interosseous membrane some-

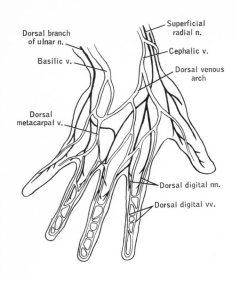

Dorsal branch of ulnar n.

Basilic v.

Dorsal metacarpal v.

Superficial radial n.

Cephalic v.

Dorsal venous arch

Dorsal digital nn.

Dorsal digital vv.

48-1   SUPERFICIAL VV. AND NN. ON BACK OF HAND

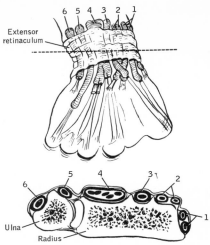

Extensor retinaculum

Ulna

Radius

1. Extensor pollicis brevis and abductor pollicis **longus**
2. Extensor carpi radialis longus and brevis
3. Extensor pollicis longus
4. Extensor digitorum and indicis
5. Extensor digiti minimi
6. Extensor carpi ulnaris

48-2   SYNOVIAL SHEATHS ON BACK OF HAND

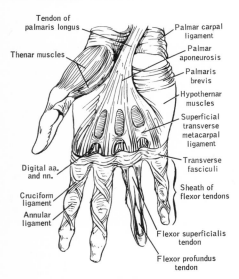

Tendon of palmaris longus

Thenar muscles

Digital aa. and nn.

Cruciform ligament

Annular ligament

Palmar carpal ligament

Palmar aponeurosis

Palmaris brevis

Hypothernar muscles

Superficial transverse metacarpal ligament

Transverse fasciculi

Sheath of flexor tendons

Flexor superficialis tendon

Flexor profundus tendon

48-3   PALMAR APONEUROSIS

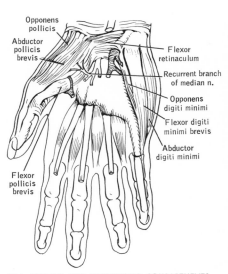

Opponens pollicis

Abductor pollicis brevis

Flexor pollicis brevis

Flexor retinaculum

Recurrent branch of median n.

Opponens digiti minimi

Flexor digiti minimi brevis

Abductor digiti minimi

48-4   THENAR AND HYPOTHENAR COMPARTMENTS

Plate 48

what above the wrist, it emerges on the dorsum of the forearm and terminates in the dorsal carpal arch.

4. Deep Nerves (Fig. 47-5)

POSTERIOR INTEROSSEOUS N. This deep branch of the radial n. arises beneath the brachioradialis muscle and winds laterally around the radius, between the superficial and deep layers of the supinator muscle to reach the back of the forearm. It descends between the superficial and deep groups of muscles accompanied by its corresponding vessels. At about the middle of the forearm, it passes deep to the extensor pollicis longus muscle and descends on the interosseous membrane to the wrist. It terminates as an enlargement which gives off twigs to the intercarpal joints.

Muscular Branches. To the extensor carpi radialis brevis and supinator muscles and the other extensors except the brachioradialis and extensor carpi radialis longus muscles.

HAND

The hand is that part of the upper limb distal to the forearm. It is divided into:

wrist. Consisting of eight carpal bones.

hand proper. Consisting of five metacarpal bones.

digits. Five in number; the first is known as the *pollex.* The *phalanges* are the bones of the digits.

DORSUM

1. Fascia   *2. Deep arteries*

3. Fascial spaces

The dorsum of the hand extends from the back of the wrist to the tips of the digits.

1. Fascia

SUPERFICIAL. The superficial fascia of the dorsum of the hand is loosely arranged and contains:

Cutaneous Vv. (Fig. 48-1)

dorsal digital vv. Two veins are located along the margins of the back of each digit and are interconnected by oblique communicating branches. The two from the pollex join the beginning of the cephalic v. The one on the radial side of the second digit independently joins the dorsal venous arch. The one on the ulnar side of the fifth digit joins the beginning of the basilic v.

Table 53

Tendon	Location
Abductor pollicis longus................. Extensor pollicis brevis	Lateral surface of radius
Extensor carpi radialis longus............ Extensor carpi radialis brevis	Lateral wide groove on back of radius
Extensor pollicis longus..................	Narrow, oblique groove medial to dorsal tubercle of radius
Extensor digitorum...................... Extensor indicis	Medial, wide groove on back of radius
Extensor digiti minimi..................	Between radius and ulna
Extensor carpi ulnaris...................	Groove between head and styloid process of ulna

dorsal metacarpal vv. Three are formed from the remainder of the digital vv. by the union of those from adjacent sides.

dorsal venous arch. Proximal to the heads of the metacarpals, it receives the dorsal metacarpal vv. The radial and ulnar ends mark the beginning of the cephalic and basilic vv., respectively.

Cutaneous Nerves (Figs. 46-1, 46-2)

superficial (branch of) radial n. Piercing the deep fascia in the distal third of the forearm along its lateral border, it continues downward, supplying the overlying skin, and finally divides into its five digital nn., which supply the skin on the back of the proximal phalanges of the first 3½ digits.

First digital n. Innervates the skin on the radial side and the eminence of the thumb.

Second digital n. Innervates the skin on the ulnar side of the thumb.

Third digital n. Innervates the skin on the radial side of the index finger.

Fourth digital n. Descends, divides, and innervates the skin on the adjacent sides of the index and middle fingers.

Fifth digital n. Joins an ulnar digital n. and descends to divide and innervate the skin on adjacent sides of the middle and ring fingers.

dorsal branch of ulnar n. Arising in the lower half of the front of the forearm, it descends, curving medially around the medial side of the ulna. It pierces the deep fascia a little above the wrist and passes down the back of the hand. It supplies the overlying skin and divides into three digital nn., which supply the skin on the back of the proximal phalanges of the last 1½ digits.

First digital n. Innervates the skin on the ulnar side of the little finger.

Second digital n. Descends, divides, and innervates the skin on the adjacent sides of the little and ring fingers.

Third digital n. Joins a radial digital n. and runs down to divide and innervate the skin on adjacent sides of the middle and ring fingers.

palmar digital branches of the median and ulnar nn. They provide branches that supply the skin on the back of the middle and distal phalanges.

DEEP. The fascia is very thin on the back of the hand. It is attached medially to the dorsum of the fifth metacarpal bone and laterally to the dorsum of the second metacarpal bone. It envelops the extensor tendons and their expansions.

Extensor Retinaculum (Fig. 48-2). The thickened band of deep fascia at the junction of the wrist and forearm extends from the anterolateral border of the distal end of the radius to the triquetrum and styloid process of the ulna. Five septums extend from the deep aspect of the retinaculum to the back of the head of the ulna and the ridges on the back of the distal end of the radius. Six compartments are formed which contain the extensor tendons and their synovial sheaths. These are arranged from lateral to medial, as shown in Table 53.

Synovial Sheaths. They extend from the upper border of the extensor retinaculum. Those enveloping tendons which are inserted into metacarpal bones end just short of their insertions. The sheaths investing the tendons that are inserted into phalanges reach only to about the middle of the metacarpals. There are six synovial sheaths for the nine tendons that pass under the extensor retinaculum.

Dorsal Interosseous Fascia. Attached to the dorsal surfaces of the second to fifth metacarpal bones, it covers the intervening dorsal interosseous muscles and may be considered a deep layer of the deep fascia.

2. Deep Arteries (Fig. 47-5)

They course beneath the extensor tendons within the dorsal interosseous fascia.

RADIAL A. After reaching the wrist, it winds backward around the lateral side of the carpus and passes deep to the tendons of the abductor pollicis longus and extensor pollicis longus and brevis muscles. When it reaches the proximal end of the first intermetacarpal space, it dips between the heads of the first dorsal interosseous muscle to enter the palm.

Dorsal Carpal Branch. Crossing the distal row of carpal bones medialward and under the extensor tendons, it anastomoses with the corresponding branch from the ulnar a. and the terminal part of the anterior and posterior interosseous aa. to form the *dorsal carpal arch.* From the arch, three *dorsal metacarpal aa.* descend on the dorsal interossei to the level of the heads of the metacarpal bones where they bifurcate, forming the *proper dorsal digital aa.* These arteries descend on the sides of the contiguous digits to supply the proximal phalangeal area. The proper palmar digital aa. supply the greater part of the digits. The dorsal metacarpal aa. are linked with the palmar arterial arches by two sets of anastomoses. The proximal anastomosis occurs between the superior perforating branches of the dorsal metacarpal aa. and the perforating branches of the deep palmar arch. The distal connection occurs between the inferior perforating branches of the dorsal metacarpal aa. and the perforating branches of the common palmar digital aa. of the superficial palmar arch.

3. Fascial Spaces (Fig. 49-3)

Two clefts are present on the dorsum of the hand between the layers of fascia.

Dorsal Subcutaneous Space. It extends between the superficial and deep fascia.

Dorsal Subaponeurotic Space. It extends between the deep fascia and the dorsal interosseous fascia.

PALM

1. Fascia   *2. Compartments of the hand*

The front of the hand extends from the distal crease at the wrist to the tips of the digits.

1. Fascia

SUPERFICIAL. A moderate amount of fat is divided into fine lobules by septums that connect the skin to the deep fascia. This layer contains vessels, nerves, and a muscle.

Unnamed Cutaneous Vessels

Cutaneous Nerves (Fig. 46-3)

palmar cutaneous branch of ulnar n. The ulnar n. provides a branch in the distal third of the forearm which descends beneath the deep fascia. Near the wrist it pierces the deep fascia and passes superficial to the flexor retinaculum to innervate the skin of the hypothenar eminence.

palmar cutaneous branch of median n. Near the wrist the median n. provides a branch that pierces the deep fascia. It passes superficial to the flexor retinaculum to innervate the skin of the central part of the hand and the medial side of the thenar eminence.

first dorsal digital branch of the radial n. It supplies the radial side of the thenar eminence.

Palmaris Brevis. It is a flat, square muscle.

Origin: Ulnar margin of the palmar aponeurosis.

Insertion: Skin on the ulnar border of the hand.

Action: Draws skin on the ulnar side inwards to provide a firmer grasp.

Nerve supply: Superficial branch of the ulnar n.

DEEP. The antebrachial fascia of the front of the forearm is continuous with the fascia of the dorsum of the hand. It is thickened at the wrist to form the *palmar carpal ligament*. The deep fascia is thin over the thenar and hypothenar eminences but is thickened at the wrist to form the flexor retinaculum, in the central part of the palm to form the palmar aponeurosis, and over the fingers to form the fibrous flexor sheaths.

Flexor Retinaculum (Fig. 48-2). The fascia is attached to the pisiform bone and hamulus of the hamate on the ulnar side and to the tubercle of the scaphoid bone and lips of the groove of the trapezium on the radial side. The flexor retinaculum is in contact with the palmar carpal ligament, proximally. This transverse, fibrous band converts the arch of the carpus into a fibroosseous tunnel for the passage of the flexor tendons (enclosed in their synovial sheaths) and the median nerve into the palm. The tendon of the flexor carpi radialis muscle lies in the groove of the trapezium between the attachments of the retinaculum to that bone.

Palmar Aponeurosis (Fig 48-3). There are two layers of fibers. The superficial longitudinal stratum begins at the apex of the aponeurosis as a continuation of the tendon of the palmaris longus muscle and divides near the base into four digital slips that lie superficial to the flexor tendons. The deeper transverse stratum is continuous with the thenar and hypothenar fascia at its sides and with the palmar carpal ligament, proximally. The transverse fibers that interconnect the diverging digital slips are thickened near the heads of the metacarpals to form the *superficial transverse metacarpal ligaments*. Distally, at the root of the fingers, the webs are reinforced by transverse fibers known as the *transverse fasciculi,* which are attached to the fibrous flexor sheaths at the bases of the first phalanges. In the short intervals between the superficial transverse metacarpal ligament and the transverse fasciculi, the digital vessels and nerves are visible. The digital slips provide superficial fibers which become attached to the skin creases of the palm and at the base of the digit. The deeper portion of each slip is divided into three parts by the flexor tendons that pierce them. The central part contributes to the formation of a fibrous flexor sheath; the marginal processes arch deeply between the heads of the metacarpus to become attached to a deep transverse metacarpal ligament. There is no digital slip to the thumb, but longitudinal fibers extend from the palmar aponeuroses onto the thenar fascia.

Fibrous Flexor Sheaths. Each sheath is attached to the margins of the palmar ligaments of the joints, to the margins of the proximal and middle phalanges, and to the palmar surface of the distal phalanges beyond the insertion of the flexor tendon. As a result osseoaponeurotic canals for these tendons are formed by the fascia of the fibrous flexor sheaths. Opposite the bodies of the phalanges the sheath is strong and made up of transverse fibers known as *annular ligaments.* Opposite the interphalangeal joints it is thin, has oblique fibers, and is known as the *cruciform ligaments.* The outer layer of the synovial sheaths which envelop the tendons serve as the linings of the fibrous sheaths.

2. Compartments of the Hand

Septums extend backward from the margins of the palmar aponeurosis to subdivide the hand. The thenar septum extends down to attach to the palmar aspect of the first metacarpal bone and separate the thenar compartment. The hypothenar septum extends down to attach to the radial side of the fifth metacarpal and separates the thenar compartment. The central compartment lies between the two septums.

Thenar Compartment (Fig. 48-4)

The thenar compartment has the following boundaries, formed by the structures indicated:

Anterior boundary: deep fascia

Posterior boundary: first metacarpal bone

Lateral boundary: attachment of deep fascia to carpals and side of first metacarpal

Medial boundary: thenar septum

The contents of the thenar compartment are:

SHORT MUSCLES OF THE THUMB. All the muscles of this group are innervated by the recurrent branch of the median n.

Abductor Pollicis Brevis. It forms greater part of the thenar eminence.

Origin: Flexor retinaculum, tubercle of the scaphoid, ridge of the trapezium.

Insertion: Radial side of base of the proximal phalanx of the thumb.

Action: Abducts the thumb by flexion at the carpometacarpal joint.

Flexor Pollicis Brevis. It is located medial to the abductor muscle.

Origin: Flexor retinaculum and ridge of the trapezium.

Insertion: Radial side of base of proximal phalanx of thumb by a tendon containing sesamoid bones.

Action: Flexes the proximal phalanx.

Opponens Pollicis. It extends beneath the preceding two muscles.

Origin: Flexor retinaculum and ridge of the trapezium.

Insertion: Entire radial border of the first metacarpal bone.

Action: Opposition of thumb; i.e., flexion, adduction, and medial rotation so that the tip of the thumb can meet each of the tips of the four fingers.

SUPERFICIAL PALMAR BRANCH OF RADIAL A. (Fig. 49-4). Supplying the thenar muscles, it arises in the forearm, curves around to the back of the hand, courses deep to the abductor pollicis brevis muscle, and helps complete the superficial palmar arch.

RECURRENT BRANCH OF MEDIAN N. (Fig. 48-4). As the median n. emerges from under the flexor retinaculum, it provides a branch that courses directly under the deep fascia and curves radially to supply the muscles of the thenar compartment (except the adductor pollicis).

PART OF TENDON OF FLEXOR POLLICIS LONGUS MUSCLE
FIRST METACARPAL BONE

Hypothenar Compartment (Fig. 48-4)

The boundaries of the hypothenar compartment are as follows:
Anterior boundary: deep fascia
Posterior boundary: fifth metacarpal bone
Lateral boundary: hypothenar septum
Medial boundary: attachment of deep fascia to fifth metacarpal
Its contents are:

SHORT MUSCLES OF THE LITTLE FINGER. All are innervated by the deep branch of the ulnar n.

Abductor Digiti Minimi. It is the most lateral muscle of the group.
Origin: Pisiform bone.
Insertion: Ulnar side of base of the proximal phalanx of the little finger.
Action: Abducts the little finger at the metacarpophalangeal joint.

Flexor Digiti Minimi Brevis. It extends on the radial side of the abductor muscle.
Origin: Flexor retinaculum and hamulus of the hamate.
Insertion: Tendon fuses and inserts with the abductor muscle.
Action: Flexes the proximal phalanx.

Opponens Digiti Minimi
Origin: Flexor retinaculum and hook of the hamate.
Insertion: Entire ulnar margin of the fifth metacarpal.
Action: Opposition; flexion, adduction, and rotation of the fifth metacarpal.

ULNAR N. (Fig. 50-1). The ulnar 1½ digits are supplied by the nerve that crosses superficial to the flexor retinaculum and passes to the base of the hypothenar eminence, where it divides into superficial and deep (p. 171) palmar branches. The former courses beneath the palmaris brevis muscle and divides into two digital branches: (1) a proper digital branch that descends along the ulnar side of the little finger; (2) a common digital branch that descends to the web of the fourth interdigital space and divides into two proper digital nn. that supply the contiguous sides of the ring and little fingers. The superficial branch also sends a communicating branch to the third common palmar digital branch of the median n.

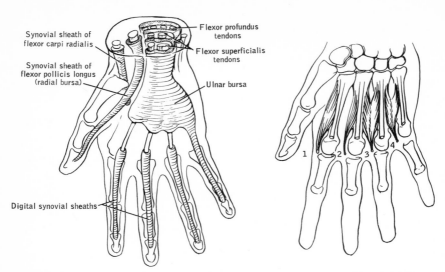

Synovial sheath of
flexor carpi radialis

Synovial sheath of
flexor pollicis longus
(radial bursa)

Flexor profundus
tendons

Flexor superficialis
tendons

Ulnar bursa

Digital synovial sheaths

49-1 SYNOVIAL SHEATHS OF FLEXOR TENDONS

1 2 3 4

49-2 LUMBRICAL MUSCLES

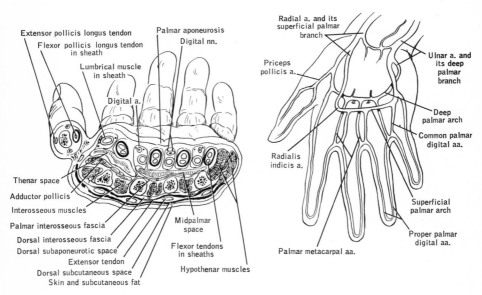

Extensor pollicis longus tendon
Flexor pollicis longus tendon
in sheath

Palmar aponeurosis
Digital nn.

Lumbrical muscle
in sheath

Digital a.

Thenar space
Adductor pollicis
Interosseous muscles
Palmar interosseous fascia
Dorsal interosseous fascia
Dorsal subaponeurotic space
Extensor tendon
Dorsal subcutaneous space
Skin and subcutaneous fat

Midpalmar
space

Flexor tendons
in sheaths

Hypothenar muscles

49-3 HORIZONTAL SECTION THROUGH PALM

Radial a. and its
superficial palmar
branch

Priceps
pollicis a.

Radialis
indicis a.

Ulnar a. and
its deep
palmar
branch

Deep
palmar arch

Common palmar
digital aa.

Superficial
palmar arch

Proper palmar
digital aa.

Palmar metacarpal aa.

49-4 ARTERIES OF THE PALM

Plate 49

166

ULNAR A. (Fig. 49-4). It passes superficially to the flexor retinaculum. At the base of the hypothenar eminence it divides into superficial and deep (p. 171) branches. The former provides a proper palmar digital a. which runs along the ulnar side of the little finger. It curves laterally to join in the formation of the superficial palmar a.

FIFTH METACARPAL BONE

Central Compartment (Fig. 49-3)

The central compartment of the hand has the following boundaries:

Anterior boundary: palmar aponeurosis

Posterior boundary: volar interosseous fascia overlying the third, fourth, and fifth metacarpals and intervening interossei

Lateral boundary: thenar septum

Medial boundary: hypothenar septum

SUPERFICIAL PALMAR ARCH (Fig. 49-4). The distal curved terminal portion of the ulnar a. and the superficial palmar branch of the radial a. (or occasionally the radialis indicis or princeps pollicis branches of the radial a.) form the superficial palmar arch. The arch lies deep to the palmar aponeurosis between the two transverse skin creases and is accompanied by venae comitantes. It provides branches to the medial 3½ digits.

Common Palmar Digital Aa. Three arteries arise from the arch and descend on the lumbrical muscles, between the flexor tendons, to the webs of the fingers. Each artery anastomoses with a palmar metacarpal a. of the deep arch and a distal perforating branch from a dorsal metacarpal a. The short trunks thus formed divide into two proper volar digital aa. which supply the contiguous sides of the fingers. These arteries provide branches to the skin, tendons, and joints of the digits, and to the dorsum of the middle and distal phalanges.

MEDIAN N. (Fig. 50-1). Supplying the radial 3½ digits, it passes deep to the flexor retinaculum to enter the palm of the hand on the radial side of the tendon of the palmaris longus muscle. It immediately gives rise to the *recurrent branch*, which supplies the thenar muscles and then ramifies into three common palmar digital nn.

First Common Palmar Digital N. It ramifies into three proper palmar digital nn. The first of these supplies the radial side of the thumb, the second supplies the ulnar side of the thumb, and the third supplies the radial side of the index finger and first lumbrical muscle.

Second Common Palmar Digital N. It descends to the web of the finger and divides into two proper palmar digital nn. for the adjacent sides of the index and middle fingers. In the palm, it gives off a twig to the second lumbrical muscle.

Third Common Palmar Digital N. Descending to the web of the finger, it divides into two proper digital nn. for the adjacent sides of the middle and ring fingers.

FLEXOR TENDONS, THEIR SHEATHS, AND THE LUMBRICALS (Figs. 49-1 to 49-3)

Tendons of the Flexor Digitorum Superficialis. They pass deep to the flexor retinaculum and into the palm. There each tendon runs towards its finger, where it enters a fibrous flexor sheath and divides above the proximal phalanx to allow passage for its corresponding profundus tendon. Above the base of the middle phalanx, the dorsal margins of two halves reunite and form a gutter for the profundus tendon. It divides again and inserts into the margins of the middle phalanx.

Tendons of the Flexor Digitorum Profundus. In the wrist, they lie between the flexor superficialis tendons and the carpus. In the palm, the diverging tendons give origin to the lumbrical muscles and each runs towards its finger, where it enters its fibrous flexor sheath. Above the proximal phalanx it passes through its corresponding superficialis tendon to insert in the base of the distal phalanx.

Sheath of the Flexor Longus (Radial Bursa). This extends from somewhat proximal to the flexor retinaculum and encloses the tendon as far as its insertion.

Sheath of the Flexor Carpi Radialis. This extends from somewhat proximal to the flexor retinaculum and encloses the tendon as far as its insertion. The tendons of the palmaris longus and flexor carpi ulnaris muscles are not enclosed in synovial sheaths.

Common Flexor Sheath (Ulnar Bursa) (Fig. 49-1). Enveloping the flexor superficialis and profundus tendons, which are arranged in two rows, it extends from above the flexor retinaculum to the middle of the palm. Its medialmost part is prolonged to the insertion of the profundus tendon of the fifth digit at its distal phalanx. The main part of the sheath envelops both the flexor tendons and the proximal part of the lumbrical muscles.

Digital Synovial Sheaths (Fig. 49-1). The individual sheaths extend from the bases to the heads of the metacarpals, over which they lie, and terminate at the bases of the distal phalanges. Within the fibrous flexor sheaths of each digit, vincula, or vascular folds, represent duplications between the outer and inner synovial sheaths. The *vincula longa* extend between the tendons and the proximal phalanges. The triangular *vincula brevia* are located near the insertion of each tendon.

Lumbrical Muscles (Fig. 49-2). These are four cylindrical muscles.

Origin: Tendons of the flexor digitorum profundus muscle.

First: Radial side of the tendon to the index finger.

Second: Radial side of the tendon to the middle finger.

Third: Contiguous sides of the tendons for the middle and ring fingers.

Fourth: Contiguous sides of the tendons for the ring and little fingers.

Each muscle passes distalward between the tendons and deep to the digital vessels and nerves. It passes in front of the deep transverse metacarpal ligament and then obliquely backwards on the radial sides of the metacarpophalangeal joints where it fans out.

Insertion: Radial border of the extensor expansions at the level of the proximal phalanx.

Action: Flex the proximal phalanges and extend the middle and distal phalanges.

Nerve supply:

Two lateral lumbrical muscles: First and second common digital branches of the median n.

Two medial lumbrical muscles: By the deep branch of the ulnar n.

DEEP PALMAR SPACES (Fig. 49-3). These fascial clefts, or potential spaces in the palm, should not be confused with the fascial compartments.

Thenar Space. The thenar space extends from the thenar eminence to the third metacarpal and from the flexor retinaculum to 1 in. proximal to the webs. Its boundaries are:

Anterior boundary: first lumbrical and flexor tendons of index finger

Posterior boundary: transverse head of adductor pollicis m.

Lateral boundary: flexor pollicis longus tendon and sheath

Medial boundary: posterior half of fibrous septum extending from palmar aponeurosis to third metacarpal

Midpalmar Space. This extends from the third metacarpal to the hypothenar eminence and from the flexor retinaculum to 1 in. proximal to the webs. Its boundaries are as follows:

Anterior boundary: second, third, and fourth lumbrical muscles and flexor tendons of medial 3 digits

Posterior boundary: medial 2½ metacarpals and enclosed interosseous muscles

Lateral boundary: posterior half of fibrous septum extending from the palmar aponeurosis to third metacarpal

Medial boundary: hypothenar septum

RADIAL A. (Fig. 49-4). This artery enters the palm from the back of the hand by passing between the heads of origin of the first dorsal interosseous muscle at the base of the first intermetacarpal space. It then begins to curve medially and gives off two branches.

Princeps Pollicis A. It descends along the ulnar border of the first metacarpal to the head of this bone, where it divides into two proper digital aa. which descend on both sides of the thumb.

Radialis Indicis A. Arising in common with its other branch and descending between the transverse head of the adductor pollicis muscle and the first dorsal inter-

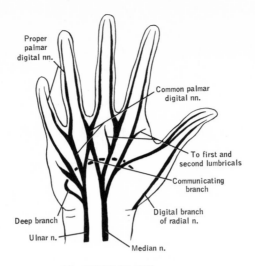

Proper
palmar
digital nn.

Common palmar
digital nn.

To first and
second lumbricals

Communicating
branch

Digital branch
of radial n.

Deep branch

Ulnar n.

Median n.

50-1   NERVES OF PALM

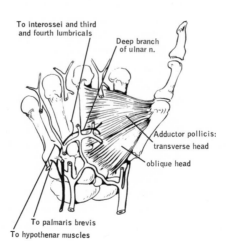

To interossei and third
and fourth lumbricals

Deep branch
of ulnar n.

Adductor pollicis:
transverse head

oblique head

To palmaris brevis

To hypothenar muscles

50-2   ADDUCTOR POLLICIS AND DEEP NERVES

Plate 50

170

osseous muscle, this artery runs along the radial side of the index finger and can be considered a proper digital artery.

DEEP PALMAR ARCH (Fig. 49-4). It is formed by the union of the terminal portion of the radial a. and the deep branch of the ulnar a. The former, after giving off its two branches in the first intermetacarpal space, curves medially across the front of the second metacarpal and its surrounding interossei, between the transverse and oblique heads of the adductor pollicis muscle, then across the third and fourth metacarpals and their interossei, to the base of the fifth metacarpal, where it joins the deep branch of the ulnar a.

Palmar Metacarpal Aa. Three arteries arise from the convexity of the arch and descend in the palmar interosseous fascia where they supply the interossei and lumbrical muscles. Near the webs of the fingers they join their corresponding common palmar digital aa. from the superficial palmar arch.

Recurrent Carpal Branches. Small branches ascend to the wrist where they supply the intercarpal joints and terminate in the palmar carpal network.

Perforating Branches. These branches pass backwards through the proximal parts of the intermetacarpal spaces between the heads of origin of the dorsal interossei muscles. They anastomose with their corresponding dorsal metacarpal aa., which arise from the arterial arch on the dorsum of the hand.

Deep Branch of the Ulnar A. (Fig. 49-4). On the radial side of the pisiform bone, the ulnar a. provides a branch that descends between the abductor and flexor digiti minimi muscles and then curves laterally through the origin of the opponens muscle to anastomose with the radial a. It supplies the adjacent muscles, the third and fourth lumbricals, and the interossei.

DEEP BRANCH OF THE ULNAR N. (Fig. 50-2). At the root of the hypothenar eminence, the ulnar n. provides a branch that curves laterally to supply the hypothenar muscles and then runs across the palm with the deep palmar arch, to supply the third and fourth lumbricals and all the interossei. It terminates by supplying the adductor pollicis muscle.

DEEP MUSCLES. The deepest layer of this compartment consists of the adductor pollicis and the interossei muscles and the second to fifth metacarpal bones. The interossei and metacarpals are enclosed by two fascial membranes, the dorsal and palmar interosseous fasciae.

Adductor Pollicis (Fig. 50-2). It is triangular in shape.

Origin:

Oblique head: Capitate, and bases of the second and third metacarpal bones.
Transverse head: Palmar surface of the third metacarpal bone.

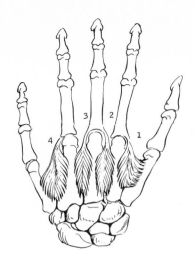

50-3   DORSAL INTEROSSEI

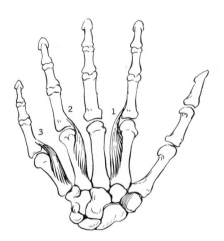

50-4   PALMAR INTEROSSEI

Plate 50   (Continued)

Insertion: Ulnar side of the base of the proximal phalanx of the thumb by a sesa-moid-containing tendon.

Action: Adducts the thumb.

Nerve supply: Deep branch of the ulnar n.

Interossei. The hand has seven interossei muscles: four dorsal and three palmar. Some consider the medial part of the flexor pollicis brevis as the first palmar inter-osseous muscle, thus making the total number of interossei eight. Except for the first dorsal and palmar interossei their tendons pass behind the deep transverse liga-ments. All the interossei are innervated by the deep branch of the ulnar n.

Dorsal Interossei (Fig. 50-3)

Origin: Two heads from adjacent sides of the metacarpal bones between which they lie.

Insertion: Radial sides of second and third digits and ulnar sides of third and fourth digits and the extensor expansion.

Action: Abducts digits from the longitudinal axis of the third finger.

Palmar Interossei (Fig. 50-4)

Origin: Palmar surfaces of first, second, third, and fifth metacarpal bones.

Insertion: Ulnar sides of the proximal phalanges of the first and second digits and radial side of the proximal phalanges of the fourth and fifth digits and the extensor expansions.

Action: Adducts digits toward the longitudinal axis of the third finger.

SECOND TO FOURTH METACARPAL BONES

BONES OF UPPER EXTREMITY

1. Shoulder girdle: clavicle and scapula

2. Arm: humerus

3. Forearm: ulna and radius

4. Hand: carpus, metacarpus, and phalanges

Each of the four regions of the upper extremity has its bony framework.

1. Shoulder Girdle

Clavicle

The clavicle (Figs. 51-1, 51-2) is S-shaped, with its medial half convex forward and its lateral half convex backward.

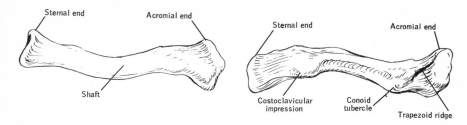

51-1   CLAVICLE: SUPERIOR SURFACE

51-2   CLAVICLE: INFERIOR SURFACE

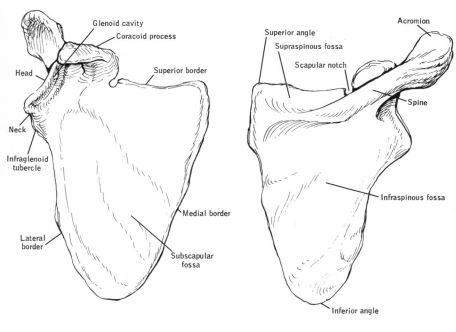

51-3   SCAPULA: COSTAL SURFACE

51-4   SCAPULA: DORSAL SURFACE

Plate 51

Sternal End. It has a saddle-shaped facet that continues inferiorly to provide an articular surface for the cartilage of the first rib.

Acromial End. It has a small oval facet.

Shaft. It presents three landmarks.

costoclavicular impression. Rough impression on the inferior surface.

conoid tubercle. A projection at the posterior margin of the underside of the clavicle.

trapezoid ridge. An oblique ridge or line running anterolaterally from the conoid tubercle.

Scapula

The scapula (Figs. 51-3, 51-4) is a flat, triangular bone.

Surfaces. The scapula has the following two surfaces:

costal. Presents a broad concavity, the *subscapular fossa,* which contains several ridges.

dorsal. Unequally divided by the spine into the smaller *supraspinous* and the larger *infraspinous fossae.*

Borders. The three borders of the scapula are as follows:

superior. The shortest and thinnest border extends from the superior angle to the coracoid process. The *scapular notch* is at the lateral end of the border.

medial. The longest border extends from the superior to the inferior angle. It parallels the vertebral column.

lateral. The thickest border extends from the glenoid cavity to the inferior angle. The *infraglenoid tubercle* is the rough impression at its upper end.

Angles. There are three angles of the scapula:

superior. The junction of the superior and medial borders.

inferior. The junction of the medial and lateral borders.

lateral. The junction of the lateral and superior borders. It is thickened to form the *head* of the scapula, which is separated from the rest of the scapula by a constricted *neck.* Laterally, the head has the shallow, piriform-shaped *glenoid cavity.* Above the upper apex of the cavity is the *supraglenoid tubercle.*

Spine of the Scapula. Extending from the neck to the medial border, it is triangular and projects backwards from the dorsal surface where it is attached at its root. Its posterior surface, or crest, is subcutaneous.

Acromion. This bony ledge projects laterally from the crest of the spine to overhang the shoulder joint. Its medial border has an ovoid articular facet.

Coracoid Process. Extending from the neck of the scapula, it consists of a flattened vertical base and a horizontal projecting portion.

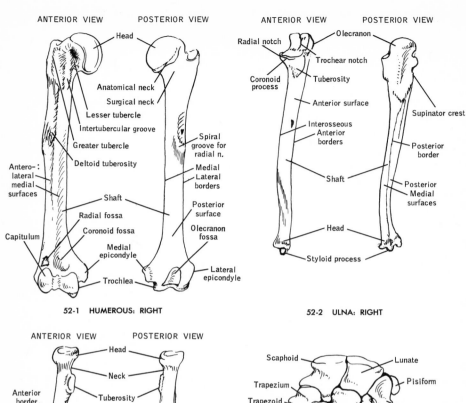

ANTERIOR VIEW   POSTERIOR VIEW

Head
Anatomical neck
Surgical neck
Lesser tubercle
Intertubercular groove
Greater tubercle
Deltoid tuberosity
Antero-:
lateral
medial
surfaces
Shaft
Radial fossa
Coronoid fossa
Capitulum
Medial
epicondyle
Trochlea

Spiral
groove for
radial n.
Medial
Lateral
borders
Posterior
surface
Olecranon
fossa
Lateral
epicondyle

52-1   HUMEROUS: RIGHT

ANTERIOR VIEW   POSTERIOR VIEW

Radial notch
Coronoid
process
Olecranon
Trochear notch
Tuberosity
Anterior surface
Interosseous
Anterior
borders
Shaft
Head
Styloid process
Supinator crest
Posterior
border
Posterior
Medial
surfaces

52-2   ULNA: RIGHT

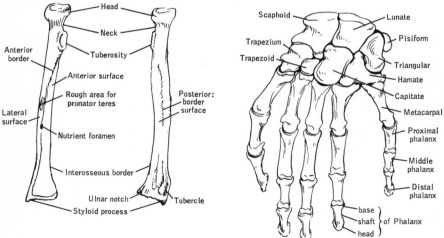

ANTERIOR VIEW   POSTERIOR VIEW

Head
Neck
Tuberosity
Anterior
border
Anterior surface
Rough area for
pronator teres
Lateral
surface
Nutrient foramen
Interosseous border
Ulnar notch
Styloid process
Posterior:
border
surface
Tubercle

52-3   RADIUS: RIGHT

Scaphoid
Trapezium
Trapezoid
Lunate
Pisiform
Triangular
Hamate
Capitate
Metacarpal
Proximal
phalanx
Middle
phalanx
Distal
phalanx
base
shaft }of Phalanx
head

52-4   BONES OF THE LEFT HAND: DORSAL SURFACE

Plate 52

2. Arm

Humerus

The humerus (Fig. 52-1) is the longest and largest bone of the upper limb.

Proximal End. It articulates with the glenoid cavity of the scapula.

head. Large, convex, smooth, and hemispherical.

anatomic neck. The slight constriction around the margin of the head.

greater tubercle. Projects laterally just below the anatomic neck and presents on its upper surface three facets (for muscular attachments).

lesser tubercle. Projects anteriorly, on the medial side just below the neck of the humerus.

intertubercular groove. Located between the tubercles and extended down onto the shaft. The lips of the groove below the tubercles are formed by their crests.

surgical neck. The constriction of the humerus below the tubercles.

Shaft. It has three borders and three surfaces.

medial border. Extends from the lesser tubercle to the medial epicondyle. Near the middle it is associated with a nutrient foramen and distally it is part of the *medial supracondylar ridge.*

lateral border. Extends from the back of the greater tubercle to the lateral epicondyle. Proximally it is indistinct, in the middle it is interrupted by the spiral groove (see below) and distally it is part of the *lateral supracondylar ridge.*

anterior border. Extends from the greater tubercle to the lateral lip of the trochlea. Proximally it is part of the crest of the greater tubercle. In the middle it forms the anterior margin of the deltoid tuberosity. Below the middle it is ill-defined, and distally it is part of the ridge between the radial and coronoid fossae.

anteromedial surface. Proximally it forms the floor of the intertubercular groove. In the middle it is rough; distally it is smooth.

anterolateral surface. It is smooth proximally, and in its middle is located the triangular *deltoid tuberosity.*

posterior surface. Characterized by the *spiral groove* that runs inferolaterally from the junction of the upper and middle third of the shaft to the junction of the middle and lower third.

Distal End. It articulates with the radius and ulna and is the *condyle* of the humerus.

medial epicondyle. Large and prominent, it has a groove on its posterior side.

lateral epicondyle. Small; it lies above the capitulum.

capitulum. This round eminence forms the lateral part of the articular surface. Above it lies the *radial fossa.*

trochlea. The spool-shaped medial part of the articular surface articulates with the ulna. Its medial lip is more prominent, but the lateral lip separates the trochlea from the capitulum. The small *coronoid fossa* lies above the trochlea in the front, and the triangular *olecranon fossa* lies above it posteriorly.

3. Forearm

Ulna

The ulna (Fig. 52-2) is the medial and longer bone of the forearm.

Proximal End. It articulates with the humerus.

olecranon. The projection from the shaft onto the back of the elbow has a smooth, concave anterior surface and forms the upper part of the trochlear notch. The posterior surface is smooth and triangular; the superior surface and the medial and lateral margins are rough.

coronoid process. The triangular projection from the front of the ulna has a smooth superior surface and forms the lower part of the trochlear notch. The anterior surface is rough and presents the *tuberosity of the ulna* where it meets the shaft. The concave *radial notch* is the lateral surface.

trochlear notch. The wide concavity that consists of the anterior surface of the trochlea and superior surface of the coronoid process. It is divided into two parts by a longitudinal ridge.

Shaft. Tapering gradually from above downward, it has three borders and three surfaces.

anterior border. Extends from the tuberosity to the styloid process. Its lower fourth is part of the *pronator ridge.*

interosseous border. Prominent in the middle and indistinct distally. From both margins of the radial notch extend ridges, which enclose the triangular *supinator fossa.* The interosseous border commences from the apex of this fossa.

posterior border. Extends from the back of the olecranon to the styloid process.

anterior surface. The upper three-fourths is concave. The nutrient foramen is present on its proximal part.

medial surface. Smooth and distally subcutaneous.

posterior surface. It has an *oblique ridge* on its upper part that extends from the posterior end of the radial notch to the posterior border. From the oblique ridge a *vertical ridge* extends downward, dividing this surface into medial and lateral parts.

Distal End. It articulates with the radius.

head. Its semilunar articular surface is received into the ulnar notch of the radius.

styloid process. Short and blunt, it projects from the posteromedial end of the shaft. It has a pit at its base, and posteriorly there is a groove.

Radius

The radius (Fig. 52-3) is the lateral bone of the forearm.

Proximal End. It articulates with the humerus and the ulna.

head. A disk the upper surface of which has a concave *fovea.*

neck. The constricted portion below the head.

tuberosity of the radius. On the medial side below the neck.

Shaft. It has three borders and three surfaces:

anterior border. It begins at the tuberosity, curves laterally to pass below the rough area for the pronator teres muscle, and terminates in a tubercle at the anterior part of the base of the styloid process. This border is more commonly known as the anterior oblique line.

interosseous border. Extending from behind the tuberosity, it divides distally into two parts to enclose the triangular area above the ulnar notch.

posterior border. Extending from the back of the neck to the posterior part of the base of the styloid process, it is indistinct except in its middle third.

anterior surface. It has a nutrient foramen on its proximal part.

lateral surface. Characterized by the rough oval impression in the middle.

posterior surface. Convex.

Distal End. Quadrilateral, it presents five surfaces, two of which are articular for the ulna and carpus.

medial surface. Presents an *ulnar notch.*

lateral surface. Narrow and prolonged downward as the *styloid process.*

anterior surface. Concave; ends in a rough forward-projecting ridge.

posterior surface. Convex; characterized by its dorsal tubercle near the middle and by its three grooves.

carpal surface. Concave articular surface divided by a slight anteroposterior ridge into two parts.

4. Hand (Fig. 52-4)

CARPUS. This bone consists of eight carpal bones, arranged in two rows and named from lateral to medial:

proximal row: Scaphoid, lunate, triangular (triquetral), and pisiform.

distal row: Trapezium, trapezoid, capitate, and hamate.

All the bones except the pisiform are cuboid, having six surfaces, of which only the dorsal and palmar are nonarticular and give attachment to ligaments. The proximal surfaces are generally convex and the distal surfaces concave.

METACARPUS. It consists of five metacarpal bones set between the carpal bones and the digits. They are numbered from one to five, from the thumb to the little finger. They articulate primarily with the corresponding distal row of carpal bones. The fourth metacarpal articulates with both the capitate and the hamate. Each metacarpal consists of three parts. The *base* is cuboid; it bears articular facets proximally for its corresponding carpal bone and on the sides for the adjacent metacarpals. Its dorsal and palmar surfaces are rough for the attachment of ligaments. The *shaft* is narrow, prismatic, convex above, and concave below. The *head*, or convex distal end, articulates with the base of the proximal phalanx. Its sides are flattened; dorsally at the junction of the head and shaft it has tubercles for the attachment of collateral ligaments of the metacarpophalangeal joint. Its palmar surface is notched for the flexor tendon that passes through.

PHALANGES. Each digit has three phalanges, except the first, which has two. They are called *proximal, middle,* and *distal.* Each phalanx consists of a *base* (which has a cuplike facet), a short *shaft,* and a pulley-like *head,* except for the distal phalanx which bears the phalangeal tuberosity.

JOINTS OF UPPER EXTREMITY

1. *Clavicular joints*   4. *Radioulnar joints*
2. *Shoulder joint*   5. *Wrist joint*
3. *Elbow joint*   6. *Joints of the hand*

The joints of the upper extremity are classified into six groups.

1. Clavicular Joints

Sternoclavicular Joint (Fig. 53-1)

Type: The sternoclavicular joint is of the double arthrodial type.

Articulating elements: The sternal end of the clavicle articulates with the superolateral angle of the manubrium and the adjacent part of the first costal cartilage.

Ligaments:

Articular capsule. It is attached to the margins of the articular surfaces.

Anterior sternoclavicular ligament. A broad band, it strengthens the capsule and is attached in front to the articular margins.

Posterior sternoclavicular ligament. A broad band that strengthens the capsule, it is attached behind to the articular margins.

Interclavicular ligament. A flattened band that strengthens the capsule above, it extends from the sternal end of one clavicle to the other and is attached to the superior margin of the manubrium in the middle.

Costoclavicular ligament. A short, strong band, it extends from the upper part of the cartilage of the first rib obliquely to the costoclavicular impression on the undersurface of the clavicle.

Articular disk. A flat, fibrocartilaginous disk dividing the joint into two cavities, it is attached above to the upper border of the sternal end of the clavicle and below to the cartilage of the first rib near its junction with the manubrium. In front and in back it is fused with the articular capsule. A separate synovial membrane lines each of the cavities.

Movements: This joint provides a limited amount of movement in every direction; thus functionally it belongs to the ball-and-socket type.

The blood supply to the sternoclavicular joint is provided by the clavicular branch of the thoracoacromial a. The joint is innervated by the medial supraclavicular n.

Acromioclavicular Joint (Fig. 53-2)

Type: The acromioclavicular joint is of the arthrodial (plane) type.

Articulating elements: The acromial end of the clavicle articulates with the medial margin of the acromion.

Ligaments:

Articular capsule. It is attached to the articular margins and lined with a synovial membrane.

Acromioclavicular ligament. This band strengthens the capsule on its superior surface and is attached to the articular margins.

Articular disk. When present, it hangs down from the articular capsule and divides the cavity incompletely.

Coracoclavicular ligament. This accessory ligament has two parts:

trapezoid ligament. Flat, quadrilateral, and located anterolaterally, it extends between the upper surface of the coracoid process and the trapezoid ridge on the undersurface of the clavicle. Its lateral border is free. Medially it is continuous with the second part of the ligament.

conoid ligament. It is triangular and located posteromedially. Its apex is attached near the root of the coracoid process. Its base is fixed to the conoid tubercle on the undersurface of the clavicle. Its medial border is free. Laterally it is continuous with the trapezoid ligament.

Movements: It permits gliding and rotation of the scapula on the clavicle.

The blood supply is provided by the acromial branch of the thoracoacromial a. The joint is innervated by the lateral pectoral and suprascapular nn.

Accessory (scapular) ligaments: They do not extend across a joint but connect one part of the scapula with another.

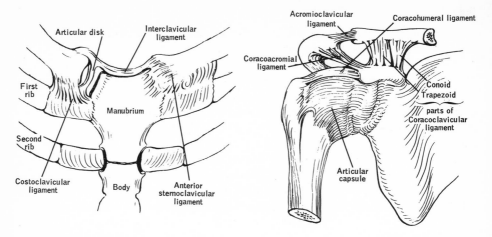

53-1 STERNOCLAVICULAR JOINT

Articular disk
Interclavicular ligament
First rib
Manubrium
Second rib
Costoclavicular ligament
Body
Anterior sternoclavicular ligament

53-2 SHOULDER JOINT

Acromioclavicular ligament
Coracohumeral ligament
Coracoacromial ligament
Conoid
Trapezoid
parts of Coracoclavicular ligament
Articular capsule

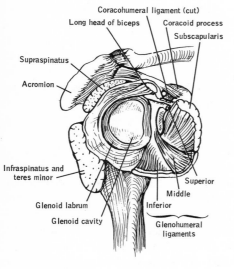

53-3 INTERIOR OF SHOULDER JOINT

Coracohumeral ligament (cut)
Long head of biceps
Coracoid process
Subscapularis
Supraspinatus
Acromion
Infraspinatus and teres minor
Glenoid labrum
Glenoid cavity
Superior
Middle
Inferior
Glenohumeral ligaments

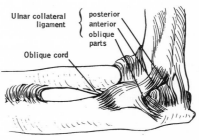

53-4 ELBOW JOINT: MEDIAL VIEW

Ulnar collateral ligament
posterior
anterior
oblique
parts
Oblique cord

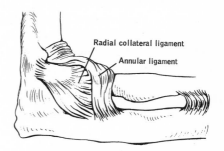

53-5 ELBOW JOINT: LATERAL VIEW

Radial collateral ligament
Annular ligament

Plate 53

182

Coracoacromial ligament. The apex of this triangular ligament is at the tip of the acromion; its base is at the lateral border of the coracoid process.

Transverse scapular ligament. Extending from the base of the coracoid process to the medial border of the scapular notch, it converts the notch into a foramen.

Spinoglenoid ligament. It extends from the lateral border of the spine of the scapula to the margin of the glenoid cavity.

2. Shoulder Joint (Figs. 53-2, 53-3)

Type: The shoulder joint is of the enarthrodial (spheroidal) type.

Articulating elements: The head of the humerus articulates with the glenoid cavity of the scapula. The cup is deepened by the *glenoid labrum,* a fibrocartilaginous ring of triangular cross section which is attached to the rim of the acetabulum.

Ligaments:

Articular capsule. This loose, thin capsule is attached above to the circumference of the glenoid cavity and below to the anatomic neck of the humerus. It is strengthened by its fusion with the tendons of insertion of the supraspinatus, infraspinatus, teres minor, and subscapularis muscles. There are two openings in the capsule: (1) at the upper end of the intertubercular groove for passage of the tendon of the long head of the biceps muscle (the transverse humeral ligament extends across this); (2) located anteriorly, below the coracoid process where the synovial cavity of the joint communicates with the subscapular bursa. A synovial membrane lines the articular capsule and passes over the anatomic neck of the humerus and on to the labrum. It envelops the tendon of the long head of the biceps muscle as a tubular sheath which extends down the intertubercular groove. It protrudes through the other opening in the capsule to form the subscapular bursa.

Coracohumeral ligament. A broad band, intimately connected to the capsule, it extends from the lateral margin of the root of the coracoid process over the articular capsule to the greater tuberosity of the humerus.

Glenohumeral ligaments. They consist of three bands between the synovial membrane and the anterior part of the articular capsule. The superior band extends from the labrum, anterior to the attachment of the biceps tendon, to the upper part of the lesser tuberosity. The middle band arises near the superior ligament and extends to the front of the lesser tuberosity. The inferior band extends from the anterior border of the glenoid cavity obliquely to the medial side of the humerus to the undersurface of its neck.

Movements: All are possible.

The blood supply to the shoulder joint is provided by branches of the transverse scapular, and the anterior and posterior humeral circumflex aa. The joint is innervated by branches of the suprascapular, upper subscapular, and axillary nn.

3. Elbow Joint (Figs. 53-4, 53-5)

Type: The elbow joint is of the ginglymus (hinge) type.

Articulating elements: The capitulum of the humerus articulates with the fovea of the head of the radius; and the trochlea of the humerus articulates with the semilunar notch of the ulna.

Ligaments:

Articular capsule. In front, it is thin and is attached superiorly to the upper margins of the radial and coronoid fossae and to the epicondyles, extending inferiorly to the anterior border of the coronoid process of the ulna and the annular ligament of the radius. Behind it is very thin and is attached superiorly to the margins of the olecranon fossa and to the epicondyles, extending inferiorly to the borders of the olecranon. The capsule is thickened on its sides by the collateral ligaments. A synovial membrane lines the articular capsule and the intracapsular bony surfaces to their articular margins. Subsynovial fat pads lie outside of the synovial membrane adjacent to the articular fossae.

Ulnar collateral ligament. This triangular ligament, fanning out from the medial epicondyle consists of three components. The anterior band is attached to the medial margin of the coronoid process. The oblique (posterior) band extends between the olecranon and the coronoid process. The intermediate part is thin and triangular, extending between the other two parts.

Radial collateral ligament. This triangular ligament fans out from the depression below the lateral epicondyle to the annular ligament and the margins of the radial notch of the ulna.

Movements: The elbow joint provides for flexion and extension.

The blood supply to the elbow joint is derived from the anastomoses around the joint. The joint is innervated anteriorly, by branches of the musculocutaneous, median, and radial nn.; posteriorly, by the ulnar n. via the radial branch to the anconeus.

4. Radioulnar Joints

Proximal Radioulnar Joint (Fig. 53-4)

Type: The proximal radioulnar joint is of the trochoid (pivot-joint) type.

Articulating elements: The head of the radius articulates with the radial notch of the ulna and the annular ligament.

Ligaments:

Articular capsule. The same as that enveloping the elbow joint. Its synovial membrane is continuous with that of the elbow joint.

Annular ligament. A strong curved band that forms most of the ring around the head of the radius, it is attached by its ends to the anterior and posterior margins of the radial notch. The ring is narrower below than above.

Quadrate ligament. This band extends from the inferior border of the annular ligament to the neck of the radius.

Movements: See below.

The arteries and nerves to this joint are the same as those to the lateral side of the elbow joint.

Oblique cord. This thick band extends from the tubercle of the ulna to the radius a little below its tuberosity.

Interosseous membrane. Extending between the interosseous borders of the radius and the ulna, it begins a little below the radial tuberosity and extends to the capsule of the superior radioulnar joint. It has an oval aperture a little above its lower margin for the passage of the anterior interosseous vessels to the back of the hand.

Distal Radioulnar Joint (Fig. 54-1)

Type: The distal radioulnar joint is also of the trochoid (pivot) type.

Articulating elements: The head of the ulna articulates with the ulnar notch of the radius.

Ligaments:

Articular capsule. It extends between the margins of the articular surfaces. A synovial membrane lines the L-shaped joint and projects above the level of the articular surfaces, enclosing a space, the *recessus sacciformis.*

Articular disk. This triangular disk is attached by its base to the sharp medial margin of the distal end of the radius and by its apex to the depression at the lateral side of the root of the styloid process. The margins of the fibrocartilaginous disk are attached to the articular capsule; its upper surface is concave and articulates with the head of the ulna; its undersurface is concave and participates in the formation of the radiocarpal joint.

Movements: At the radioulnar joints both pronation and supination is possible.

The arteries and nerves to this joint are derived from the anterior and posterior interosseous aa. and nn.

5. Wrist (Radiocarpal) Joint (Fig. 54-1)

Type: The wrist joint is condyloid in type.

Articulating elements: The distal end of the radius and the articular disk of the inferior radioulnar joint articulate with the proximal row of carpal bones.

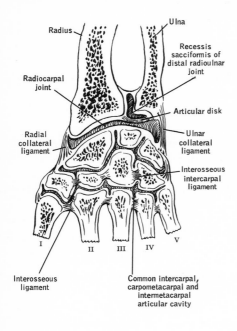

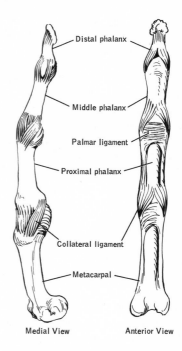

54-1   VERTICAL SECTION THROUGH WRIST JOINTS

54-2   METACARPAL AND PHALANGEAL JOINTS

Plate 54

Ligaments:

Articular capsule. It extends between the margins of the articular surfaces. Its synovial membrane lines the deep surface of the capsule.

Palmar radiocarpal ligament. It extends downwards and medially from the anterior margin of the distal end of the radius and its styloid process to the proximal row of carpal bones and to the capitate.

Dorsal radiocarpal ligament. It extends downward and medially from the posterior margin of the distal end of the radius to the back of the proximal row of carpal bones.

Radial collateral ligament. It extends from the tip of the styloid process of the radius to the sides of the scaphoid and trapezium bones.

Ulnar collateral ligament. It extends from the styloid process of the ulna to the pisiform bone and to the adjacent part of the flexor retinaculum.

Movements: The wrist joint is capable of flexion and extension; abduction and adduction; and circumduction.

The blood supply to the wrist joint is provided by branches of the palmar and dorsal carpal networks. The joint is innervated by branches of the anterior and posterior interosseous nn. and the dorsal and deep branches of the ulnar n.

6. Joints of the Hand

Intercarpal Joints (Fig. 54-1)

JOINTS BETWEEN THE PROXIMAL ROW OF CARPAL BONES

Type: They are of the arthrodial (gliding) type.

Articulating elements: They are the scaphoid and triangular bones.

Ligaments: They are the dorsal, palmar, and interosseous intercarpal ligaments.

JOINTS BETWEEN THE DISTAL ROW OF CARPAL BONES

Type: These joints are also of the arthrodial (gliding) type.

Articulating elements: They consist of the bones of the distal row.

Ligaments: They are the dorsal, palmar, and interosseous intercarpal ligaments.

JOINTS BETWEEN THE TWO ROWS: MIDCARPAL JOINT

Type: There is a central ball-and-socket type, as well as two arthrodial types.

Articulating elements: The head of the capitate and the apex of the hamate articulate with the cup-shaped scaphoid and lunate bones; the trapezium and trapezoid articulate with the scaphoid, and the hamate articulates with the triangular bone.

Ligaments: They are the palmar and dorsal intercarpal and collateral ligaments. The pisiform bone has its own articulation with the palmar surface of the triangular bone. The bones are united by a thin articular capsule lined with a synovial membrane. The pisiform bone is also connected by the pisohamate ligament to the hamulus of the hamate and by the pisometacarpal ligament to the base of the fifth metacarpal. These ligaments are part of the insertion of the flexor carpi ulnaris.

The synovial membrane of the intercarpal joint (Fig. 54-1) is very extensive. It lines the midcarpal joint and sends prolongations upward and downward between the carpals of the proximal and distal rows. It extends into the carpometacarpal joints (except the thumb) and also into the intermetacarpal joints. It does not communicate with the wrist joint or with the pisiform joint, both of which have separate synovial cavities.

Movements: At the intercarpal joint motion occurs simultaneously with motion at the wrist joint. The principle site of movement is at the midcarpal joint, which contributes to flexion and extension of the hand.

The blood supply to the intercarpal joints is derived from the palmar and dorsal carpal networks. The nerves to these joints are derived from the anterior and posterior interosseous nn. and the deep and dorsal branches of the ulnar n.

Carpometacarpal Joints (Fig. 54-1)

CARPOMETACARPAL JOINT OF THE THUMB

Type: This joint is of the saddle type.

Articulating elements: The trapezium articulates with the base of the first metacarpal bone.

Ligaments: The articular capsule is thick but loose. It extends between the margins of the articular surfaces. A synovial membrane lines the capsule of this separate cavity.

Movements: This joint provides for flexion, extension, abduction, adduction, circumduction, and opposition.

The arteries and nerves are derived from nearby rami which pass to the thumb.

CARPOMETACARPAL JOINTS OF THE OTHER FOUR DIGITS

Type: They are arthrodial in type.

Articulating elements: The distal row of carpal bones articulates with the bases of the second to fifth metacarpal bones.

Ligaments: They are the dorsal, palmar, and interosseous carpometacarpal ligaments.

Intermetacarpal Joints (Fig. 54-1)

Type: They are arthrodial in type.

Articulating elements: They are the contiguous sides of the bases of the second to fifth metacarpal bones.

Ligaments: They are the dorsal, palmar, and interosseous metacarpal ligaments.

Deep transverse metacarpal ligament. This narrow band extends across the palmar surfaces of the heads of the second to fifth metacarpal bones.

Metacarpophalangeal Joints (Fig. 54-2)

Type: They are condyloid in type.

Articulating elements: The head of the metacarpals articulates with the proximal end of the phalanges.

Ligaments: They are the articular capsule and the collateral ligament.

Palmar ligaments. Dense fibrocartilaginous plates are located between the collateral ligaments.

Movements: They consist mainly of flexion and extension, with some abduction and adduction.

Interphalangeal Joints (Fig. 54-2)

Type: They are of the hinge type.

Articulating elements: The head of the proximal phalanx articulates with the base of the distal phalanx.

Ligaments: They are the articular capsule and the collateral and palmar ligaments.

Movements: These joints provide for flexion and extension.

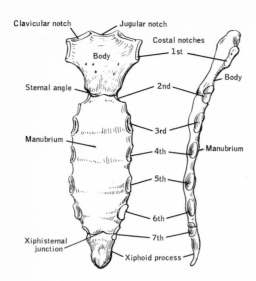

Clavicular notch   Jugular notch

Costal notches
1st

Body

Sternal angle   2nd   Body

Manubrium   3rd

4th   Manubrium

5th

6th

Xiphisternal junction   7th

Xiphoid process

55-1   STERNUM: FRONT VIEW   SIDE VIEW

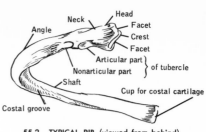

Neck   Head

Angle   Facet
Crest
Facet
Articular part
Nonarticular part   of tubercle
Shaft
Cup for costal cartilage

Costal groove

55-2   TYPICAL RIB (viewed from behind)

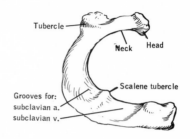

Tubercle

Neck   Head

Scalene tubercle

Grooves for:
subclavian a.
subclavian v.

55-3   FIRST RIB (viewed from above)

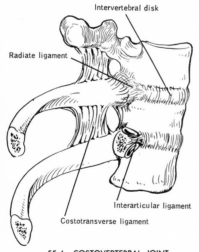

Intervertebral disk

Radiate ligament

Interarticular ligament

Costotransverse ligament

55-4   COSTOVERTEBRAL JOINT

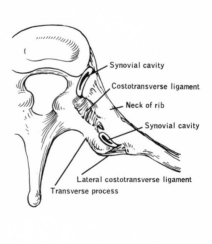

Synovial cavity

Costotransverse ligament

Neck of rib

Synovial cavity

Lateral costotransverse ligament

Transverse process

55-5   COSTOTRANSVERSE JOINT

Plate 55

THORAX

The thorax contains the respiratory and circulatory organs. It communicates with the neck at the thoracic inlet (superior thoracic aperture) and it is closed at its thoracic outlet by the diaphragm. The thorax will be described in terms of its structural framework and the contents of the thoracic cavity.

THORACIC BONES AND JOINTS

1. *Sternum* 2. *Ribs*
3. *Joints*

The sternum and ribs comprise the bony thorax and provide protection for the heart and lungs as well as the sites of attachment for muscles of the thorax, upper limb, back, and abdomen.

1. Sternum (Fig. 55-1)

The sternum consists of three parts:

Manubrium. The manubrium presents a *jugular notch* above, and a pair of *clavicular notches* on the lateral sides of the upper border. Laterally there are a pair of facets for the first costal cartilage and demifacets for the second costal cartilage. Inferiorly, the manubrium is united with the body of the sternum by a fibrocartilage at the *sternal angle.*

Body. The body of the sternum presents, above, the other demifacets for the second costal cartilage and, laterally, costal notches for the third to sixth costal cartilages and a demifacet for the seventh. The lower end is united with the xiphoid process, at the *xiphisternal junction,* by an intervening fibrocartilage and by ligaments.

Xiphoid Process. It presents a demifacet for the seventh rib.

2. Ribs (Fig. 55-2)

There are usually twelve ribs, or costae, on each side of the body. The first seven, the *true ribs,* join the sternum by means of their costal cartilages. The remaining five are the *false ribs;* the costal cartilages of the eighth, ninth, and tenth ribs join the seventh costal cartilage to reach the sternum. The eleventh and twelfth ribs are free and are called *floating ribs.*

Typical Ribs (Third to Ninth)

Each typical rib can be divided into three parts:

Head. The head is wedge-shaped; the apex is the *crest* of the head. It presents two facets which articulate with the numerically corresponding vertebra and with the vertebra above.

Neck. It presents a crest on the upper border of the constriction, a *tubercle* posteriorly where the neck and shaft meet, a facet for articulation with the transverse process of the next lower vertebra, and a nonarticular rough elevation.

Shaft. This thin, long, curved shaft presents a ridge at the *angle*, or point of maximum curvature, and a *costal groove* on the inner lower edge.

Atypical Ribs

There are five atypical ribs.

First Rib (Fig. 55-3). The first rib is short. Its head has only one facet for articulation with Tv 1; its neck is long. A prominent tubercle is present at the junction of the neck and shaft. On the upper surface of the latter are two shallow grooves, which are separated by the *scalene tubercle* at the inner margin of the shaft. A costal groove is absent.

Second Rib. It is longer than the first rib but similar to it. The shaft is not twisted but has a rough eminence on its external surface. The costal groove is not very distinct.

Tenth Rib. It is atypical only in presenting a single facet on its head.

Eleventh Rib. This short rib presents a slight angle and no neck or tubercles.

Twelfth Rib. This very short rib has no neck, tubercles, angle, or costal grooves.

Costal Cartilages. These bars of hyaline cartilage prolong the ribs anteriorly. The upper seven articulate with the sternum; the next three join the seventh cartilage; the last two are tips terminating in the abdominal wall. The thoracic vertebrae are discussed on p. 358.

3. Joints of the Ribs and Sternum

Costovertebral Joints (Fig. 55-4)

Type: They are arthrodial in type.

Articulating elements: The head of the rib articulates with demifacets of two adjacent vertebrae.

Ligaments:

Articular capsule. It is attached to the margins of articular surfaces and is thickened anteriorly as the radiate ligament.

Interarticular ligament. Extending between the crest of the head to the intervertebral disk, it attaches to the capsule in front and behind.

Costotransverse Joints (Fig. 55-5)

Type: They are arthrodial joints.

Articulating elements: The tubercle of the rib articulates with the adjacent transverse process.

Ligaments:

Costotransverse ligament. It extends between the back of the neck of the rib and the front of the transverse process.

Lateral costotransverse ligament. It extends obliquely between the apex of the transverse process and the nonarticular portion of the tubercle of the rib.

Superior costotransverse ligament. It extends between the crest of the neck of the rib to the lower border of the transverse process above.

Costochondral Joints

They permit gliding of the lateral end of each costal cartilage with the sternal end of its rib.

Interchondral Joints

They permit gliding between each of the fifth to ninth costal cartilages with the one below. Each joint is enclosed by an articular capsule.

Costosternal Joints

The first rib is directly united with the sternum. These joints refer to the second to seventh ribs.

Type: They are arthrodial joints.

Articulating elements: The costal cartilage articulates with the sternum.

Ligaments:

Articular capsule. It is strengthened by radiate ligaments.

Intraarticular ligament. It divides the joint into two cavities.

Sternal Joints

A fibrocartilage unites the manubrium with the body of the sternum; the xiphoid process and body are united by a cartilage that ossifies at puberty.

THORACIC WALLS

1. Intrinsic muscles	*3. Veins*
2. Arteries	*4. Nerves*

Various parts of the anterior thoracic wall have already been discussed (cutaneous nn., p. 127; breast, p. 129; pectoral fascia and muscles, p. 130).

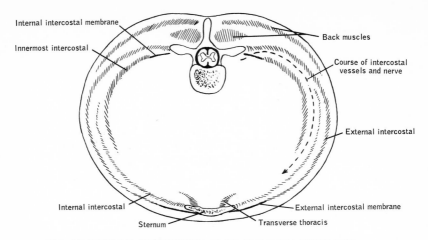

56-1 DIAGRAMMATIC REPRESENTATION OF THE INTERCOSTAL MUSCULATURE

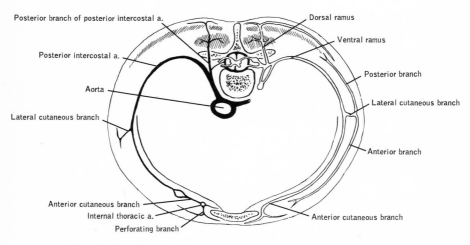

56-2 DIAGRAMMATIC REPRESENTATION OF AN INTERCOSTAL ARTERY AND NERVE

Plate 56

1. Intrinsic Muscles (Fig. 56-1)

EXTERNAL INTERCOSTALS. Extending from the tubercle of a rib, each is continuous at the costochondral junction with its *external intercostal membrane*. Their fibers are directed downward and forward.

Origin: Lower margin of each of the first 11 ribs.

Insertion: Upper margin of the rib below.

Action: Elevates the ribs.

Nerve supply: Corresponding intercostal or thoracoabdominal nn.

INTERNAL INTERCOSTALS. They extend from the side of the sternum to the angle of the ribs, where they are continuous with the *internal intercostal membrane*. The fibers are directed downwards and backwards.

Origin: Costal cartilages and upper margin of the costal groove of first 11 ribs.

Insertion: Upper margin of the rib below.

Action: Elevates the ribs.

Nerve supply: Corresponding intercostal or thoracoabdominal n.

TRANSVERSUS THORACIS

Origin: Posterior surface of xiphoid process and lower third of sternum.

Insertion: Inner surface of costal cartilage of the second to sixth ribs.

Action: Draws anterior part of the thorax downward.

Nerve supply: Intercostal nn.

INNERMOST INTERCOSTAL. Variable in extent, it is considered a deep layer of the internal intercostal muscles, from which it is separated by the intercostal nn. and vessels. The innermost intercostal muscles extend between the ribs and are connected by fascia with the transversus thoracic muscle above and the subcostal muscle below.

SUBCOSTAL. It consists of variable slips.

Origin: Inner surface of the lower ribs near their angle.

Insertion: Inner surface of the second or third rib below the rib of origin.

Action: Draws adjacent ribs together.

Nerve supply: Intercostal nn.

LEVATORES COSTARUM. They are 12 small, fan-shaped muscles.

Origin: Transverse processes of Cv 7 and Tv 1 to Tv 11.

Insertion: Ribs medial to their angles.

Action: Raise ribs and increase size of the thoracic cavity.

Nerve supply: Intercostal nn.

2. Arteries (Fig. 56-2)

INTERNAL THORACIC A. Arising in the root of the neck from the first part of the subclavian a., it descends medialward behind the clavicle and first costal cartilage

Table 54

Branches	Course	Area supplied
Pericardiacophrenic a.....	With phrenic nerve	Diaphragm, pericardium, pleura
Anterior mediastinal a....	Descends	Fat, thymus, pericardium
Anterior intercostal aa....	Laterally; 2 for each of upper 6 spaces	Intercostal mm.
Perforating branches.....	Anteriorly	Pectoralis major m. and breast
Musculophrenic a........	Downward and lateralward	Intercostal mm. and lower pericardium
Superior epigastric a......	Descends into rectus sheath	Diaphragm and abdominal aa.

Table 55

Branch	Area supplied
Posterior branch.................	Muscles of back and vertebral canal (via spinal branch)
Collateral intercostal branch.......	Anastomoses with lower of two anterior intercostal aa.
Muscular branches................	Intercostals and pectoralis major and minor mm.
Lateral cutaneous branches........	Accompany corresponding nerves
Mammary branches..............	From third to fifth costal spaces

and then parallel with the margin of the sternum. It ends behind the sixth intercostal space by dividing into its two terminal branches; the superior epigastric and the musculophrenic aa. Its branches are given in Table 54.

POSTERIOR INTERCOSTAL AA. They have two sites of origin.

Superior Intercostal A. Arising from the costocervical trunk at the neck of the first rib, it provides a branch, the first posterior intercostal a., and continues down as the second posterior intercostal a.

Third to Eleventh Posterior Intercostal Aa. Arising from the back of the descending aorta, they pass to the costal grooves, where they anastomose with the upper of the two anterior intercostal aa. The branches of each artery are shown in Table 55.

SUBCOSTAL A. Arising from the back of the lowest part of the thoracic aorta, it passes behind the structures of the wall to enter the abdomen.

3. Veins

INTERNAL THORACIC VV. These are venae comitantes of the internal thoracic a. They are formed by union of the companion veins of the musculophrenic and superior epigastric aa. and course on both sides of the internal thoracic a. to unite near the third costal cartilage. This vessel ascends along the medial side of the artery to terminate in the brachiocephalic v. at the thoracic inlet.

Table 56

Branches	Area supplied
White ramus communicans....	Sympathetic fibers to the sympathetic trunk
Muscular branches............	Intercostals
Lateral cutaneous branch......	Anterior branch over pectoralis major m. and posterior branch over serratus anterior m.
Anterior cutaneous branch.....	Medial branch over sternum, lateral branch over front of thorax

ANTERIOR INTERCOSTAL VV. Two veins are present in the upper spaces; they terminate in the internal thoracic v.

POSTERIOR INTERCOSTAL VV. One vein is present in each intercostal space. Each has tributaries that correspond to the arteries. The veins terminate on both sides among the brachiocephalic, azygos, or hemiazygos vv.

4. Nerves (Fig. 56-2)

Typical Intercostal Nn. (Third to Sixth)

The typical intercostal nn. are the ventral rami of the thoracic spinal nn. Each lies below its corresponding vein and artery and passes along the posterior intercostal membrane to enter the costal groove. It continues between the intercostal muscles to terminate as the anterior cutaneous branch by piercing the anterior thoracic wall near the sternum. The branches of each nerve are shown in Table 56.

Atypical Intercostal Nn.

The atypical intercostal nn. also are ventral rami of the thoracic spinal nerves but have the following distinct characteristics:

FIRST THORACIC N. This short nerve joins the brachial plexus. It is purely motor, and its potential sensory supply area is covered by the supraclavicular nn.

SECOND THORACIC N. It provides a lateral cutaneous branch innervating the flcor of the axilla and the posterior medial side of the arm.

SEVENTH TO ELEVENTH THORACIC NN. Coursing to the point where the corresponding cartilages curve upwards, they continue their courses behind the cartilages and between the digitations of the diaphragm to enter the abdominal wall. They finally pierce the rectus abdominis muscle and become cutaneous.

SUBCOSTAL N. (Tn 12). Passing obliquely behind the psoas major muscle and in front of the quadratus lumborum muscle, it enters the abdominal wall.

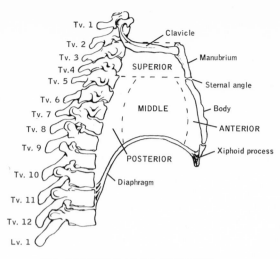

Tv. 1

Tv. 2

Tv. 3

Tv.4

Tv. 5

Tv. 6

Tv. 7

Tv. 8

Tv. 9

Tv. 10

Tv. 11

Tv. 12

Lv. 1

Clavicle

Manubrium

SUPERIOR

Sternal angle

MIDDLE

Body

ANTERIOR

POSTERIOR

Xiphoid process

Diaphragm

57-1   SUBDIVISIONS OF THE MEDIASTINUM

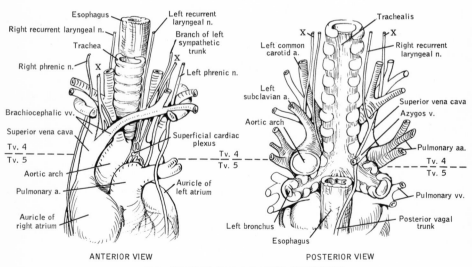

Esophagus

Right recurrent laryngeal n.

Trachea

Right phrenic n.   X

Brachiocephalic vv.

Superior vena cava

Tv. 4

Tv. 5

Aortic arch

Pulmonary a.

Auricle of
right atrium

Left recurrent
laryngeal n.

Branch of left
sympathetic
trunk

X

Left phrenic n.

Superficial cardiac
plexus

Auricle of
left atrium

ANTERIOR VIEW

Trachealis

X   X

Left common
carotid a.

Right recurrent
laryngeal n.

Left
subclavian a.

Superior vena cava

Azygos v.

Aortic arch

Pulmonary aa.

Tv. 4

Tv. 5

Tv. 4

Tv. 5

Pulmonary vv.

Left bronchus

Posterior vagal
trunk

Esophagus

POSTERIOR VIEW

57-2   CONTENTS OF THE SUPERIOR MEDIASTINUM

Plate 57

198

MEDIASTINUM

The mediastinum is the region of the thoracic cavity between the two pleural sacs. It is divided by the pericardium into four parts: superior, anterior, middle, and posterior mediastinum (Fig. 57-1).

SUPERIOR MEDIASTINUM

1. Boundaries   *2. Contents*

The superior mediastinum is the part of the thoracic cavity containing the structures passing directly to and from the neck.

1. Boundaries (Fig. 57-1)

The superior mediastinum has the following boundaries:
Anterior boundary: manubrium sterni
Posterior boundary: Tv 1 to 4
Superior boundary: thoracic inlet
Inferior boundary: line between base of manubrium and Tv 4

2. Contents (Fig. 57-2)

The contents of the superior mediastinum are the following:

THYMUS. It lies on the front of the trachea, between the carotid aa. and above the left brachiocephalic v.

BRACHIOCEPHALIC VV. Arising in the neck, they unite on the right side of the superior mediastinum to form the superior vena cava. In the thorax they receive the internal thoracic and inferior thyroid vv.

SUPERIOR VENA CAVA. It originates behind the first costal cartilage near the sternum, where it receives the azygos v. It enters the superior mediastinum, by piercing the pericardium opposite the second costal cartilage, and descends vertically to join the right atrium opposite the third costal cartilage.

ARCH OF AORTA. Beginning behind the right sternal margin opposite the second cartilage, it passes to the left and backward to end at the lower border of Tv 4. It lies behind the lower half of the manubrium. It provides the brachiocephalic a. opposite the center of the manubrium, which ascends to the right into the neck. On the left side, the left common carotid and left subclavian aa. arise and ascend into the neck.

TRACHEA. This fibrocartilaginous tube lies in the median plane. It extends from the lower border of the cricoid cartilage, opposite the lower border of Cv 6, and ends by dividing into two extrapulmonary bronchi opposite the sternal angle. From 15 to 20 incomplete cartilaginous rings keep the tube open. The posterior deficiency is completed by the *trachealis* muscle.

ESOPHAGUS. The thoracic part of the esophagus lies behind the trachea, separated from the vertebral column by prevertebral fascia and the longus colli muscle. It begins at the end of the pharynx at the level of Cv 6, descends through the superior and posterior mediastinum, and passes through the diaphragm to join the stomach.

PHRENIC NN. They originate from the cervical plexus. The *right phrenic n.* enters the thorax on the lateral side of the right brachiocephalic v. and descends on the lateral side of the superior vena cava and the heart. The *left phrenic n.* enters the thorax on the lateral side of the left brachiocephalic v. and descends over the arch of the aorta; the pleura and lung are lateral to it. Both nerves are accompanied by the pericardiacophrenic vessels and provide branches to the parietal pleurae, pericardium, and diaphragm, which they pierce.

VAGUS NN. They originate in the cranial cavity. The *right vagus n.* enters the thorax between the common carotid a. and the right brachiocephalic v. It descends toward the medial side of the arch of the azygos v. and provides branches to the esophagus, deep cardiac plexus, and anterior pulmonary plexus. It ramifies, forming a posterior pulmonary plexus on the back of the root of the right lung. The *left vagus n.* enters the thorax by passing between the left common carotid a. and the left brachiocephalic v. It passes over the left subclavian a. and the arch of the aorta to the root of the left lung, where it ramifies into the posterior pulmonary plexus. As it crosses the arch it provides branches to the anterior pulmonary plexus and then the recurrent laryngeal n. The vagus nn. also provide cardiac branches in the thorax.

ANTERIOR MEDIASTINUM

> *1. Boundaries*   *2. Contents*

The anterior mediastinum is the narrowest of the regions of the thoracic cavity.

1. Boundaries (Fig. 57-1)

The boundaries of the anterior mediastinum are as follows:
Anterior boundary: body of sternum
Posterior boundary: anterior surface of pericardium
Superior boundary: line between base of manubrium and Tv 4
Inferior boundary: diaphragm

2. Contents

The anterior mediastinum contains the lowest part of the thymus, lymph glands, areolar tissue, and small blood vessels.

MIDDLE MEDIASTINUM

1. Boundaries   *2. Contents*

The volume of the middle mediastinum determines the extent of the adjacent mediastinal regions.

1. Boundaries (Fig. 57-1)

The middle mediastinum has the following boundaries:
Anterior boundary: anterior pericardium
Posterior boundary: posterior pericardium
Superior boundary: line between base of manubrium and Tv 4
Inferior boundary: diaphragm

2. Contents

The contents of the middle mediastinum are as follows:

Pericardium (Fig. 58-1)

The pericardium is a fibroserous sac that encloses the heart and great vessels. It is conical in shape and consists of two layers:

FIBROUS PERICARDIUM. It consists of tough fibrous tissue.

SEROUS PERICARDIUM. It consists of the following two layers:

Parietal Layer. It lines the fibrous pericardium.

Visceral Layer. It covers the heart and great vessels. The part of the thin layer that encloses the aorta and pulmonary a. is the *arterial mesocardium;* that enclosing the superior and inferior venae cavae and the four pulmonary vv. is the *venous mesocardium.* The visceral and parietal layers are continuous at the lines of reflection and are separated by a potential space, the *cavity of the pericardium.*

SINUSES OF PERICARDIUM. Two recesses are present within the pericardial sac.

Transverse Sinus. This horizontal tubelike recess is bounded by the serous pericardium located between the aorta, pulmonary a., and the atria.

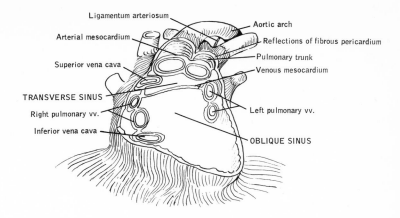

Ligamentum arteriosum
Arterial mesocardium
Superior vena cava
TRANSVERSE SINUS
Right pulmonary vv.
Inferior vena cava

Aortic arch
Reflections of fibrous pericardium
Pulmonary trunk
Venous mesocardium
Left pulmonary vv.
OBLIQUE SINUS

58-1   PERICARDIUM: REFECTIONS AND SINUSES

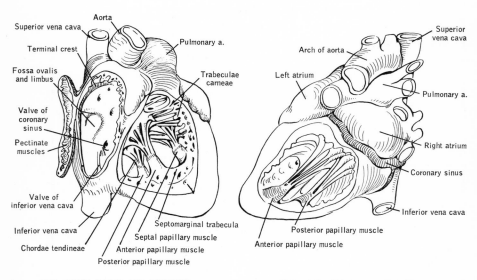

Superior vena cava
Terminal crest
Fossa ovalis and limbus
Valve of coronary sinus
Pectinate muscles
Valve of inferior vena cava
Inferior vena cava
Chordae tendineae

Aorta
Pulmonary a.
Trabeculae carneae

Septomarginal trabecula
Septal papillary muscle
Anterior papillary muscle
Posterior papillary muscle

58-2   RIGHT ATRIUM AND VENTRICLE

Superior vena cava
Arch of aorta
Left atrium
Pulmonary a.
Right atrium
Coronary sinus
Inferior vena cava
Posterior papillary muscle
Anterior papillary muscle

58-3   LEFT ATRIUM AND VENTRICLE

Plate 58

Oblique Sinus. This wide recess lies between the left atrium and the back of the pericardium. It is bounded superiorly by the serous pericardial reflections, at the sides by the venous mesocardium; it is open inferiorly.

The neurovascular system of the pericardium is supplied by:

arteries: Branches of thoracic aorta, internal thoracic, pericardiacophrenic, and phrenic aa.

veins: Correspond to the aortic branches and drain into the azygos v.

nerves: Branches of the phrenic, vagi, and sympathetic nn. via the esophageal plexus.

Heart

The heart is a cone-shaped muscular organ with an apex and base and three surfaces: anterior, inferior, and left. It consists of four chambers (two atria and two ventricles), whose boundaries are demarcated by sulci.

SULCI OF THE HEART

coronary sulcus. It separates the two atria from the two ventricles and contains the trunks of the coronary vv. (see below).

interatrial sulcus. This vertical groove is not very prominent and lies on the back of the heart.

anterior interventricular sulcus. Extending from the left side of the root of the pulmonary trunk, it runs obliquely to the lower margin near the apex.

posterior interventricular sulcus. It extends from the base of the heart to the right side of the apex.

LAYERS OF THE HEART. The heart consists of three layers.

epicardium. The epicardium is another name for the visceral layer of serous pericardium (see p. 201).

myocardium. The myocardium is the striated cardiac muscle. It is thin in the atria and thickest in the left ventricle. The muscle fibers of the heart are arranged into complex sheets with the musculature of the atria and ventricles being separate.

endocardium. This thin fibroelastic membrane is covered with endothelial cells which are continuous with those lining the blood vessels. At the orifices of the blood vessels this layer is duplicated to form the cusps of the valves.

ATRIA OF THE HEART. The atria form the basal part of the heart. An ear-shaped pouch, the *auricle,* extends anteriorly. An *interatrial septum* separates both chambers.

Right Atrium (Fig. 58-2). It forms the right border of the heart. The interior of this chamber presents:

opening of superior vena cava. In the superoposterior part of the atrium; it contains no valves.

opening of inferior vena cava. In the posteroinferior wall of the atrium; it contains a rudimentary valve in the form of a crescentic vertical flap of endocardium.

opening of coronary sinus. Between the atrioventricular orifice and the valve of the inferior vena cava and partially guarded by a semicircular valve.

openings of anterior cardiac vv. On the anterior wall below the auricle.

openings of venae minimae. In some of the pits near the septum below the superior vena cava.

fossa ovalis. A shallow depression on the septum above the opening of the inferior vena cava.

limbus fossae ovalis. The curved ridge that forms its oval margin, and is especially distinct above and at the sides of the fossa. Hidden under cover of the upper part of the limbus may be a slit, the remnant of the fetal foramen ovale.

terminal crest. The smooth vertical ridge on the right wall of the chamber which extends between the anterior margins of the openings of both venae cavae. The crest is reflected on the outside by an indistinct line, the *terminal sulcus.*

pectinate muscles. These extend as parallel ridges from the terminal crest over the anterior and right walls of the auricle.

Left Atrium (Fig. 58-3). It forms part of the base and of the posterior surface of the heart. Internally it is smooth and presents only the openings of the pulmonary vv. on its posterior wall.

VENTRICLES OF THE HEART. The ventricles form the anterior left and lower parts of the heart. The two chambers are completely separated by an interventricular septum.

Right Ventricle (Fig. 58-2). It is triangular in outline and presents internally:

trabeculae carneae. This is a lacework of muscular ridges, one of which, the *septomarginal trabecula* may be conspicuous and extend across the right ventricle. It extends from the interventricular septum to the anterior papillary muscle.

papillary muscles. They are conical muscular projections, to the apices of which are connected slender, fibrous threads, the *chordae tendineae.* These are inserted into the underside of the flaps of the tricuspid valve. Three muscles belong to this group: *anterior,* arising from the sternocostal wall; *inferior,* arising from the diaphragmatic wall; and *septal,* arising from the interventricular septum.

Left Ventricle (Fig. 58-3). This forms the apex of the heart and the greater part of its diaphragmatic surface. It presents internally:

trabeculae carneae. Although similar to the trabeculae carneae on the right side, it usually has no septomarginal trabecula.

papillary muscles. Two are present. They arise from the anterior and posterior walls and have chordae tendineae which are attached to the cusps of the mitral valve.

VALVES OF THE HEART (Fig. 59-1). There is no muscular continuity between the atria and the ventricles. At the level of the *coronary sulcus,* dense, circular *fibrous rings* serve to strengthen the atrioventricular orifices and semilunar valves. A *fibrous trigone* lies between the atrioventricular orifices and the aortic semilunar valve. An oval membranous septum extends down from the trigone to form the upper part of the interventricular septum.

The valves are located at the following four orifices:

Right Atrioventricular Orifice. This is guarded by a (tricuspid) valve which consists of three triangular cusps attached to a fibrous ring. The *anterior cusp* is largest, the *posterior cusp* is related to the diaphragmatic wall, and the *medial cusp* is related to the septum.

Left Atrioventricular Orifice. It is guarded by a (bicuspid) valve which consists of two triangular *cusps, anterior* and *posterior,* attached to a fibrous ring.

Pulmonary Orifice. This is located at the upper end of the prolonged narrow tube of the anterior surface of the ventricle, the *infundibulum.* Its semilunar valve consists of three *cusps: left, right,* and *anterior.* The free edge of each cusp consists of a central thickening, the *nodule,* and thinner sides, the *lunules.* The shallow outward bulging of the wall produces the *sinuses* (Figs. 59-2, 59-3).

Aortic Orifice. It is also guarded by a semilunar valve consisting of three *cusps; left, right,* and *posterior.* These have the same structure as the pulmonary valves. Three sinuses are present because of the pronounced outward bulging of the aortic wall; one anterior and two posterior.

ARTERIES OF THE HEART (Fig. 59-4). The blood vessels lie between the epi- and myocardial layers.

Right Coronary A. Originating from the anterior aortic sinus, it courses in the atrioventricular sulcus to the right lower border of the heart. It curves around the back of the heart and then obliquely to anastomose with the left coronary a. Its branches are:

Unnamed branches. They supply the aorta, pulmonary trunk, and right auricle, atrium, and ventricle.

Marginal a. Coursing along the lower border of the heart, it supplies the right ventricle.

Posterior interventricular a. Arising near the termination of the right coronary a., it descends in the interventricular groove to the apex of the heart and supplies the left ventricle.

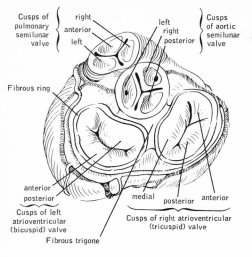

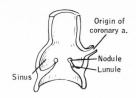

59-2 SEMILUNAR VALVE: SAGITTAL SECTION

59-1 VALVES OF THE HEART

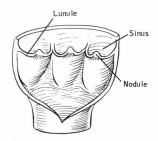

59-3 SEMILUNAR VALVE: OPENED

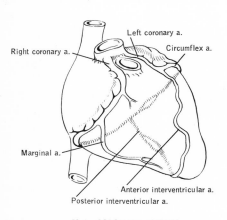

59-4 CORONARY ARTERIES

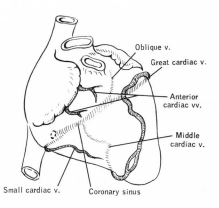

59-5 CORONARY VEINS

Plate 59

Left Coronary A. Originating from the left posterior aortic sinus, it lies in the atrioventricular sulcus and anastomoses with its counterpart, at the back of the heart. Its branches are:

Unnamed branches. They supply the aorta, pulmonary trunk, and the left auricle, atrium, and ventricle.

Anterior interventricular a. Arising as the coronary a., it enters its groove. It descends towards the apex in the anterior interventricular groove and supplies both ventricles.

Circumflex a. Coursing in the left part of the coronary sulcus, it provides branches to the left atrium and ventricle.

VEINS OF THE HEART (Fig. 59-5)

Venae Cordis Minimae. These minute veins open primarily in the right atrium (see above).

Anterior Cardiac Vv. Lying on the front of the right atrium and ventricle, they have independent openings into the former.

Coronary Sinus. Lying in the atrioventricular sulcus between the left atrium and ventricle, it is a continuation of the great cardiac v. and terminates in the right atrium, where its orifice has a unicuspid valve (see above). Its tributaries are:

Great cardiac v. Beginning at the apex of the heart, it ascends in the anterior interventricular sulcus, and curves around the heart in the coronary sulcus, to continue as the coronary sinus.

Middle cardiac v. Beginning at the apex of the heart, it passes on the back of the heart in the posterior interventricular groove, and joins the coronary sinus near its termination.

Small cardiac v. Coursing along the lower border of the anterior surface of the heart, it curves around its right margin to enter the coronary sinus near its termination.

Oblique v. Passing across the back of the left atrium, it joins the coronary sinus.

NERVES OF THE HEART. The heart has two systems of nervous supply.

Cardiac Plexuses (Fig. 60-1). This system controls the force or frequency of the heart contractions. The cardiac plexus consists of sympathetic and parasympathetic (vagus) nerves. The plexus consists of two parts:

Superficial. Lying in the concavity of the aortic arch, this plexus consists of the inferior cervical cardiac branch of the left vagus n. and the superior cervical cardiac branch of the left sympathetic trunk.

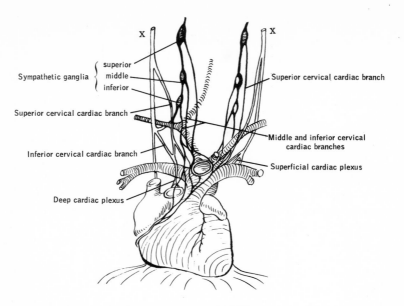

X   X

Sympathetic ganglia { superior
middle
inferior

Superior cervical cardiac branch

Superior cervical cardiac branch

Middle and inferior cervical
cardiac branches

Inferior cervical cardiac branch

Superficial cardiac plexus

Deep cardiac plexus

60-1   NERVE SUPPLY TO THE HEART

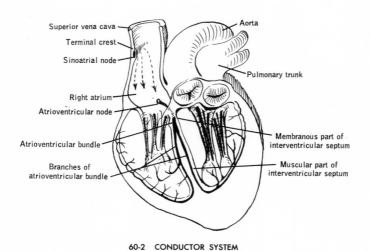

Superior vena cava

Terminal crest

Sinoatrial node

Aorta

Pulmonary trunk

Right atrium

Atrioventricular node

Atrioventricular bundle

Branches of
atrioventricular bundle

Membranous part of
interventricular septum

Muscular part of
interventricular septum

60-2   CONDUCTOR SYSTEM

Plate 60

Table 57

Plexus	Distribution
Right half of deep plexus......	Right atrium; right anterior pulmonary and right and left coronary plexuses
Left half of deep plexus.......	Left atrium; left anterior pulmonary and left coronary plexuses
Superficial plexus............	Left half of deep, left anterior pulmonary, and right coronary plexuses

Deep. Lying upon the tracheal bifurcation, it consists of cardiac branches from all the cervical sympathetic ganglions of both sides except the superior left, together with superior and inferior cervical and thoracic cardiac branches of the right vagus n. and superior cervical and thoracic branches of the left vagus n. The branches from the plexus to the heart are shown in Table 57.

The coronary plexuses accompany these arteries and innervate the areas they supply.

Conductor System (Fig. 60-2). This system is responsible for the orderly sequence of the cardiac cycle. It consists of:

Sinoatrial node. This mass of specialized myocardium is located in front of the opening for the superior vena cava. This node appears to initiate the heart beat and to produce contraction of the atrial musculature.

Atrioventricular node. A similar mass is located in the interatrial septum just above the opening of the coronary sinus. In response to the initial stimulus, this node transmits an impulse for contraction of the ventricle musculature.

Atrioventricular bundle. This specialized myocardium courses in the interventricular septum. It divides at the lower border of the membranous septum into right and left branches which continue onto the respective ventricular walls.

POSTERIOR MEDIASTINUM

1. Boundaries   *2. Contents*

The posterior mediastinum is the narrow region behind the pericardium.

1. Boundaries (Fig. 57-1)

The boundaries of the posterior mediastinum are:

Anterior boundary: posterior surface of pericardium

Posterior boundary: bodies of Tv 5 to 12

Superior boundary: line between base of manubrium and Tv 4

Inferior boundary: diaphragm

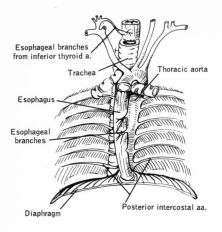

Esophageal branches
from inferior thyroid a.

Trachea

Thoracic aorta

Esophagus

Esophageal
branches

Diaphragm

Posterior intercostal aa.

61-1   ESOPHAGUS AND THORACIC AORTA

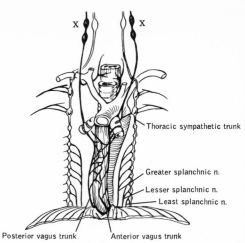

X   X

Thoracic sympathetic trunk

Greater splanchnic n.

Lesser splanchnic n.

Least splanchnic n.

Posterior vagus trunk   Anterior vagus trunk

61-2   ESOPHAGEAL PLEXUS AND SPLANCHNIC NERVES

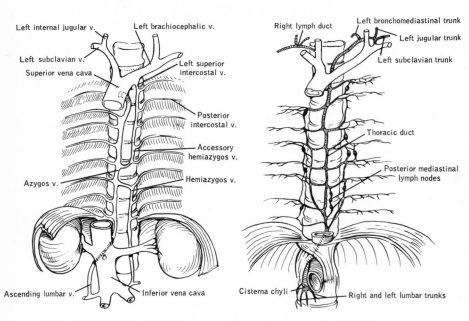

Left internal jugular v.

Left brachiocephalic v.

Left subclavian v.

Superior vena cava

Left superior
intercostal v.

Posterior
intercostal v.

Accessory
hemiazygos v.

Azygos v.

Hemiazygos v.

Ascending lumbar v.

Inferior vena cava

61-3   AZYGOS SYSTEM OF VEINS

Right lymph duct

Left bronchomediastinal trunk

Left jugular trunk

Left subclavian trunk

Thoracic duct

Posterior mediastinal
lymph nodes

Cisterna chyli

Right and left lumbar trunks

61-4   THORACIC DUCT

Plate 61

2. Contents

The posterior mediastinum has the following contents:

THORACIC AORTA (Fig. 61-1). This continuation of the aortic arch extends from the left side of the lower border of Tv 4 to the lower border of Tv 12. It is continuous with the abdominal aorta.

Posterior Intercostal and Subcostal Aa. Ten pairs.

Superior Phrenic A. Small branches to the posterior diaphragm.

Esophageal Branches. At least two help supply the esophagus.

Pericardial Branches. A few small vessels to the back of the pericardium.

Mediastinal Branches. They supply the lymph nodes of this region.

Left Bronchial Aa. These two arteries descend laterally to the back of the left bronchus and accompany it into the lung. The right bronchial a. usually arises from the first right aortic intercostal a.

ESOPHAGUS (Fig. 61-1). Entering the posterior mediastinum to the right of the aorta and descending from Tv 5 to Tv 7, it curves gradually forward until it lies in front of the aorta. It pierces the diaphragm at the level of Tv 9.

VAGI (Fig. 61-2). The *right vagus* emerges from the posterior pulmonary plexus as one or two cords, passing to the back of the esophagus to ramify into a plexus. The *left vagus* also emerges from the posterior pulmonary plexus as one or two cords, passing over the aorta to the front of the esophagus to ramify. Both vagi form the *esophageal plexus,* which receives branches from the greater splanchnic n. and the thoracic sympathetic trunk. The esophageal plexus supplies the smooth musculature and glands of the lower two-thirds of the esophagus. The upper third is supplied by the recurrent laryngeal nn. Just above the diaphragm the anterior and posterior vagal trunks emerge from the esophageal plexus. They enter the abdomen beside the esophagus.

THORACIC SYMPATHETIC TRUNK (Fig. 61-2). The continuation of the cervical sympathetic trunk enters the thorax by passing over the neck of the first rib. It descends under the parietal pleura to pierce the diaphragm and to continue as the lumbar trunk. As the first may be fused with the inferior cervical and others also may be fused, there are about eleven ganglions. Various branches arise from the ganglions.

Gray Rami Communicantes.

Esophageal Branches. They follow the arteries to form the esophageal plexus with the vagal branches.

Aortic Branches. They participate in forming the aortic plexus.

Cardiac Branches. They contribute to the cardiac plexus, the primary source of which is the cervical ganglions.

Pulmonary Branches. They follow the posterior intercostal aa. to the posterior pulmonary plexus.

Greater Splanchnic N. Arising from the fifth to ninth ganglions as a trunk that descends on the lateral side of the azygos or hemiazygos vv., respectively, it pierces the crus of the diaphragm and ends in the celiac ganglion.

Lesser Splanchnic N. Arising from the tenth and eleventh ganglions, it pierces the crus of the diaphragm and ends in the aorticorenal ganglion.

Lowest Splanchnic N. Arising from the twelfth ganglion, it pierces the diaphragm and ends in the renal plexus.

AZYGOS V. (Fig. 61-3). Usually arising from the ascending lumbar v. at the level of the renal v., it ascends on the right crus of the diaphragm and enters the thorax through the aortic hiatus. It continues up on the front of the vertebral column to Tv 4, where it arches anteriorly over the root of the right lung to enter the superior vena cava near its termination.

Right Subcostal and Lower Eight Posterior Intercostal Vv.

Right Superior Intercostal V. From second to fifth intercostal spaces.

Phrenic V. From the back of the diaphragm.

Esophageal, Pericardial, and Mediastinal Branches

Right Bronchial V. From the lung.

HEMIAZYGOS V. (Fig. 61-3). Arising from the ascending lumbar v., it pierces the left crus of the diaphragm, and enters the thorax. It ascends on the side of the vertebral bodies to the level of Tv 9, where it curves sharply to the right, passing behind the aorta, esophagus, and thoracic duct to terminate in the azygos v. Its principle tributaries are the left subcostal and lower four left posterior intercostal vv. Other tributaries are the left mediastinal vv. and lower esophageal vv.

ACCESSORY HEMIAZYGOS V. (Fig. 61-3). Arising at the vertebral end of the fourth intercostal space, it descends on the side of the vertebral bodies to the level of Tv 8, where it curves sharply to the right and joins the azygos v. Its tributaries are the left bronchial v. and the fifth to eighth left posterior intercostal vv.

THORACIC DUCT (Fig. 61-4). The largest lymphatic channel arises from a sac, the *cisterna chyli*, which lies on the surface of Lv 2 to the right of the abdominal aorta. It enters the thorax via the aortic hiatus and ascends along the vertebral column between the aorta and the azygos v. At the level of Tv 5 it curves to the left and continues its ascent along the left margin of the esophagus to enter the root of the neck. It then passes lateralward between the carotid sheath and the vertebral a., arches in front of the subclavian a., and joins the left subclavian v. in the angle of junction with the internal jugular v.

The tributaries of the thoracic duct are shown in Table 58.

On the right side, the bronchomediastinal, jugular, and subclavian trunks terminate in the brachiocephalic, internal jugular, and subclavian vv., respectively. Also

Table 58

Tributary	Lymph transmitted from	Area joined
Right and left lumbar trunks.....	Lower extremity	Cisterna chyli
Intestinal trunk................	Digestive organs	Left lumbar trunk
Descending trunks (2)..........	Back of thorax	Cisterna chyli
Left mediastinal trunk..........	Left half of thorax	Thoracic duct
Left jugular trunk..............	Left side of head	Thoracic duct
Left subclavian trunk...........	Left side of neck	Thoracic duct

Table 59

Group name	Region drained	Draining nodes
Parietal:		
Sternal...................	Breast; anterior thoracic wall	Bronchomediastinal trunk
Intercostal................	Posterolateral thoracic wall	Thoracic duct
Phrenic:		
Anterior set..............	Surface of liver, diaphragm	Sternal nodes
Middle set...............	Middle part of diaphragm	Anterior phrenic nodes
Posterior set.............	Posterior part of diaphragm	Posterior mediastinal nodes
Visceral:		
Anterior mediastinal........	Thymus, pericardium, pleura	Bronchomediastinal trunk
Posterior mediastinal........	Esophagus, pericardium	Thoracic duct
Tracheobronchial............	Trachea, bronchi, lung	Bronchomediastinal trunk

the right jugular and right subclavian trunks may unite at the medial border of the scalenus anterior muscle to form the right lymphatic duct, which descends across the front of the first part of the subclavian a. to join the brachiocephalic v.

LYMPHATICS. They are shown in Table 59.

PLEURA AND LUNGS

On each side of the thoracic mediastinum a lung is enveloped in its serous sac, the pleura.

PLEURA

      1. Layers   *2. Lines of pleural reflection*

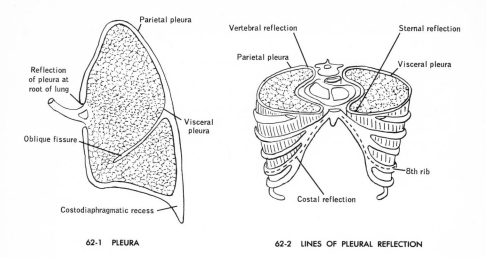

Parietal pleura

Reflection of pleura at root of lung

Oblique fissure

Visceral pleura

Costodiaphragmatic recess

62-1   PLEURA

Vertebral reflection

Sternal reflection

Parietal pleura

Visceral pleura

8th rib

Costal reflection

62-2   LINES OF PLEURAL REFLECTION

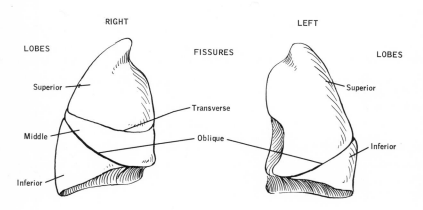

RIGHT

LEFT

LOBES

FISSURES

LOBES

Superior

Transverse

Superior

Middle

Oblique

Inferior

Inferior

Inferior

62-3   LUNGS (seen from the front)

Plate 62

1. Layers

The pleura takes the form of an invaginated sac (Fig. 62-1). Thus the parietal pleura clothes the thoracic wall; the visceral pleura is intimately associated with the lung and follows its fissures. The parietal pleura may be subdivided into four pleurae:

costal pleura. Lines the ribs and intercostal muscles.

mediastinal pleura. Lines the mediastinal surface.

diaphragmatic pleura. Lines the thoracic surface of the diaphragm.

cervical pleura. Forms the *cupola* in the neck.

The two layers of pleura are continuous on the mediastinal surface as a narrow tube, the upper part of which envelops the structures of the root of the lung and the collapsed lower part of which forms the *pulmonary ligament.*

2. Lines of Pleural Reflection (Fig. 62-2)

These lines are the margins where the pleura passes from the costal surface to mediastinal surfaces. They are the:

vertebral reflection. At the front of the vertebral column.

sternal reflection. From the back of the sternum.

costal reflection. At the diaphragmatic border.

At two points potential spaces are formed by separation of the parietal pleural layers. These are the:

costomediastinal recess. Behind the sternum and the fourth and fifth left intercostal spaces.

costodiaphragmatic recess. Between the eighth to tenth intercostal spaces.

The neurovascular system of the pleura is supplied by:

arteries: The arteries are branches from adjacent arteries.

veins: The veins correspond to the arteries.

nerves: The nerves for the parietal pleura stem from the phrenic, intercostal, vagal, and sympathetic nn. Those for the visceral pleura stem from the vagus and sympathetic nn. via the pulmonary plexus.

LUNGS

1. *Surfaces and borders*   3. *Root*
2. *Fissures and lobes*   4. *Bronchial tree*

The lungs are the essential organs of respiration.

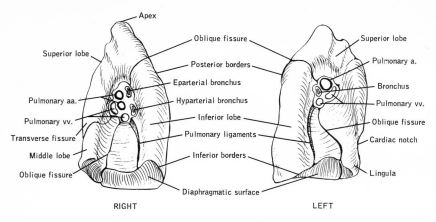

63-1 MEDIASTINAL SURFACE OF LUNG

RIGHT   LEFT

LOBES
Superior: 1, 2, 3
Middle: 4, 5
Inferior: 6, 7, 8, 9, 10

LOBES
Superior: 1+2, 3, 4, 5
Inferior: 6, 7+8, 9, 10

SEGMENTS
1. Apical
2. Posterior
3. Anterior
4. Lateral
5. Medial
6. Superior
7. Anterior basal
8. Medial basal
9. Lateral basal
10. Posterior basal

SEGMENTS
1+2. Apical-Posterior
  3. Anterior
  4. Superior
  5. Inferior
  6. Superior
7+8. Anterior medial basal
  9. Lateral basal
 10. Posterior basal

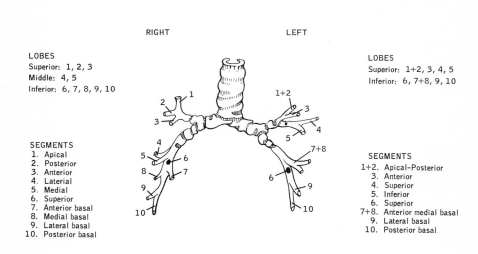

63-2 BRONCHOPULMONARY SEGMENTS

Plate 63

216

1. Surfaces and Borders

The lungs are conical in shape; they have the following surfaces and borders:

apex. It rises to the neck of the first rib and is covered by a cupola of the pleura.

costal surface. This large and convex surface conforms to the curvature formed by the ribs.

mediastinal surface. It bears the impressions of the heart and other structures. The hilus, or wedge-shaped area above and behind the cardiac impression, contains the structures of the root of the lung (see below) and is bounded below by the pulmonary ligament.

diaphragmatic surface. It forms the concave base of the lung.

anterior border. This margin separates the costal from the mediastinal surfaces. On the left side it has a deep indentation, the *cardiac notch.*

posterior border. It is an ill-defined line between the costal surface and the posterior part of the medial surface.

inferior border. This sharp margin separates the diaphragmatic surface from the costal and mediastinal surfaces.

2. Fissures and Lobes (Fig. 62-3)

Both lungs are divided by an oblique fissure extending from the posterior border somewhat below the apex to the inferior border near the midclavicular line. The right lung has a transverse fissure which extends from near the middle of the anterior border to the oblique fissure. The fissures divide the lungs into lobes.

Right Lung. It consists of superior, middle, and inferior lobes.

Left Lung. It consists of superior and inferior lobes.

The number of lobes, however, may vary, being increased by the presence of an extra fissure or decreased by fusion.

3. Root (Fig. 63-1)

It consists of:

bronchi. They lie behind the blood vessels.

pulmonary a. Single; it divides into branches that accompany the bronchi.

pulmonary vv. Paired; they take an independent course within the lung.

bronchial aa. One on the right side, of variable origin, and two on the left, which arise from the thoracic aorta. They supply the bronchi, pulmonary vessels, and pleurae.

bronchial vv. These originate near the hilus and drain into the azygos v. on the right side and the accessory hemiazygos v. on the left.

nerves. Branches of the vagus and sympathetic nn. via the anterior and posterior pulmonary plexuses.

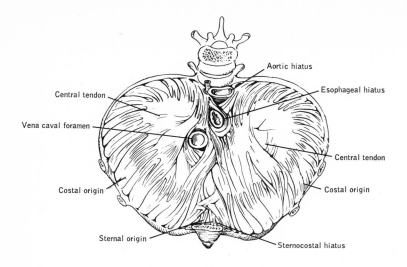

64-1 DIAPHRAGM AND ITS MAJOR ORIFICES (superior view)

Aortic hiatus

Esophageal hiatus

Central tendon

Vena caval foramen

Central tendon

Costal origin

Costal origin

Sternal origin

Sternocostal hiatus

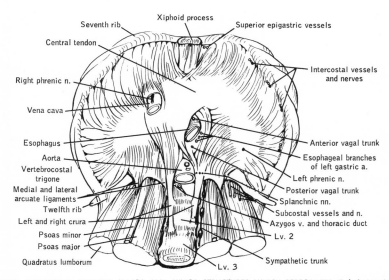

64-2 DIAPHRAGM AND THE MAJOR AND MINOR STRUCTURES WHICH PERFORATES IT (inferior view)

Seventh rib

Xiphoid process

Superior epigastric vessels

Central tendon

Right phrenic n.

Intercostal vessels and nerves

Vena cava

Esophagus

Anterior vagal trunk

Aorta

Esophageal branches of left gastric a.

Vertebrocostal trigone

Left phrenic n.

Posterior vagal trunk

Medial and lateral arcuate ligaments

Splanchnic nn.

Twelfth rib

Subcostal vessels and n.

Left and right crura

Azygos v. and thoracic duct

Psoas minor

Lv. 2

Psoas major

Quadratus lumborum

Sympathetic trunk

Lv. 3

Plate 64

4. Bronchial Tree (Fig. 63-2)

The trachea bifurcates at the level of the intervertebral disk between Tv 4 and Tv 5 into right and left *main bronchi*. Each of these bronchi descends into the hilus of the lung. Three *lobar bronchi* arise on the right side and two on the left; each divides into *segmental bronchi*. The portion of the lobe of the lung supplied by a segmental bronchus is known as a *bronchopulmonary segment*.

DIAPHRAGM

            1. Structure   *2. Openings*

The diaphragm is the convex musculofascial partition between the thorax and the abdomen.

1. Structure (Fig. 64-1)

Origin: Extensive; from the circumference of the thoracic outlet, namely:
    Back of xiphoid process by a pair of short, narrow slips.
    Inner surfaces of the lower six costal cartilages by wide slips.
    Lateral arcuate ligament from the twelfth rib to the transverse process of Lv 1.
    Medial arcuate ligament from the transverse process of Lv 1 to the body of Lv 2.
    Crura, or bundles, down to the bodies of Lv 2 and Lv 3.
    Median arcuate ligament from the left to right crus.
Insertion: Crescentic central tendon divided into right, left, and median lobes.
Action: Chief muscle of respiration.
Nerve supply: Phrenic n.
Arterial supply: Pericardiacophrenic, musculophrenic, superior and inferior phrenic aa.
Vertebrocostal Trigone. This gap in the origin of the diaphragm between the twelfth rib and the lateral arcuate ligament is closed by a thin sheet of fibrous tissue.

2. Openings (Fig. 64-2)

aortic hiatus. Between the crura and behind the median arcuate ligament. It transmits the aorta, thoracic duct, and azygos v.

esophageal hiatus. This is anterosuperior to and at the right of the aortic hiatus. It transmits the esophagus, esophageal branches of the left gastric a. and v., and the anterior and posterior vagal trunks.

vena caval foramen. Lying between the right and median lobes of the central tendon, it transmits the inferior vena cava, right phrenic n., and lymphatics. Smaller structures passing through the diaphragm are shown in Table 60.

Table 60

Structure	*Site of passage*
Superior epigastric vessels	Between xiphoid process and seventh costal cartilage
Musculophrenic vessels	Between seventh and eighth costal cartilages
Hemiazygos v.	Through the left crus
Subcostal vessels and n.	Behind lateral arcuate ligament
Lower 5 intercostal vessels and nn.	Between slips from seventh to twelfth cartilages
Sympathetic trunk	Behind medial arcuate ligament
Three splanchnic nn.	Through crura
Left phrenic n.	Left lobe of central tendon

ABDOMEN

The abdomen is the part of the trunk located between the thorax and the pelvis. It contains most of the digestive system and some of the urinary organs. It is bounded above by the diaphragm and below by the horizontal plane of the pelvic inlet; the abdominal and pelvic cavities are continuous.

ANTERIOR ABDOMINAL WALL

1. *Fascia*   3. *Inguinal region*
2. *Muscles*   4. *Deep arteries*
              5. *Deep nerves*

The anterior wall of the abdomen is supported by a muscular framework.

1. Fascia

SUPERFICIAL FASCIA. This layer is characterized by its variable fat content. It consists of two distinct strata in the inguinal region (see below). It contains:

Cutaneous Nn. (Fig. 65-1). They are comprised of the anterior and lateral cutaneous branches of the seventh to eleventh intercostal nn. (Tn 7 to 11) and the anterior cutaneous branches of the subcostal (Tn 12) and iliohypogastric nn. (Ln 1).

Cutaneous Aa. (Fig. 65-1). The branches of the lower intercostal aa. accompany the lateral cutaneous nn. The branches of the superior and inferior epigastric aa. accompany the anterior cutaneous nn. Three superficial inguinal aa. are branches of the femoral a.

Cutaneous Vv. The superficial inguinal vv. accompany the corresponding arteries and end in the long saphenous v.

Cutaneous Lymphatics. They drain into the axillary nodes from the upper part of the abdomen and into the inguinal nodes from the lower part of the abdomen.

DEEP. It is extremely thin and fuses with the external oblique aponeurosis.

2. Muscles (Fig. 65-2)

The abdominal muscles flatten the anterior abdominal wall, compress the viscera, and help flex and rotate the vertebral column. They are innervated by the seventh to twelfth intercostal, subcostal, iliohypogastric and iliolumbar nn.

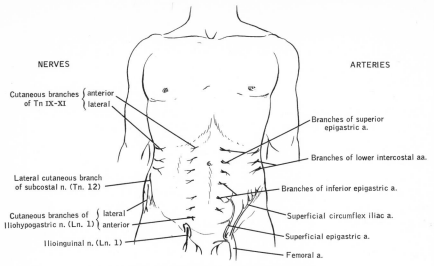

NERVES

Cutaneous branches { anterior
of Tn IX-XI { lateral

Lateral cutaneous branch
of subcostal n. (Tn. 12)

Cutaneous branches of { lateral
Iliohypogastric n. (Ln. 1) { anterior

Ilioinguinal n. (Ln. 1)

ARTERIES

Branches of superior
epigastric a.

Branches of lower intercostal aa.

Branches of inferior epigastric a.

Superficial circumflex iliac a.

Superficial epigastric a.

Femoral a.

65-1   ANTERIOR ABDOMINAL WALL: NERVES AND ARTERIES

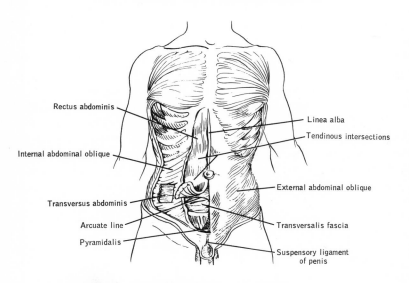

Rectus abdominis

Internal abdominal oblique

Transversus abdominis

Arcuate line

Pyramidalis

Linea alba

Tendinous intersections

External abdominal oblique

Transversalis fascia

Suspensory ligament
of penis

65-2   ANTERIOR ABDOMINAL WALL: MUSCLES

Plate 65

EXTERNAL ABDOMINAL OBLIQUE. The fibers extend downwards and forwards.

Origin: Lower eight ribs interdigitating with serratus anterior and latissimus dorsi muscles.

Insertion: Anterior half of the outer lip of the iliac crest, xiphoid process, linea alba, pubic crest, and pectineal line.

INTERNAL ABDOMINAL OBLIQUE. The fibers extend upward and forward.

Origin: Lumbar fascia, anterior two-thirds of iliac crest, and lateral half of inguinal ligament.

Insertion:

Fleshy fibers: Inferior margin of the ninth to twelfth costal cartilages and ribs.

Aponeurosis: Dividies to form anterior and posterior laminae of the rectus sheath.

TRANSVERSUS ABDOMINIS. The fibers run horizontally.

Origin: Lumbar fascia, inner surfaces of the sixth to twelfth costal cartilages, anterior two-thirds of inner lip of the iliac crest, lateral third of the inguinal ligament.

Insertion: Xiphoid process, linea alba, pubic crest, and pectineal line.

Linea Alba. This band extends from the xiphoid process to the pubic symphysis. It is formed by the interlocking insertions of the aponeuroses of the flat abdominal muscles.

RECTUS ABDOMINIS. It is enclosed within the rectus sheath and presents three *tendinous intersections.*

Origin: Pubic crest and anterior ligament of symphysis pubis.

Insertion: Anterior surface of xiphoid process and fifth to seventh costal cartilages.

Transversalis Fascia. This internal fascial lining of the anterior abdominal wall is separated from the peritoneum by a thin layer of extraperitoneal areolar tissue.

PYRAMIDALIS. It is small and triangular, and may be absent.

Origin: Pubic crest.

Insertion: Linea alba below the umbilicus.

Action: Tightens the linea alba.

Nerve supply: Subcostal n.

Rectus Sheath (Fig. 66-1). The aponeurosis of the flat abdominal muscles forms a sheath around the rectus abdominis. The arrangement varies on three levels, as shown in Table 61.

contents of sheath. Rectus abdominis, pyramidalis, superior and inferior epigastric vessels, terminal parts of the sixth to twelfth intercostal nn.

arcuate line. A curved ridge where the aponeurosis of the tranversus abdominis muscle passes onto the anterior wall of the rectus sheath.

E. O. = External abdominal oblique
I. O. = Internal abdominal oblique
T. A. = Transversus abdominis

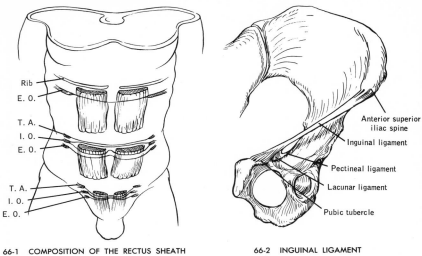

Rib
E. O.
T. A.
I. O.
E. O.
T. A.
I. O.
E. O.

Anterior superior
iliac spine

Inguinal ligament

Pectineal ligament

Lacunar ligament

Pubic tubercle

66-1   COMPOSITION OF THE RECTUS SHEATH

66-2   INGUINAL LIGAMENT

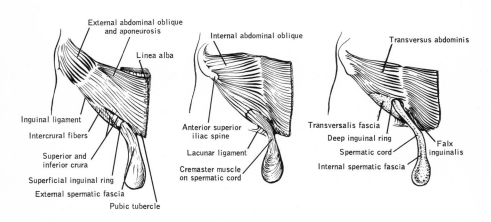

External abdominal oblique
and aponeurosis

Linea alba

Inguinal ligament

Intercrural fibers

Superior and
inferior crura

Superficial inguinal ring

External spermatic fascia

Pubic tubercle

Internal abdominal oblique

Anterior superior
iliac spine

Lacunar ligament

Cremaster muscle
on spermatic cord

Transversus abdominis

Transversalis fascia

Deep inguinal ring

Spermatic cord

Internal spermatic fascia

Falx
inguinalis

66-3   WALLS OF THE INGUINAL CANAL

Plate 66

Table 61

| Level | Components of rectus sheath | |
	Anterior wall	Posterior wall
Above rib margin..........	Aponeurosis of external oblique	Only costal cartilages
From rib margin to lower.... fourth of sheath	Aponeurosis of external oblique Anterior lamina of internal oblique	Posterior lamina of inferior oblique Aponeurosis of transversus abdominis, transversalis fascia
In lower fourth of sheath...	Aponeurosis of external oblique Aponeurosis of internal oblique Aponeurosis of transversus abdominis	Transversalis fascia

3. Inguinal Region

This triangular region is bounded by the inguinal ligament, the lateral margin of the rectus muscle, and a horizontal imaginary line drawn from the anterior superior iliac spine to the margin of the rectus abdominis.

Layers

Superficial Fascia. It consists of Camper's layer, which is fatty and contains the cutaneous vessels, and Scarpa's layer, which is membranous and passes down over the inguinal ligament to join the fascia lata of the thigh.

Aponeurosis of External Abdominal Oblique. This later gives rise to three ligaments (Fig. 66-2):

inguinal ligament. The thickened, rolled lower border of the aponeurosis of the external abdominal oblique muscle extends from the anterior superior iliac spine to the pubic tubercle.

lacunar ligament. The triangular extension of the medial part of the inguinal ligament attaches to the pubic tubercle at its apex and to the pectineal line below. Its base forms the medial margin of the femoral ring.

pectineal ligament. A fibrous extension from the base of the lacunar ligament.

Internal Abdominal Oblique (Fig. 66-3). This muscle originates in part from the lateral half of the inguinal ligament. Its aponeurosis fuses with that of the transversus abdominis muscle to form the *falx inguinalis* (conjoined tendon), which is attached medially to the end of the linea alba and inferiorly to the pectin pubis.

Transversus Abdominis (Fig. 66-3). It contributes to the formation of the falx inguinalis. As the muscle fibers arch over the cord from its deep surface, fibers arise that arch down to the inguinal ligament just medial to the deep inguinal ring. This band, of variable strength, is known as the *interfoveolar ligament.*

Transversalis Fascia (Fig. 66-3). Medially it forms the posterior wall of the rectus sheath and the inguinal canal (see below). It is carried into the thigh, below the inguinal ligament, as the anterior wall of the femoral sheath. Laterally it is continuous with the iliac fascia and the lateral part of the inguinal ligament.

Inguinal Canal

The inguinal canal is a passage, 1½ in. long, above the medial half of the inguinal ligament and directed medially, downward, and forward. The ends of the canal are:

Superficial Inguinal Ring (Fig. 66-3). A triangular aperture in the aponeurosis of the external oblique muscle just above the pubic tubercle and the medial end of the inguinal ligament. The margins of the ring are known as the *medial* and *lateral crura;* they are held together by the *intercrural fibers.*

Deep Inguinal Ring (Figs. 66-3, 67-1). A circular aperture in the transversalis fascia is located about ½ in. above the mid-inguinal point. This is the point on the inguinal ligament equidistant from the pubic symphysis and the anterior superior iliac spine.

The boundaries of the deep inguinal ring are as follows:

Anterior boundary: aponeurosis of external abdominal oblique muscle

Posterior boundary: transversalis fascia and falx inguinalis

Roof: lower border of internal abdominal oblique muscle

Floor: inguinal and lacunar ligaments

It contains:

Male: spermatic cord, terminal parts of ilioinguinal and genital branch of genitofemoral n., cremasteric a. and v.

Female: round ligament of the uterus and genital branch of the genitofemoral n.

In the male the spermatic cord becomes enveloped by several of the layers of the anterior abdominal wall during the course of the descent of the testicle from the abdominal cavity to the scrotal sac. These layers and the corresponding coverings of the spermatic cord are shown in Table 62.

In the female the ovaries descend but only as far as the true pelvis. The round ligament and its vessels also receive homologues of the spermatic fascia as they pass through the smaller inguinal canal. Although these layers are difficult to delineate, a few cremasteric fibers are usually observable.

The scrotum is discussed on p. 285.

Table 62

Layer of anterior abdominal wall	Covering of spermatic cord
Transversalis fascia..............	Internal spermatic fascia
Transversus abdominis	
Internal abdominal oblique.......	Cremaster muscle
External abdominal oblique.......	External spermatic fascia

4. Deep Arteries (Fig. 67-2)

MUSCULOPHRENIC A. This terminal branch of the internal thoracic a. enters the abdomen between slips of the diaphragm from the ninth and tenth costal cartilages and passes along the deep surface of the costal margin. It provides branches to the anterior abdominal wall and the anterior intercostal aa. to the seventh to ninth intercostal spaces.

SUPERIOR EPIGASTRIC A. Another terminal branch of the internal thoracic a., it enters the abdomen between the sternal and first costal slips of the diaphragm, and pierces the upper end of the posterior wall of the rectus sheath to ramify in the muscle and provide cutaneous branches.

INFERIOR EPIGASTRIC A. One of the two branches of the external iliac a., it ascends behind the middle inguinal point and curves medially. It pierces the transversalis fascia and courses vertically to the arcuate line, where it ramifies and sinks into the rectus abdominis muscle. In addition to muscular and cutaneous branches, it gives rise to:

Pubic Branch. Descending behind the inguinal ligament, it anastomoses with the pubic branch of the obturator a.

Cremasteric A. Passing into the deep inguinal ring and through the canal, it anastomoses with the testicular a. in the male. It is the artery of the round ligament in the female.

DEEP CIRCUMFLEX ILIAC A. The other branch of the external iliac a., it ascends along the back of the inguinal ligament to the anterior superior iliac spine, where it gives rise to an ascending branch and pierces the transversalis fascia. Continuing along the iliac crest, it supplies the adjacent muscles.

5. Deep Nerves (Fig. 67-2)

THORACOABDOMINAL INTERCOSTAL NN. (Tn 7 to 11). They leave the intercostal spaces deep to the cartilages and enter the abdominal wall by passing through the slips of origin of the diaphragm and the transversus abdominis muscle. These nerves course anteroinferiorly between the transversus abdominis and internal oblique muscles to the rectus sheath, which they pierce to emerge as the anterior cutaneous nn. (see above). They give off muscular branches and lateral cutaneous nn., which arise in line with the upper intercostals and branch accordingly.

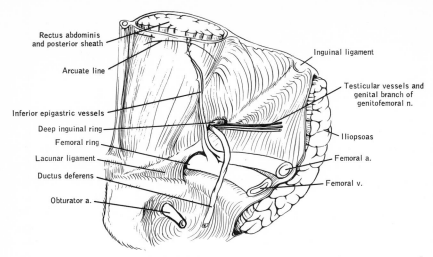

Rectus abdominis
and posterior sheath

Arcuate line

Inferior epigastric vessels

Deep inguinal ring

Femoral ring

Lacunar ligament

Ductus deferens

Obturator a.

Inguinal ligament

Testicular vessels and
genital branch of
genitofemoral n.

Iliopsoas

Femoral a.

Femoral v.

67-1   INGUINAL REGION (viewed from within)

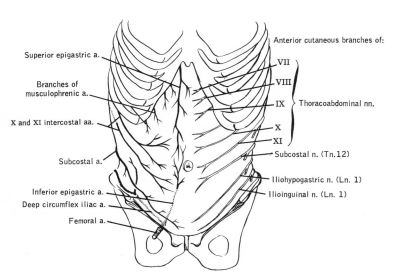

Superior epigastric a.

Branches of
musculophrenic a.

X and XI intercostal aa.

Subcostal a.

Inferior epigastric a.

Deep circumflex iliac a.

Femoral a.

Anterior cutaneous branches of:

VII

VIII

IX   } Thoracoabdominal nn.

X

XI

Subcostal n. (Tn.12)

Iliohypogastric n. (Ln. 1)

Ilioinguinal n. (Ln. 1)

67-2   ARTERIES AND NERVES OF THE ANTERIOR ABDOMINAL WALL

Plate 67

SUBCOSTAL N. (Tn 12). The subcostal n. enters the abdomen by passing behind the lateral arcuate ligament of the diaphragm. It takes a course below and parallel to the lowest intercostal n., provides a lateral cutaneous branch to the gluteal region, some muscular branches and terminates as an anterior cutaneous branch.

ILIOHYPOGASTRIC N. (Ln 7). A branch of the lumbar plexus, it courses inferolaterally, piercing the aponeurosis of the transversus abdominis muscle, then curves anteroinferiorly between the transversus abdominis and internal oblique muscles, to pierce the latter in front of the anterior superior iliac spine. There it provides a lateral cutaneous branch to the gluteal region. It pierces the external oblique muscle a little above the superficial inguinal ring, to become the anterior cutaneous branch (see above).

ILIOINGUINAL N. (Ln 7). This nerve has the same origin and takes the same course as the iliohypogastric n., except that the ilioinguinal is a little below the iliohypogastric n. After piercing the internal oblique muscle, it passes into the inguinal canal and emerges from the superficial inguinal ring to innervate the thigh and the scrotum or mons pubis. It has no lateral cutaneous branch.

PERITONEUM

1. General   2. Peritoneal cavity
3. Anterior parietal peritoneum

The peritoneum, like the pleura, is an invaginated serous sac.

1. General

The peritoneum lines the abdominal walls as the parietal peritoneum, and is reflected on the viscera as the visceral peritoneum. Some of the viscera are held against the posterior abdominal wall; other viscera are connected by duplications called mesenteries, omenta, and ligaments.

omenta. Duplications connecting the stomach with another organ.

mesentery. Duplications connecting the intestine to the posterior abdominal wall.

ligaments. All other peritoneal duplications.

The position of the organs and peritoneal folds results from the rotation of the gut during fetal development and is described in standard embryology texts.

The derivatives from the various parts of the primitive mesentery are shown in Table 63.

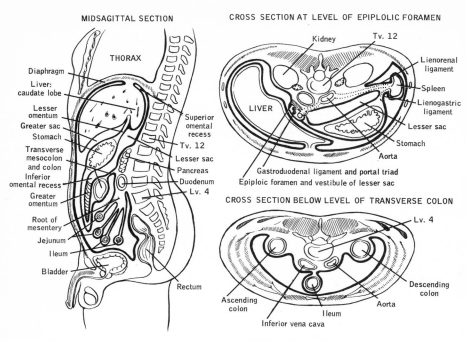

MIDSAGITTAL SECTION

THORAX

Diaphragm
Liver: caudate lobe
Lesser omentum
Greater sac
Stomach
Transverse mesocolon and colon
Inferior omental recess
Greater omentum
Root of mesentery
Jejunum
Ileum
Bladder

Superior omental recess
Tv. 12
Lesser sac
Pancreas
Duodenum
Lv. 4

Rectum

CROSS SECTION AT LEVEL OF EPIPLOIC FORAMEN

Kidney
Tv. 12
Lienorenal ligament
Spleen
Lienogastric ligament
Lesser sac
Stomach
Aorta
LIVER

Gastroduodenal ligament and portal triad
Epiploic foramen and vestibule of lesser sac

CROSS SECTION BELOW LEVEL OF TRANSVERSE COLON

Lv. 4
Descending colon
Ascending colon
Ileum
Aorta
Inferior vena cava

68-1   SCHEMATIC PRESENTATION OF THE ARRANGEMENT OF THE PERITONEUM

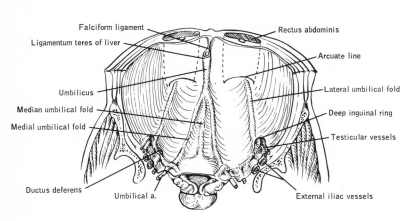

Falciform ligament
Ligamentum teres of liver
Umbilicus
Median umbilical fold
Medial umbilical fold
Ductus deferens
Umbilical a.

Rectus abdominis
Arcuate line
Lateral umbilical fold
Deep inguinal ring
Testicular vessels
External iliac vessels

68-2   ANTERIOR ABDOMINAL WALL (seen from within)

Plate 68

Table 63

Dorsal mesentery	Dorsal mesogastrium	Ventral mesogastrium
The mesentery	Greater omentum	Lesser omentum
Transverse mesocolon	Phrenicolienal ligament	Falciform ligament
Sigmoid mesocolon	Phrenicocolic ligament	Coronary ligament
Mesoappendix		Triangular ligaments

2. Peritoneal Cavity (Figs. 68-1, 69-3)

The peritoneal cavity is the potential space between the visceral and the parietal peritoneum. It is completely closed in the male but communicates with the outside in the female via the uterine tubes. The cavity is divided into two parts:

Greater Sac. The major part of the peritoneal cavity is subdivided by the greater omentum and the transverse colon into supra- and infracolic compartments.

Lesser Sac (Omental Bursa). This is a diverticulum from the greater sac. Its anterior wall consists of the caudate lobe of the liver, the lesser omentum, the posterior surface of the stomach, and the anterior two layers of the greater omentum. The posterior wall consists of the transverse mesocolon and the posterior two layers of greater omentum. The lesser sac consists of a series of recesses.

vestibule. Narrow canal extending from the epiploic foramen.

superior omental recess. Between the caudate lobe and the diaphragm.

lienal recess. Between the spleen and the stomach.

inferior omental recess. Between the layers of the greater omentum.

Epiploic Foramen. The opening between the greater and lesser sacs, it boundaries are as follows:

Anterior boundary: free border of lesser omentum containing portal triad

Posterior boundary: inferior vena cava and right crus of diaphragm

Superior boundary: caudate process of caudate lobe of liver

Inferior boundary: first part of duodenum

In the lower abdominal cavity, between the root of the mesentery and the colon on both sides, are two "gutters" resulting from the rotation of the gut. They consist of right and left paracolic gutters. The various peritoneal fossae will be discussed with their respective organs.

3. Anterior Parietal Peritoneum (Fig. 68-2)

On the peritoneal surface of the umbilical region five ridges of peritoneum are produced by the underlying cords, which are remnants of fetal tubes.

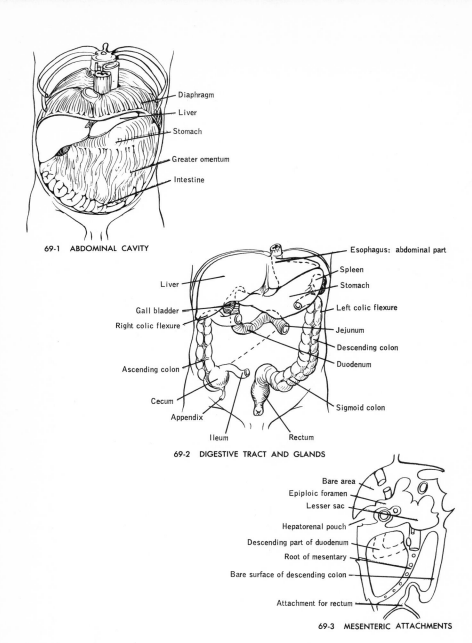

69-1 ABDOMINAL CAVITY

Diaphragm
Liver
Stomach
Greater omentum
Intestine

Esophagus: abdominal part
Spleen
Stomach
Left colic flexure
Jejunum
Descending colon
Duodenum
Sigmoid colon
Rectum

Liver
Gall bladder
Right colic flexure
Ascending colon
Cecum
Appendix
Ileum

69-2 DIGESTIVE TRACT AND GLANDS

Bare area
Epiploic foramen
Lesser sac
Hepatorenal pouch
Descending part of duodenum
Root of mesentary
Bare surface of descending colon
Attachment for rectum

69-3 MESENTERIC ATTACHMENTS

Plate 69

median umbilical fold. Produced by the urachus, it extends from the bladder to the umbilicus.

medial umbilical folds. Produced by the obliterated umbilical aa., they converge from the sides of the bladder to the umbilicus.

lateral umbilical folds. Produced by the inferior epigastric aa. (functional), they extend from the side of the deep inguinal ring to the arcuate line.

ligamentum teres. The round ligament of the liver is produced by the obliterated umbilical v., and lies in the margin of the falciform ligament, which extends from the umbilicus to the inferior border of the liver.

ESOPHAGOGASTROINTESTINAL TRACT

1. *Abdominal part of esophagus*
2. *Stomach*
3. *Small intestine*
4. *Large intestine*
5. *Arteries*
6. *Portal venous system*
7. *Nerves*
8. *Lymphatics*

The gastrointestinal tract provides for the digestion of food, the resorption of its breakdown products, and the elimination of its indigestible material.

1. Abdominal Part of Esophagus (Fig. 69-2)

A short stump extends from the esophageal opening of the diaphragm to the cardiac opening of the stomach. This part of the esophagus receives its blood supply from esophageal branches of the left gastric a.

2. Stomach (Fig. 70-1)

The piriform-shaped dilated part of the alimentary canal is located in the upper left part of the abdomen. It presents anterior and posterior surfaces, and a concave *lesser curvature* and a convex *greater curvature* which extend from the cardiac to the pyloric opening.

Parts

cardia. It adjoins the esophagus and is separated from the fundus by the *cardiac notch.*

fundus. It is the rounded upper end above the level of the esophageal opening.

body. The body is the portion of the stomach between the fundus and the pyloric antrum. It is separated from the pyloric antrum by the *angular notch.*

pyloric antrum. This is the slightly dilated part of the stomach below the body.

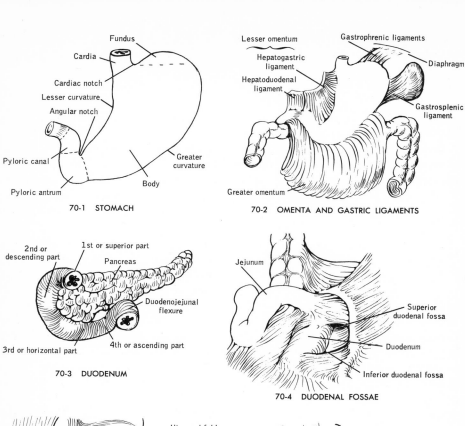

70-1   STOMACH

Fundus
Cardia
Cardiac notch
Lesser curvature
Angular notch
Pyloric canal
Pyloric antrum
Greater curvature
Body

70-2   OMENTA AND GASTRIC LIGAMENTS

Lesser omentum
Gastrophrenic ligaments
Hepatogastric ligament
Diaphragm
Hepatoduodenal ligament
Gastrosplenic ligament
Greater omentum

70-3   DUODENUM

2nd or descending part
1st or superior part
Pancreas
Duodenojejunal flexure
3rd or horizontal part
4th or ascending part

70-4   DUODENAL FOSSAE

Jejunum
Superior duodenal fossa
Duodenum
Inferior duodenal fossa

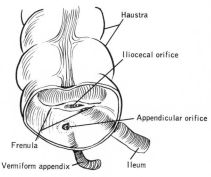

70-5   CECUM

Iliocecal fold
Retrocecal fossa
Tenia coli
Appendices epiploica
Superior and inferior iliocecal fossae
Mesentery of appendix

70-6   ILIOCECAL VALVE

Haustra
Iliocecal orifice
Appendicular orifice
Frenula
Vermiform appendix
Ileum

Plate 70

pyloric canal. The pyloric canal is the cylindric portion of the stomach between the antrum and the pyloric constriction.

Peritoneal Attachments

Both surfaces of the stomach are covered with peritoneum. At the curvatures the peritoneum forms duplications that connect to other organs. These are:

Lesser Omentum (Fig. 70-2). It extends from the first inch of the duodenum (hepatoduodenal ligament), from the lesser curvature of the stomach, and from the diaphragm (hepatogastric ligament) to the margins of the porta hepatis of the liver. Its right border is free; it forms the anterior boundary of the epiploic foramen and encloses the bile duct, hepatic artery, and portal vein.

Greater Omentum (Figs. 69-1, 70-2). This omentum consists of four layers. The anterior two layers are attached to the greater curvature of the stomach and hang down almost to the pelvis, where they turn back as the posterior two layers. These reach the transverse colon and fuse with its mesentery. This new layer extends to the lower border of the pancreas, where it divides to pass upwards and downward over the structures of the posterior abdominal wall. The four layers of the greater omentum extending below the transverse colon are fused. The lower part of the lesser sac separates them above this level. The gastroepiploic vessels lie between the anterior two layers near the margin of the greater curvature of the stomach.

Gastrophrenic Ligament. It extends to the diaphragm from the fundus near the esophageal opening.

Gastrosplenic Ligament (Fig. 70-1). Extending from the upper third of the greater curvature to the hilus of the spleen, it is continuous with the gastrophrenic ligament above and with the anterior two layers of the greater omentum below. The anterior layer invests the surfaces of the spleen and comes into relation again with the posterior layer. The two layers pass from the hilus to the posterior abdominal wall over the left kidney as the lienorenal ligament. Both these ligaments contribute to forming the left boundary of the lesser sac.

The neurovascular system of the stomach is supplied by:

arteries: Gastric, gastroepiploic, and short gastric from the splenic a.

veins: They accompany the arteries to the splenic, superior mesenteric, or portal vv.

nerves: Gastric nn. from the vagi and branches of the celiac plexus.

3. Small Intestine

DUODENUM (Fig. 70-3). This C-shaped tube, being retroperitoneal, has no mesentery (except for the hepatoduodenal part of the lesser omentum from the first inch). It is attached to the body wall and is subdivided into four parts, as shown in Table 64.

Table 64

Part of duodenum	Course
First, or superior.........	From pylorus to right side of body of Lv 1
Second, or descending.....	In front of right renal vessels
Third, or horizontal.......	Across right iliopsoas, inferior vena cava, and aorta
Fourth, or ascending......	Along left side of aorta to flexure

Duodenojejunal Flexure (Fig. 70-3). This sharp curvature in the digestive tract is held in place by the *suspensory muscle of the duodenum*. This is a fibromuscular band ascending behind the pancreas from the flexure to the diaphragm.

Duodenal Folds (Fig. 70-4). The peritoneum between the posterior wall and the lateral sides of the duodenum may be pinched up to form folds which cover the superior and inferior duodenal fossae.

The neurovascular system of the duodenum is supplied by:

arteries: Superior and inferior pancreaticoduodenal aa. and the duodenal branches of the hepatic a.

veins: They terminate in the portal v. and the superior and inferior mesenteric vv.

nerves: Sympathetic and vagus nn. via plexuses.

JEJUNUM. This portion of the intestine extends for about 8 ft from the duodenojejunal flexure, at the left side of Lv 2 to the ileum. No distinct line of demarcation is grossly evident at the jejunoileal junction.

ILEUM. The ileum is the continuation of the jejunum that extends for about 12 ft, terminating in the right iliac fossa at the cecum. The characteristics of the jejunum that differentiate it from the ileum are (1) it lies in upper left part of the intestinal area; (2) its walls are thicker and more vascular; (3) its lumen is wider; (4) the circular folds on its internal surface are large and closer set; (5) aggregate nodules are absent from the internal surface.

The Mesentery (Fig. 69-3). This is a broad fold that connects the jejunum and ileum with the posterior abdominal wall. Its root is about 6 in. in length and extends obliquely from the left side of Lv 2 to about the right sacroiliac joint. It crosses the third part of the duodenum, the aorta, the inferior vena cava, the right ureter, and some vessels and nerves.

The neurovascular system of the small intestine is supplied by:

arteries: Jejunal and ilial aa. from the superior mesenteric a.

veins: They terminate in the superior or inferior mesenteric vv.

nerves: They are the vagal and sympathetic branches.

4. Large Intestine

The colon begins in the right iliac fossa as the *cecum* (Fig. 70-5). This is a blind pouch that is enveloped by peritoneum but has no mesentery. The ileum projects

Table 65

Part of colon	Course
Ascending..............	From right iliac fossa to inferior surface of the liver
Transverse..............	From right colic flexure to lower part of the spleen
Descending.............	From left colic flexure to left iliac fossa
Pelvic, or sigmoid........	S-shape loop extending to middle piece of the sacrum

into the posteromedial wall of the junction of the cecum and colon, producing the slitlike *ileocecal valve* (Fig. 70-6). Mucous membrane folds, the *frenula*, extend from both ends of the valve. The *vermiform appendix* extends from the posteromedial wall of the cecum. The appendix has a considerable range of locations. It is enveloped by peritoneum and has its own triangular mesenteriolum, which is attached to the left lamina of the mesentery. The colon is divided into four parts, as shown in Table 65.

The ascending and descending parts of the colon, being retroperitoneal, are fixed to the posterior abdominal wall. The transverse and pelvic colon are intraperitoneal structures and thus are completely invested with peritoneum and each has its own mesocolon. The colon is characterized by:

appendices epiploicae. They are fat-filled finger-like projections of peritoneum.

teniae coli. These three equidistant muscular brands, representing the outer longitudinal coat of the large intestine, extend from the root of the appendix to the rectum. They spread out again as a continuous layer. Because the tenia are shorter than the colon, they produce its pouches or sacculations, the *haustra*.

Peritoneal Recesses

retrocecal recess. Extends upward behind the cecum.

superior ileocecal recess. Behind the ileocecal fold.

inferior ileocecal recess. Between the ileocecal fold and the mesentery of the appendix.

The neurovascular system of the large intestine is supplied by:

arteries: Colic and sigmoid branches of the mesenteric a.

veins: Its veins terminate in the superior and inferior mesenteric vv.

nerves: From the vagi and sympathetic plexuses.

5. Arteries (Fig. 71-1)

Celiac Trunk

The celiac trunk arises from the front of the abdominal aorta a little below the diaphragm. It extends for about ½ in. over the upper border of the pancreas and divides into the following:

LEFT GASTRIC A. It ascends obliquely to the esophageal opening of the stomach and then curves sharply and descends along the lesser curvature, giving branches

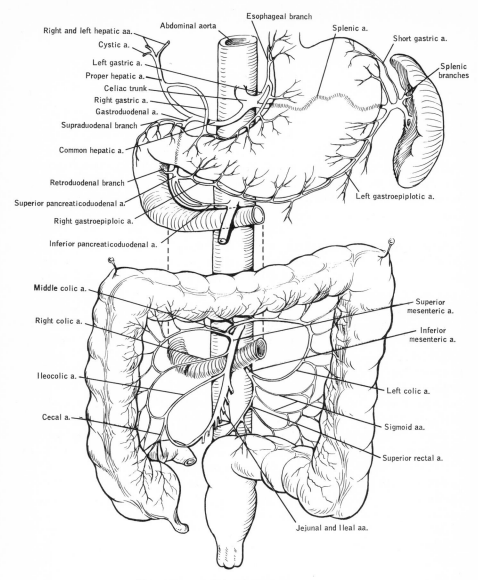

Right and left hepatic aa.

Cystic a.

Left gastric a.

Proper hepatic a.

Celiac trunk

Right gastric a.

Gastroduodenal a.

Supraduodenal branch

Common hepatic a.

Retroduodenal branch

Superior pancreaticoduodenal a.

Right gastroepiploic a.

Inferior pancreaticoduodenal a.

Abdominal aorta

Esophageal branch

Splenic a.

Short gastric a.

Splenic branches

Left gastroepiplotic a.

Middle colic a.

Right colic a.

Ileocolic a.

Cecal a.

Superior mesenteric a.

Inferior mesenteric a.

Left colic a.

Sigmoid aa.

Superior rectal a.

Jejunal and Ileal aa.

71-1   ARTERIAL SUPPLY TO THE DIGESTIVE TRACT

Plate 71

238

to both sides of the stomach. It terminates by anastomosing with the right gastric. It also gives off *esophageal branches* which pass up to supply the thoracic part of the esophagus.

SPLENIC A. The largest branch of the celiac a. courses sinuously along the upper border of the pancreas behind the lesser sac and provides:

Pancreatic Branches. They pass to the body of the pancreas.

Short Gastric Aa. They pass in the gastrosplenic ligament to the fundus of the stomach.

Left Gastroepiploic A. Arising near the spleen, it runs in the gastrosplenic ligament and then along the greater curvature between the anterior two layers of the greater omentum, providing branches to the stomach and the omentum. It ends in anastomoses with the right gastroepiploic a.

Splenic Branches. Forming the ramified termination of the splenic a., they pass through the lienorenal ligament to enter the hilum of the spleen.

COMMON HEPATIC A. It courses to the right along the upper border of the pancreas to the first part of the duodenum and then up into the lesser omentum near its free margin. It ascends as the *proper hepatic a.* to the porta hepatis. Its branches are:

Right Gastric A. Running to the left along the lesser curvature to anastomose with the left gastric a., it gives branches to both surfaces of the pyloric portion of the stomach.

Gastroduodenal A. Descending behind the first part of the duodenum, it ends at its lower border by dividing into:

superior pancreaticoduodenal a. It divides into anterior and posterior divisions, which loop around the head of the pancreas, providing branches to both the duodenum and the pancreas. The divisions anastomose with corresponding divisions of the inferior pancreaticoduodenal a.

right gastroepiploic a. Running to the left along the greater curvature and may anastomose with the left gastroepiploic a., it gives off branches to the stomach and omentum.

Supra- and retroduodenal aa. frequently arise from the gastroduodenal a. to supply the superior and inferior aspects of the first part of the duodenum respectively.

Right and Left Hepatic Aa. Terminal branches of the proper hepatic a. enter the substance of the liver. The right hepatic a. gives a small cystic branch which descends along the cystic duct to the gallbladder.

Superior Mesenteric A.

The superior mesenteric a. arises from the front of the aorta, a little below the celiac trunk and behind the pancreas (Lv 1). Passing over the third part of the duodenum and entering the root of the mesentery, it terminates in the right iliac

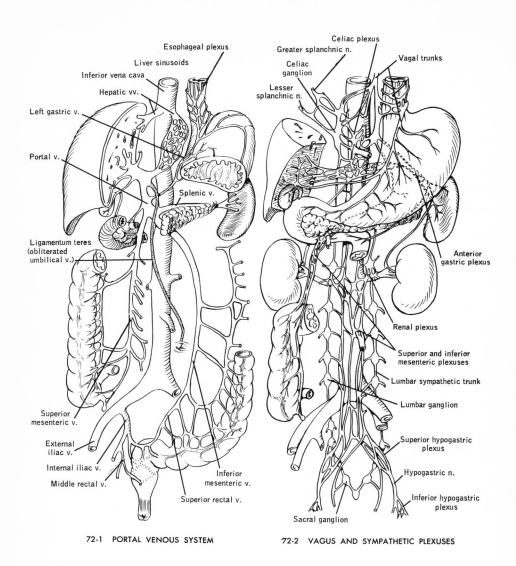

Esophageal plexus

Liver sinusoids

Inferior vena cava

Hepatic vv.

Left gastric v.

Portal v.

Splenic v.

Ligamentum teres
(obliterated
umbilical v.)

Superior
mesenteric v.

External
iliac v.

Internal iliac v.

Middle rectal v.

Inferior
mesenteric v.

Superior rectal v.

Celiac plexus

Greater splanchnic n.

Celiac
ganglion

Lesser
splanchnic n.

Vagal trunks

Anterior
gastric plexus

Renal plexus

Superior and inferior
mesenteric plexuses

Lumbar sympathetic trunk

Lumbar ganglion

Superior hypogastric
plexus

Hypogastric n.

Inferior hypogastric
plexus

Sacral ganglion

72-1   PORTAL VENOUS SYSTEM

72-2   VAGUS AND SYMPATHETIC PLEXUSES

Plate 72

240

fossa by anastomosing with a branch of the ileocolic a. Its branches, which supply the parts of the colon indicated by their names, are:

INFERIOR PANCREATICODUODENAL A. It divides into anterior and posterior divisions which anastomose with the corresponding divisions of the superior pancreaticoduodanal a.

JEJUNAL AND ILEAL AA. About 15 intestinal aa. arise and pass in the mesentery towards the jejunum and ileum. They divide and anastomose several times, forming a series of arcades, before the straight, terminal *vasa recti* are given off to the intestine proper.

MIDDLE COLIC A. Arising at the lower border of the pancreas, it runs inferoanteriorly in the transverse mesocolon, dividing into right and left branches which supply the transverse colon and anastomose with the right and left colic aa., respectively.

RIGHT COLIC A. Arising below the duodenum, it curves to the right to divide into ascending and descending branches which anastomose with the middle colic and ileocolic aa., respectively.

ILEOCOLIC A. The lowermost of the major branches descends to divide into ascending and descending branches which anastomose with the right colic a. and the end of the superior mesenteric a., respectively. The ileocolic a. also provides *ileal* and *cecal branches* as well as an *appendicular a.*

Inferior Mesenteric A.

The inferior mesenteric a. arises from the front of the aorta, a little above the bifurcation, opposite Lv 3 and behind the duodenum. It descends to the left, behind the parietal peritoneum, to terminate as the superior rectal a. Its branches are:

LEFT COLIC A. Passing laterally, it divides into ascending and descending branches which anastomose with the middle colic a. and an ascending branch of the sigmoid a., respectively.

SIGMOID AA. About three arteries descend, each dividing into ascending and descending branches which form loops from which vasa recti arise. It anastomoses primarily with the left colic aa.

SUPERIOR RECTAL A. Entering the pelvic mesocolon, it descends to supply the rectum.

6. Portal Venous System (Fig. 72-1)

PORTAL V. The union of the splenic v. and the superior mesenteric v. behind the neck of the pancreas forms the portal v. It ascends behind the first part of the duodenum to enter the lesser omentum and continues up to the porta hepatis, where it divides into right and left branches which enter the liver and ramify. The capillaries reunite into hepatic vv. that terminate in the inferior vena cava. The portal v. receives such small vessels as the coronary v. (associated with the stomach), the pyloric v., and a cystic v. Its main tributaries are:

Splenic V. Formed by the union of a number of branches from the hilus of the spleen, it passes behind the pancreas below the splenic a. to the portal v. Its tributaries correspond to branches of the splenic a. and include the inferior mesenteric v. and the superior rectal v.

Superior Mesenteric V. It ascends in the root of the mesentery to the neck of the pancreas, where it joins the portal v. Its tributaries correspond to branches of the artery and include the right gastroepiploic v., the pancreaticoduodenal v. and other pancreatic vv.

7. Nerves

VAGUS N. (Fig. 72-2). The anterior and posterior vagal trunks are formed on the esophagus and pass through the esophageal opening of the diaphragm. They provide branches which form the *gastric plexus* around the stomach. The anterior trunk provides branches to the duodenum, liver, and pancreas; the posterior trunk provides branches to the celiac plexus, the fibers of which go to all the organs of the abdomen.

SYMPATHETIC FIBERS (Fig. 72-2). A group of interconnected plexuses is located in relation to the abdominal aorta and its branches. The *celiac plexus* consists of the two celiac ganglions that lie on the diaphragmatic crura, and a dense network of preganglionic vagal and sympathetic fibers. Over the aorta is the *intermesenteric plexus,* from which are derived the subordinate plexuses around the major and minor branches of the aorta. The principal branches are the superior and inferior mesenteric, renal, and phrenic plexuses. The splanchnic nn. terminate in the upper plexuses. Rami pass from these plexuses with the arteries to the abdominal organs. The sympathetic plexus continues into the pelvis via the superior mesenteric plexus, which extends from the intermesenteric plexus across the bifurcation of the aorta.

8. Lymphatics

The visceral lymph nodes are associated with the three major branches of the abdominal aorta, as shown in Table 66.

Most of these groups of nodes may be further subdivided into several individual sets.

Table 66

Group name	Region drained	Draining nodes
Gastric.................	Stomach	
Hepatic.................	Stomach, duodenum, liver, pancreas ⎫	Celiac group of preaortic
Pancreaticolienal..........	Pancreas and spleen ⎬	
Mesenteric..............	Small intestine ⎫	
Ileocolic................	Ileum, cecum, ascending colon ⎬	Superior mesenteric group of preaortic
Mesocolic...............	Transverse colon ⎭	
Inferior mesenteric.........	Descending and sigmoid colon	Inferior mesenteric group of preaortic

LIVER, BILIARY APPARATUS, PANCREAS, AND SPLEEN

1. *Liver*   3. *Biliary ducts*
2. *Gallbladder*   4. *Pancreas*
           5. *Spleen*

The liver and pancreas are digestive glands associated with the functions of the gastrointestinal tract. The spleen is a lymphatic organ.

1. Liver (Figs. 73-1 to 73-3)

The liver is a four-sided pyramid, located in the uppermost part of the abdomen. It lies on one side, with its base on the right and its apex on the left. It presents:

Two Surfaces. The two surfaces of the liver are diaphragmatic and visceral. The visceral surface has an H-shaped division which consists of:

Left arm. It contains fissures for the ligamentum teres and ligamentum venosum.

Right arm. It contains fossae for the gallbladder and the inferior vena cava.

Cross arm. It contains the *porta hepatis*, the transverse cleft, bounded by part of the lesser omentum, which transmits the portal v., proper hepatic a., common hepatic duct, nerves, and lymphatics.

Four Lobes

right and left lobes. The right and left lobes of the liver are separated on the diaphragmatic surface by the falciform ligament.

caudate lobe. It is located above the porta hepatis and between the fissure for the ligamentum venosum and the fossa of the inferior vena cava. The *caudate process* extends from the right lower border and separates the porta hepatis from the fossa for the inferior vena cava.

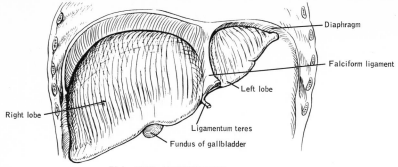

73-1 LIVER: ANTERIOR VIEW

Diaphragm

Falciform ligament

Left lobe

Ligamentum teres

Fundus of gallbladder

Right lobe

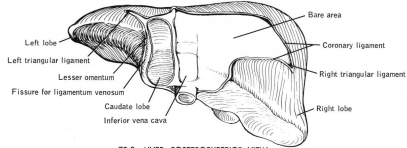

73-2 LIVER: POSTEROSUPERIOR VIEW

Bare area

Left lobe

Left triangular ligament

Lesser omentum

Fissure for ligamentum venosum

Caudate lobe

Inferior vena cava

Coronary ligament

Right triangular ligament

Right lobe

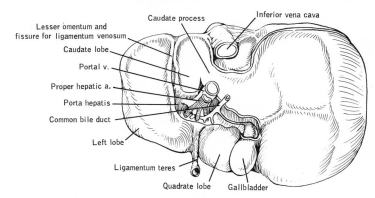

73-3 LIVER: INFERIOR VIEW

Caudate process

Inferior vena cava

Lesser omentum and
fissure for ligamentum venosum

Caudate lobe

Portal v.

Proper hepatic a.

Porta hepatis

Common bile duct

Left lobe

Ligamentum teres

Quadrate lobe

Gallbladder

Plate 73

244

quadrate lobe. It is located below the porta hepatis and between the fissure for the ligamentum teres and the fossa for the gallbladder.

The inferior surface presents the preserved impressions of the abdominal organs with which the liver comes in contact. These impressions are named after the structure involved.

The liver is clothed completely with visceral peritoneum except for the large convex area, the *bare area,* where it rests against the diaphragm, and over both fossae. The peritoneum is reflected at the liver as a number of ligaments.

Ligaments

coronary ligament. This is the single layer of peritoneum reflected from the margins of the bare area onto the diaphragm. The margins meet in the corners of the bare area to form the *right and left triangular ligaments.*

falciform ligament. This is the long, triangular fold extending between the lobes of the liver and the anterior abdominal wall as far as the umbilicus. The third border is free and encloses the *ligamentum teres,* a remnant of the fetal umbilical v., which extends in its fissure to the porta hepatis.

lesser omentum. It originates in part from the fissure for the ligamentum venosum and extends across to the lesser curvature of the stomach and first part of the duodenum.

The neurovascular system of the liver is supplied by:

artery: Proper hepatic a.

veins: Portal and hepatic vv.

nerves: Vagal and sympathetic nn.

2. Gallbladder (Fig. 74-1)

This pear-shaped organ is about 3 in. long. Its lower end, or *fundus,* projects beyond the lower margin of the liver. Its anterior surface is adherent in its fossa to the liver; its posterior surface is covered with peritoneum and lies against the beginning of the transverse colon. Its narrow, upper end, or *neck,* lies on the right side of the aorta and is continuous with the cystic duct. The main portion of the gallbladder is the *body.*

The neurovascular system of the gallbladder is supplied by:

artery: Cystic a., from the right hepatic a.

vein: Cystic v. drains into the superior mesenteric v.

nerves: Vagus and sympathetic nn.

3. Biliary Ducts (Fig. 74-1)

The canals for transmission of the bile from the gallbladder to the duodenum consist of:

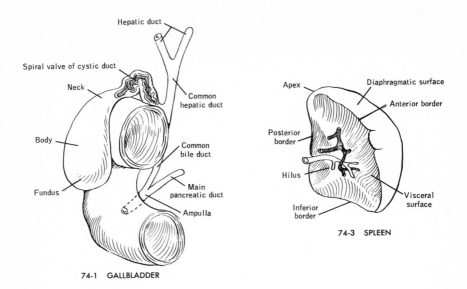

74-1 GALLBLADDER

74-3 SPLEEN

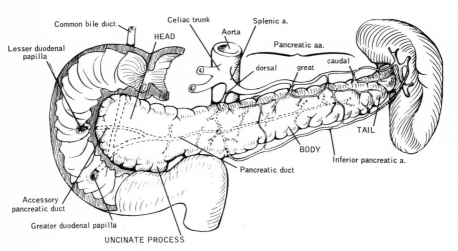

74-2 PANCREAS: ITS DUCTS AND BLOOD SUPPLY

Plate 74

CYSTIC DUCT. This very short, twisted canal extends from the neck of the gallbladder to the common hepatic duct. The mucous membrane of the duct is arranged as a series of ridges forming the *spiral valve*.

COMMON HEPATIC DUCT. It is formed in the porta hepatis by the union of the right and left hepatic ducts from the corresponding lobes of the liver.

COMMON BILE DUCT. Formed by the union of the cystic and common hepatic ducts, it descends in the free border of the lesser omentum in front of the portal v. and lateral to the hepatic a. It then passes behind the first part of the duodenum to a groove on the back of the head of the pancreas. The duct passes obliquely through the posteromedial wall of the second part of the duodenum. The duct expands near its termination to form an ampulla, which receives the pancreatic duct, and passes obliquely through the posteromedial wall to form the *greater duodenal papilla* on the inner surface of the duodenum.

4. Pancreas (Fig. 74-2)

This accessory digestive gland lies transversely across the posterior abdominal wall behind the stomach and between the duodenum and spleen. This gland is both exocrine and endocrine in function. It presents:

Four Parts

head. The expanded part of the pancreas in the C-shaped curve of the duodenum.

neck. The constricted part of the pancreas in front of the superior mesenteric vessels.

body. The main part of the pancreas is triangular in cross section.

tail. This blunt end of the pancreas extends into the lienorenal ligament.

Two Processes

unicate process. It projects from the lower part of the head behind the superior mesenteric vessels.

tuber omentale. It projects upward from the body to the lesser curvature of the stomach.

The triangular *body* presents three surfaces and three borders:

anterior surface: lying in the floor of the lesser sac.

posterior surface: lying against the posterior abdominal wall and bearing the splenic v.

inferior surface: lying in relation to the duodenojejunal flexure.

anterior border: at the separation of the layers of the transverse mesocolon.

superior border: extending from the tuber omentale and carrying the splenic a.

inferior border: separating the inferior from the posterior borders.

PANCREATIC DUCTS (Fig. 74-3). The pancreas contains two ducts.

Pancreatic Duct. Extending from the tail of the pancreas, it receives small subsidiary ducts in its course through the body of the pancreas. It curves inferoposte-

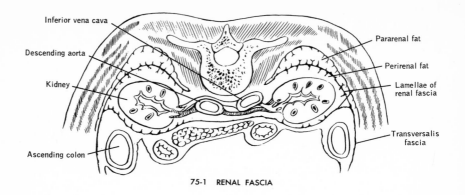

Inferior vena cava

Descending aorta

Kidney

Ascending colon

Pararenal fat

Perirenal fat

Lamellae of renal fascia

Transversalis fascia

75-1   RENAL FASCIA

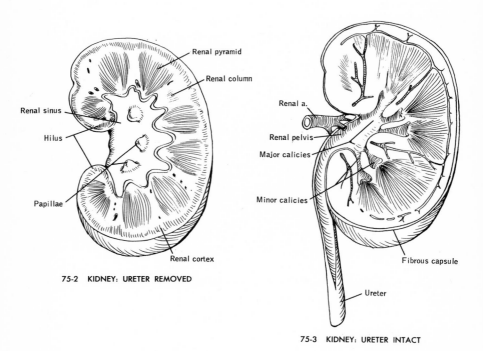

Renal pyramid

Renal column

Renal sinus

Hilus

Papillae

Renal cortex

75-2   KIDNEY: URETER REMOVED

Renal a.

Renal pelvis

Major calicies

Minor calicies

Fibrous capsule

Ureter

75-3   KIDNEY: URETER INTACT

Plate 75

riorly in the head of the pancreas and then to the right to join the common bile duct, thereby terminating in the duodenum at the *greater duodenal papilla.*

Accessory Pancreatic Duct. Variable in development, it frequently extends from the first curve of the main duct through the head of the pancreas to open in the *lesser duodenal papilla,* which is located superior to the greater duodenal papilla.

The neurovascular system of the pancreas is supplied by:

arteries: The head receives branches of the superior and inferior pancreatico-duodenal aa. The body receives branches from great, dorsal, and transverse pancreatic aa. The tail is supplied by the caudal pancreatic a.

veins: The tributaries from the head empty into the main pancreaticoduodenal v. which passes into the portal v. Those from the body empty into pancreatic vv. which pass into the splenic v. Those from the tail empty into the caudal pancreatic v. which passes into the splenic v.

nerves: Vagus and sympathetic fibers of the celiac plexus.

5. Spleen (Fig. 73-4)

A lymphatic organ located on the left side of the body between the upper part of the stomach and the diaphragm, it has its own true fibroelastic capsule, which is enveloped by peritoneum. It presents:

Two Surfaces. The diaphragmatic is convex and smooth; the visceral is triangular in outline. The visceral surface has gastric, renal, and colic impressions and a central *hilus* for the splenic vessels.

Three Borders. Anterior (notched), posterior, and inferior (base).

The neurovascular system of the spleen is supplied by:

arteries: Terminal branches of the splenic a.

veins: The splenic v. empties into the portal v.

nerves: Nerves from the celiac plexus.

KIDNEYS, URETERS, AND SUPRARENAL GLANDS

1. Kidneys   *2. Ureter*

3. Suprarenal glands

The kidneys are the essential organs of excretion, and the ureters convey the urine to the bladder. The suprarenal glands are endocrine organs.

1. Kidneys (Fig. 75-1, 75-2)

These paired bean-shaped, retroperitoneal organs lie one on each side of the vertebral column between the levels of Tv 12 and Lv 3. Each presents:

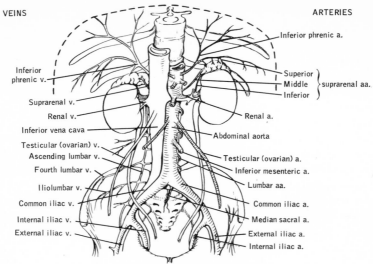

Inferior phrenic a.

Inferior phrenic v.

Superior
Middle ⎰ suprarenal aa.
Inferior ⎱

Suprarenal v.

Renal v.

Renal a.

Inferior vena cava

Abdominal aorta

Testicular (ovarian) v.

Ascending lumbar v.

Testicular (ovarian) a.

Fourth lumbar v.

Inferior mesenteric a.

Lumbar aa.

Iliolumbar v.

Common iliac v.

Common iliac a.

Internal iliac v.

Median sacral a.

External iliac v.

External iliac a.

Internal iliac a.

76-1   BLOOD VESSELS OF POSTERIOR ABDOMINAL WALL

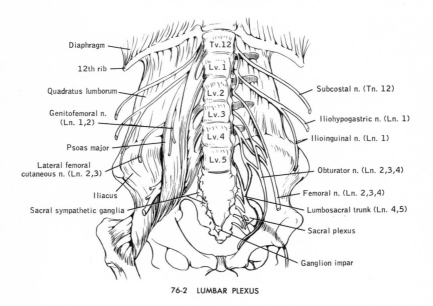

Diaphragm

Tv. 12

Lv. 1

12th rib

Lv. 2

Subcostal n. (Tn. 12)

Quadratus lumborum

Lv. 3

Iliohypogastric n. (Ln. 1)

Genitofemoral n.
(Ln. 1,2)

Ilioinguinal n. (Ln. 1)

Lv. 4

Lv. 5

Psoas major

Lateral femoral
cutaneous n. (Ln. 2,3)

Obturator n. (Ln. 2,3,4)

Femoral n. (Ln. 2,3,4)

Iliacus

Lumbosacral trunk (Ln. 4,5)

Sacral sympathetic ganglia

Sacral plexus

Ganglion impar

76-2   LUMBAR PLEXUS

Plate 76

Two Surfaces. Anterior and posterior.

Two Borders. Lateral (convex) and medial (concave).

Two Poles. Superior and inferior.

Each kidney is enclosed in a *fibrous capsule* and is enveloped by:

perirenal fat. An adipose capsule around the kidney and its vessels.

renal fascia. Derived from the subperitoneal fascia, which splits on both sides of each kidney to form the anterior and posterior lamellae, which envelop the kidney, its adipose capsule, and the suprarenal glands. The fascial layers enclose the inferior vena cava and aorta between them in the median plane.

pararenal fat. Adipose tissue between the posterior lamellae of renal fascia and transversalis fascia beneath.

Each kidney is divided into:

cortex. Outer zone composed of the cortical arches over the pyramids of the medulla and renal columns.

medulla. Consists of about 15 conical masses, the *pyramids*, the apices of which converge toward the renal sinus. They form the *papillae*, which project into the lumens of the minor calyces.

The blood vessels and ureter are associated with the medial border of the kidney at its hilus. Inside the kidney the hilus expands into a large cavity, the *renal sinus*. Within the sinus the renal pelvis of the ureter (see below) divides into two to three *major calices*, each of which ramifies into about four *minor calices*, or cup-shaped ducts that receive the renal papillae.

The neurovascular system of the kidney is supplied by:

arteries: Renal aa. (Fig. 76-1) arise from each side of the abdominal aorta at the level of the upper border of Lv 2, both arteries pass transversely to the hilum of the kidney over the crura of the diaphragm and the psoas major muscle. The right artery lies behind the inferior vena cava and the head of the pancreas. The left artery lies behind the left renal v. and the body of the pancreas. Each provides an inferior suprarenal a., which ascends to the gland, and an ureteric branch to the upper part of the ureter.

veins: Renal vv. pass in front of the arteries transversely to empty into the inferior vena cava.

nerves: They emanate from the renal plexus.

2. Ureter (Fig. 76-1)

This retroperitoneal tube conveys urine from the kidney to the bladder. It begins in the renal sinus as a dilation, the *renal pelvis*, formed by union of the major calyces. It begins to taper as it descends along the medial margin of the kidney. At the lower pole it becomes the ureter proper. Half of this 10-in. tube is within the abdomen. It crosses the origin of the external iliac a. to enter the pelvis and terminates by obliquely entering the posterolateral angle of the bladder. The ureter is constricted at the ureteropelvic junction, where it crosses the iliac vessels and where it joins the bladder.

The neurovascular system of the ureter is supplied by:

arteries: The renal pelvis and the upper ureter are supplied by the renal a. The middle ureter is supplied by the testicular (ovarian) a. The pelvic ureter is supplied by vesicle aa.

veins: They correspond to the arteries.

nerves: They stem from the inferior mesenteric, spermatic, and pelvic plexuses.

3. Suprarenal Glands (Fig. 76-1)

These endocrine glands are located on either side of the celiac a. on the superomedial aspect of the kidneys and on the crura of the diaphragm. Each is composed of a yellow cortex and a deep red medulla. The right gland is triangular; the left is semilunar in shape.

The neurovascular system of the suprarenal glands is supplied by:

arteries: The three sources are the superior suprarenal aa. from the inferior phrenic a. that descend to the gland. The middle suprarenal a. from the abdominal aorta that arise at the level of the renal aa. The inferior suprarenal a. from the renal a. that run laterally to the gland.

veins: Suprarenal vv., terminating on the right side in the inferior vena cava and on the left side in the renal v.

nerves: From the celiac plexus.

POSTERIOR ABDOMINAL WALL

1. Fascia	*4. Arteries*
2. Intrinsic muscles of back	*5. Veins*
3. Muscles of the posterior abdominal wall	*6. Nerves*

The posterior abdominal wall extends from the posterior attachment of the diaphragm to the iliac crests. It is reinforced by the lumbar vertebrae.

1. Fascia

SUPERFICIAL. The superficial fascia of the posterior abdominal wall contains a variable amount of fat beneath the skin, cutaneous tributaries of the lumbar vessels, and cutaneous branches of the dorsal rami of the lower thoracic nn.

DEEP. The deep fascia of the posterior abdominal wall consists of the fascia of the latissimus dorsi muscle, the thoracolumbar fascia, and the iliac fascia on the psoas and iliacus muscles.

2. Intrinsic Muscles of the Back (p. 351)

3. Muscles of the Posterior Abdominal Wall (Fig. 76-2)

QUADRATUS LUMBORUM. It is rectangular.

Origin: Iliolumbar ligament, iliac crest, lower lumbar transverse processes.

Insertion: Medial half of twelfth rib and the upper lumbar transverse processes.

Action: Fixes last rib during inspiration.

Nerve supply: Tn 12 and Ln 1 to 3.

PSOAS MAJOR. Long and fusiform, it lies on the side of the vertebral column of the lumbar region.

Origin: Lumbar vertebrae and fibrous arches on the sides of the bodies.

Insertion: Lesser trochanter.

Action: See below.

Nerve supply: Ln 2 to 4.

ILIACUS. It joins the psoas major muscle to form the *iliopsoas muscle.*

Origin: Floor of the iliac fossa.

Insertion: Tendon of the psoas major muscle and the lesser trochanter.

Action: Iliopsoas muscle flexes and rotates the thigh medially. After flexion it rotates the thigh laterally. It helps flex the vertebral column.

Nerve supply: Femoral n.

PSOAS MINOR. This long, slender muscle is frequently absent.

Origin: Lateral margin of Tv 12 and Lv 1 and the intervening intervertebral disk.

Insertion: Pectineal ligament and the iliacus fascia.

Action: Helps flex the vertebral column.

Nerve supply: Ln 1.

4. Arteries (Fig. 76-1)

Abdominal Aorta

It extends from its point of emergence through the diaphragm (level of the Tv 12 to Lv 1 disk) to its point of bifurcation into the common iliac aa (level of Lv 4). Its branches may be classified in three groups, located in different planes, as shown in Table 67.

PARIETAL GROUP

Inferior Phrenic Aa. Arising from the front of the abdominal aorta just below the aortic hiatus, they diverge across the crura of the diaphragm to divide into an

Table 67

Visceral (p. 237)	Paired (pp. 251, 252)	Parietal
Celiac trunk Superior mesenteric a. Inferior mesenteric a.	Suprarenal aa. Renal aa. Testicular aa.	Inferior phrenic a. Lumbar a. Median sacral a.

Table 68

Visceral (p. 242)	Paired (pp. 251, 252)	Parietal
Superior mesenteric v. Splenic v. Inferior mesenteric v.	Suprarenal vv. Renal vv. Testicular vv.	Iliolumbar v. Lumbar vv. Ascending lumbar v.

anterior branch, which ramifies on the underside of the diaphragm, and a posterior branch, which ramifies on the posterolateral body wall. The inferior phrenic aa. also provide superior suprarenal aa. to these glands.

Lumbar Aa. These four arteries are in series with the posterior intercostal aa. They arise from the back of the abdominal aorta at the levels of the bodies of the upper four lumbar vertebrae. They run laterally behind the psoas major muscle and in front of the quadratus lumborum muscle to terminate by ramifying between the transversus abdominis and internal oblique muscles. From each lumbar a. arises a posterior branch which accompanies the dorsal ramus of its corresponding spinal n. This branch divides into muscular branches to the back muscles and a spinal branch to the contents of the vertebral column.

Median Sacral A. See Pelvis, p. 261.

5. Veins (Fig. 76-1)

Inferior Vena Cava

It extends from below and at the right of the aortic bifurcation (in front of Lv 5) to its passage through the diaphragm (level of Tv 8). Its branches may be classified in three groups, located on different planes, as shown in Table 68.

PARIETAL GROUP

Iliolumbar V. Emerging at the medial side of the psoas major muscle, it descends to empty into the common iliac v. on the same side.

Lumbar Vv. They pass from the posterior abdominal wall medially behind the quadratus lumborum muscle. The fifth lumbar v. empties into the iliolumbar v. The fourth and third empty into the inferior vena cava. The second and first empty into the ascending lumbar v.

Ascending Lumbar V. Ascending from the lateral sacral vv. over the pelvic surface, it crosses the roots of the lumbar transverse processes within the substance of the psoas major muscle and joins the subcostal v. to form the azygos v.

6. Nerves (Fig. 76-2)

LUMBAR Nn. The ventral rami pass into the substance of the psoas major muscle. There Ln 1 receives a branch from Tn 12. After providing muscular branches, Ln 1 to 4 divide to form the roots of the lumbar plexus. The lower division of Ln 4 joins Ln 5 to form the lumbosacral trunk.

Lumbar Plexus

The nerves of this plexus are derived from Tn 12 and Ln 1 to 4. The branches of the plexus are:

ILIOHYPOGASTRIC N. (Ln 1). See p. 229.

ILIOINGUINAL N. (Ln 1). See p. 229.

GENITOFEMORAL N. (Ln 1, 2). Emerging on the front of the psoas major muscle, it descends behind the fascia to a variable level and divides into:

Genital Branch. Descending to the front of the lower part of the external iliac a., it passes through the deep inguinal ring into the inguinal canal. It supplies the cremaster muscle, and the skin of the scrotum in the male or the round ligament and skin of the labium majus in the female.

Femoral Branch. The lateral branch descends behind the inguinal ligament in the anterior wall of the femoral sheath and emerges through the saphenous opening to supply the skin on the uppermost part of the front of the thigh.

LATERAL FEMORAL CUTANEOUS N. (Ln 2, 3). Emerging through the lateral margin of the psoas muscle at the iliac crest, it crosses the iliacus muscle covered by its fascia, passes behind the lateral end of the inguinal ligament, and divides into anterior and posterior cutaneous branches.

FEMORAL N. (Posterior Division of Ln 2 to 4). The largest branch of the lumbar plexus emerges at the lower lateral border of the psoas major muscle. It descends behind the iliac fascia, in the groove between the psoas and iliacus muscles, to pass behind the inguinal ligament into the thigh. It gives muscular branches to the iliacus muscle in the iliac fossa.

OBTURATOR N. (Anterior Division of Ln 2 to 4). Lying medial to the femoral n., it emerges at the posteromedial margin of the psoas muscle and passes in front of the sacroiliac joint into the pelvis. It enters the thigh via the obturator foramen and supplies the adductor group of muscles.

ACCESSORY OBTURATOR N. (Ln 3, 4). This nerve is present only in about 10 per cent of cases. It descends along the medial side of the psoas major muscle and over the superior pubic ramus into the thigh. It provides a branch to the hip joint and unites with the obturator n.

Lumbar Sympathetic Trunk (Fig. 76-2)

The lumbar sympathetic trunk enters the abdomen behind the medial arcuate ligament and descends on the side of the bodies of the lumbar vertebrae. It usually contains about four ganglions. In addition to the usual rami communicantes associated with sympathetic ganglions, *lumbar splanchnic nn.* arise from both the ganglions and the trunk. These are two to four short rami which join the intermesenteric and hypogastric plexuses.

The sympathetic supply to the abdominal viscera is distributed by means of the plexuses of nerves along the abdominal aorta and its branches.

PELVIS

The pelvis is the inferior part of the trunk; the pelvic cavity is directly continuous with the abdominal cavity. The pelvis contains the bony framework which provides attachment of the lower extremities to the trunk.

PELVIC VISCERA

1. *Pelvic peritoneum*   4. *Rectum*
2. *Urinary bladder*   5. *Arteries*
3. *Urethra*   6. *Veins*

7. *Nerves*

The pelvic viscera consists of the two organs used for the collection of the body wastes prior to elimination and also of the pelvic genital organs (pp. 267 and 271).

1. Pelvic Peritoneum

The pelvic viscera are only partially covered by peritoneum. This extends from the anterior abdominal wall, behind the pubis, onto the superior surface of the bladder. In the male (Fig. 77-1), it passes over the upper ends of the seminal vesicles and the rectovesical pouch onto the rectum. In the female (Fig. 77-2), it clothes the uterus and passes over the rectouterine pouch onto the rectum.

A number of recesses, covered by peritoneum, are found in the pelvic cavity. Table 69 shows these recesses, together with their locations.

2. Urinary Bladder (Fig. 77-3)

This hollow muscular organ lies in the anteroinferior part of the pelvis. When empty and hardened it presents:

Four Angles
Anterior (apex): behind margin of pubic symphysis
Posterolateral (2): with ureters attached at these angles
Inferior (neck): resting on prostate in male, on pelvic diaphragm in female
Three Surfaces
Superior: covered by peritoneum
Inferolateral (2): forming the sides of the bladder
Inferoposterior: forming the base of the bladder
The interior of the bladder is smooth except at the *trigone*. This is the wrinkled triangular area bounded by the orifices of the ureters, at the upper angles, and by

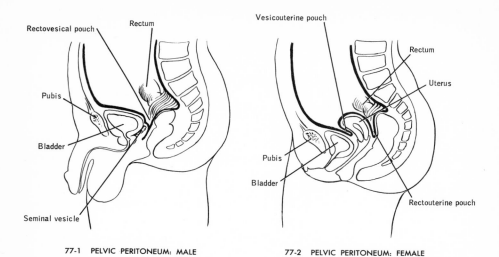

Rectovesical pouch

Rectum

Pubis

Bladder

Seminal vesicle

77-1   PELVIC PERITONEUM: MALE

Vesicouterine pouch

Rectum

Uterus

Pubis

Bladder

Rectouterine pouch

77-2   PELVIC PERITONEUM: FEMALE

Superior surface

Ureters

Anterior angle

Inferolateral surface

Posterolateral angle

Inferior angle (neck)

Prostate

Spongy urethra

77-3   URINARY BLADDER

Median umbilical ligament

Interureteric fold

Ureter

Trigone

Orifice of ureter

Uvula

Internal urethral orifice

Prostate

Prostatic urethra

Utricle

Colliculus

Prostatic sinus

Orifice of ejaculatory duct

Membranous urethra

Spongy urethra

Crus penis

77-4   VESICAL TRIGONE AND URETHRA: MALE

Plate 77

Table 69

Recess	Location
Paravesical fossae	On either side of the distended bladder
Pararectal fossae	On either side of the rectum
Rectovesical pouch	Between the rectum and bladder of male
Vesicouterine pouch	Between the bladder and uterus of female
Rectouterine pouch	Between the rectum and bladder of female

the internal urethral orifice, at the lower angle. A fold of mucous membrane, the *interureteric fold,* connects the upper angles of the trigone. Just above the internal urethral orifice is an elevation, the *uvula* of the bladder.

The bladder, like all the pelvic viscera, is embedded in extraperitoneal connective tissue, the *endopelvic fascia.* At the neck of the bladder, this fascia is differentiated into the medial and lateral *puboprostatic ligaments* of the male or the *pubovesical ligament* of the female.

The neurovascular system of the bladder is supplied by:

arteries: Superior and inferior vesical aa.

veins: The vesical plexus drains into the internal iliac v.

nerves: Hypogastric plexus and the pelvic splanchnic nn.

3. Urethra

Male (Fig. 77-4)

Both urine and spermatic fluid pass through the male urethra. It extends from the internal to the external urethral orifice, at the tip of the penis, and is divided into three parts:

Prostatic Urethra. It extends from the neck of the bladder through the prostate. The *urethral crest* is a narrow longitudinal elevation on its posterior wall. The *prostatic sinuses* are the grooves at the sides of the crest into which the prostatic ducts open. The most prominent part of the crest, the *colliculus,* has a diverticulum, the *utricle,* which extends backward and upward into the prostate. The ejaculatory ducts open at the margins of the utricle.

Membranous Urethra. Extending from the lower end of the prostate, it pierces the components of the urogenital diaphragm.

Spongy Urethra. It extends from the bulb of the penis, through the corpus spongiosum, to the external urethral orifice (p. 287).

Female (Fig. 78-1)

The prostatic and membranous portions of the female urethra correspond to the male urethra. It extends from the neck of the bladder through the pelvic diaphragm

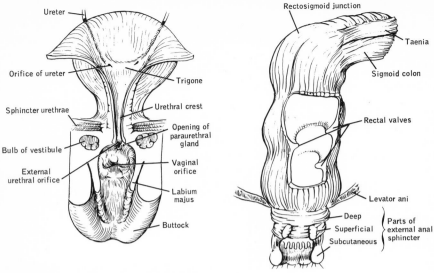

Ureter

Orifice of ureter

Trigone

Sphincter urethrae

Urethral crest

Opening of paraurethral gland

Bulb of vestibule

External urethral orifice

Vaginal orifice

Labium majus

Buttock

78-1 VESICAL TRIGONE AND URETHRA: FEMALE

Rectosigmoid junction

Taenia

Sigmoid colon

Rectal valves

Levator ani

Deep

Superficial

Subcutaneous

Parts of external anal sphincter

78-2 RECTUM

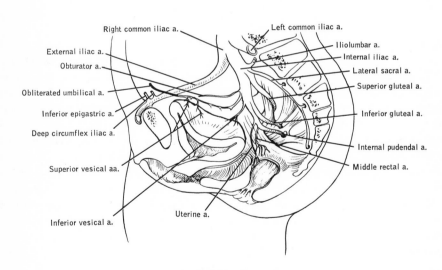

Right common iliac a.

Left common iliac a.

External iliac a.

Iliolumbar a.

Obturator a.

Internal iliac a.

Obliterated umbilical a.

Lateral sacral a.

Inferior epigastric a.

Superior gluteal a.

Deep circumflex iliac a.

Inferior gluteal a.

Superior vesical aa.

Internal pudendal a.

Middle rectal a.

Inferior vesical a.

Uterine a.

78-3 ARTERIES OF PELVIS

Plate 78

to terminate in front of the vaginal opening. In its course it is intimately associated with the anterior wall of the vagina. The prostate in the female is represented by a cluster of *paraurethral glands* at each side of the lower part of the urethra. Their ducts open into the vestibule on the sides of the external urethral orifice, and are known as the *paraurethral ducts.*

4. Rectum (Fig. 78-2)

The terminal portion of the gastrointestinal tract lies in the pelvis. It extends from the level of Sv 3 to the tip of the coccyx, where it enters the anal canal. As it descends, the rectum curves slightly to the right and then to the left. This sinuosity corresponds to the three transverse rectal valves that project inward. Peritoneum covers only the anterior and lateral surfaces of the upper third and the anterior surface of the middle third of the rectum.

The neurovascular system to the rectum is supplied by:

arteries: Superior, middle, and inferior rectal and the median sacral aa.

veins: The superior rectal v. drains into the portal system, the inferior rectal and medial sacral vv. drain to the systemic system.

nerves: Sympathetic and pelvic splanchnic nn.

5. Arteries (Fig. 78-3)

MEDIAN SACRAL A. Arising from the back of the aorta just above the bifurcation, it descends over Lv 4 and 5 and the pelvic surface of the sacrum. It provides the small pair of fifth lumbar aa. and branches to the rectum.

SUPERIOR RECTAL A. This continuation of the inferior mesenteric a. courses in the pelvic mesocolon from the middle of the left common iliac a. to Sv 3. It divides into two branches which descend on either side of the rectum. These subdivide near the end of the anus, pierce the muscularis muscle, and descend as vasa recti in the submucosa to form a series of loops at the lower end of the rectum.

INTERNAL ILIAC A. Arising from the common iliac a. in front of the sacroiliac articulation, it terminates near the upper margin of the greater sciatic foramen by dividing into anterior and posterior divisions, as shown in Table 70.

Branches of the Posterior Division

Iliolumbar a. Ascending behind the common iliac vessels and under the psoas major muscle, it divides into the following branches:

iliac branch. Supplies the iliacus muscle and providing a large nutrient a. to the ilium.

lumbar branch. Supplies the psoas major and quadratus lumborum muscles and providing a spinal branch which passes through the lumbosacral intervertebral foramen to the cauda equina.

Table 70

Anterior division		Posterior division: somatic segmental branches
Visceral branches	Perineal and limb branches	
Umbilical a. Superior vesical a. A. of ductus deferens Inferior vesical a. Middle rectal a. Uterine a. Vaginal a.	Inferior gluteal a. Internal pudendal a. Obturator a.	Iliolumbar a. Lateral sacral aa. Superior gluteal a.

Lateral sacral aa. They descend laterad to the anterior sacral foramens and branches supply the contents of the sacral canal. Their terminal branches pass out through the posterior foramens to supply the muscles and skin on the back of the sacrum.

Superior gluteal a. This continuation of the posterior division courses between the lumbosacral trunk and the first sacral n. It passes out of the pelvis, above the piriformis muscle, through the greater sciatic foramen into the gluteal region.

Branches of the Anterior Division

The visceral branches are:

Umbilical a. This vessel is almost completely obliterated; it forms a prominent fold, the medial umbilical fold, on the anterior abdominal wall. From its patent end the following also arise:

superior vesical a. Supplies the superior part of the bladder and the terminal part of the ureter.

artery of the ductus deferens. Supplies the back of the bladder and the seminal vesicles and accompanies the ductus deferens as far as the testis, where it anastomoses with the testicular a.

Inferior vesical a. It provides branches to the fundus of the bladder, prostate, seminal vesicles, and ureter.

Middle rectal a. It provides branches to the rectum, and to the prostate, seminal vesicles, and ductus deferens in the male or to the vagina in the female.

Uterine a. This large vessel descends medially to the cervix. Then it ascends tortuously between the layers of the broad ligament on the side of the uterus, curving laterally near the uterine tube to anastomose with the ovarian a. In addition to branches to the body of the uterus, branches are provided to the upper part of the vagina, medial part of the uterine tube, and round ligament of the uterus, and ligament of the ovary.

Vaginal a. It provides branches to the front and back of the vagina, to the bladder, and to the rectum.

The perineal and limb branches are:

Inferior gluteal a. The larger of the two terminal branches of the anterior division of the internal iliac a. passes back between Sn 1 and 2 (sometimes Sn 2 and 3) and leaves the pelvis through the greater sciatic foramen below the piriformis muscle to enter the gluteal region.

Internal pudendal a. The other terminal branch passes down and back and leaves the pelvis at the lower border of the greater sciatic foramen, passing between the piriformis and coccygeus muscles. After crossing the ischial spine, it reenters the pelvis through the lesser sciatic foramen and enters the pudendal canal to supply the external genitalia.

Obturator a. Descending forward on the side wall of the pelvis, it leaves through the obturator canal on the upper part of the obturator foramen. Its pelvic branches supply the iliacus muscle and the bladder. A pubic branch anastomoses with the inferior epigastric a.

6. Veins

MEDIAN SACRAL V. It is formed by a pair of venae comitantes of the corresponding artery and terminates in the left common iliac v.

SUPERIOR RECTAL V. It ascends from the pelvis to become the inferior mesenteric v.

INTERNAL ILIAC V. It begins above the greater sciatic notch and ascends, joining the external iliac v. at the pelvic rim, to form the common iliac v. Its tributaries correspond to branches of the internal iliac a. except that the umbilical is absent, and the iliolumbar usually joins the common iliac v. The visceral vv. are derived from plexuses that drain the viscera. These are the vesical, prostatic, pudendal, and rectal plexuses.

7. Nerves (Figs. 79-1, 79-2)

LUMBOSACRAL TRUNK. This thick cord is formed on the ala of the sacrum by the descending branch of Ln 4 and the ventral ramus of Ln 5. It enters the pelvis to join the formation of the sacral plexus.

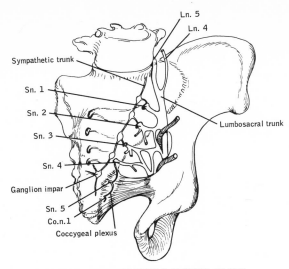

79-1 SACRAL AND COCCYGEAL PLEXUSES: IN SITU

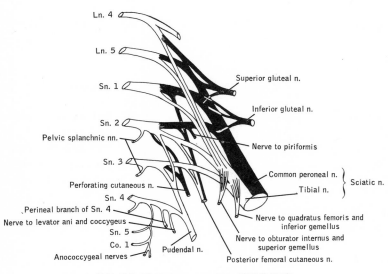

79-2 SACRAL AND COCCYGEAL PLEXUSES: COMPONENTS

Plate 79

Table 71

Anterior branches	Posterior branches	Terminal branches
Nerves to levator ani and coccygeus mm. Nerve to quadratus femoris m. Nerve to obturator internus m. Perineal branch of Sn 4 Pelvic splanchnic nn.	Nerve to piriformis m. Superior gluteal n. Inferior gluteal n. Posterior femoral cutaneous n. Perforating cutaneous n.	Sciatic n. Pudendal n.

Sacral Plexus

It is formed by the lumbosacral trunk and the ventral rami of Sn 1 to 4. The nerves forming this plexus emerge from the anterior sacral foramens. The branches of this plexus can be divided into three groups, as shown in Table 71.

ANTERIOR BRANCHES

Nerves to Levator Ani and Coccygeus (Sn 3, 4). They arise from a common loop and descend to enter the pelvic surface of these muscles.

Nerve to Quadratus Femoris (Ln 4, 5, Sn 1). It leaves the pelvis through the greater sciatic foramen beneath the sciatic n. to supply the quadratus femoris and gemellus inferior muscles in the gluteal region.

Nerve to Obturator Internus (Ln 5, Sn 1, 2). It emerges from the pelvis below the piriformis muscle to supply the obturator internus and gemellus superior muscles in the gluteal region.

Perineal Branch of Sn 4. It pierces the coccygeus muscle and enters the ischiorectal fossa.

Pelvic Splanchnic Nn. They are parasympathetic fibers that arise from Sn 2 to 4 and join the visceral sympathetic plexus (see below) for distribution to the pelvic organs.

POSTERIOR BRANCHES

Nerve to Piriformis (Sn 1, 2). It immediately enters the pelvic surface of the muscle.

Superior Gluteal N. (Ln 4, 5, Sn 1). It exits from the pelvis above the piriformis muscle to enter the gluteal region.

Inferior Gluteal N. (Ln 5, Sn 1, 2). It exits from the pelvis below the piriformis muscle medial to the sciatic n. to enter the gluteal region.

Posterior Femoral Cutaneous N. (Sn 1 to 3). Emerging from the pelvis below the piriformis muscle, it passes through the gluteal region to the back of the knee.

Perforating Cutaneous N. (Sn 2, 3). Descending to the coccygeus muscle, it pierces it and the sacrotuberous ligament, and curves around the lower border of the gluteus maximus muscle to supply the skin of the buttock.

TERMINAL BRANCHES

Sciatic N. (Ln 4, 5, Sn 1 to 3). Leaving the pelvis at the lower margin of the piriformis muscle, it enters the thigh.

Pudendal N. (Sn 2 to 4). It exits from the pelvis over the ischial spine and enters the pudendal canal for distribution to the perineum.

Coccygeal Plexus

It is formed by the union of ventral rami of parts of Sn 4 and 5 and Co. n 1, which unite on the pelvic surface of the coccygeus muscle. The *anococcygeal nn.* arise from the plexus. They pierce the coccygeus muscle and sacrotuberous ligament to supply the skin of the anal region.

Sacral Sympathetic Trunk

The lumbar trunk crosses the margin of the ala of the sacrum to enter the pelvis. It descends on the pelvic surface of the sacrum just medial to the pelvic sacral foramens. It terminates on the coccyx by the union of both trunks in the *ganglion impar.* A sacral ganglion lies adjacent to each of the sacral foramens.

Sympathetic Plexuses

The aortic plexus extends into the pelvis as the *superior hypogastric plexus,* which divides into two *hypogastric nn.* in front of the sacrum. These descend on each side of the rectum, where they ramify into the *inferior hypogastric plexus.* Subdivisions of this plexus accompany the visceral branches of the internal iliac aa. to supply the pelvic organs and are named accordingly.

PELVIC GENITAL ORGANS

1. Genital organs of the male   *2. Genital organs of the female*

In the male, the spermatozoa are produced in the testis and pass into the epididymis for storage. On emission, they pass through the ductus deferens, the ejaculatory duct, and the urethra to the external urethral orifice. The other genital organs produce the secretions that comprise the seminal fluid. In the female, the ova are extruded from the ovaries and pass down the uterine tube into the uterus.

1. Genital Organs of the Male (Fig. 80-1)

The testes, epididymides, ductus deferens, seminal vesicles, ejaculatory ducts, prostate gland, bulbourethral glands, and the penis comprise the male genitalia. The scrotum and penis, the external genital organs, are described on p. 285. The testis, being intrapelvic in the fetus, is included in the discussion of the pelvic genital organs.

TESTES (Fig. 80-2). These are paired, oval white organs, the layers of which are:

tunica vaginalis. Visceral layer.

tunica albuginea. This dense fibrous coat projects into the testis as the *mediastinum testis*. Extending from the mediastinum are septums which subdivide the testis into compartments. Within each are two or more convoluted *seminiferous tubules*. The tubules of each compartment unite near its apex to form *straight tubules*. These enter the mediastinum to form a network, the *rete testis*. About 15 *efferent ducts* emerge from the mediastinum into the head of the epididymis.

The neurovascular system of the testis is supplied by:

arteries: Testicular a. from the aorta.

veins: The pampiniform plexus gives rise to the testicular v. It terminates in the inferior vena cava on the right and in the renal v. on the left.

nerves: From the aortic and renal plexuses.

EPIDIDYMIS (Fig. 80-2). Along the posterior border of the testis is a highly coiled duct derived from the efferent ductules of the rete testis and continuous with the ductus deferens. It consists of a *head* (the enlarged upper end), a *body* (separated from the testis by the sinus of the epididymis), and a *tail* (the lower end). The blood and nerve supply are the same as for the testis.

Appendix Testis. It is a small vestigial body on the upper end of the testis.

Appendix of the Epididymis. It is a small vestigial body on the head of the epididymis.

DUCTUS DEFERENS (Fig. 80-1). This continuation of the epididymis ascends from the scrotum in the spermatic cord to enter the pelvis at the deep inguinal ring. It courses subperitoneally along the side wall of the pelvis and curves medially, passing over the ureters. It expands into an *ampulla* behind the bladder. Behind the neck of the bladder, the ductus deferens narrows and joins the duct of the seminal vesicle to form the ejaculatory duct (see below).

The neurovascular system of the ductus deferens is supplied by:

arteries: Inferior vesical a. and branches from the middle rectal a. to the ampulla.

veins: The veins correspond to the arteries.

nerves: The nerves originate in the pelvic sympathetic plexus.

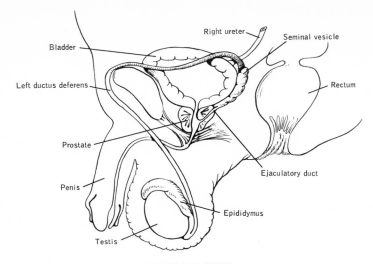

80-1   MALE GENITAL SYSTEM

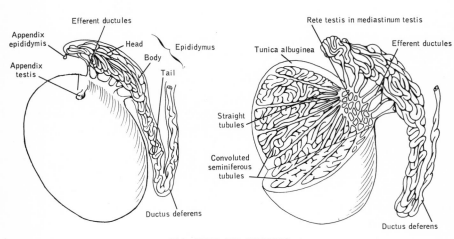

80-2   TESTIS AND EPIDIDYMIS

Plate 80

Table 72

Constituent	Association
Ductus deferens.................	Epididymis
Artery of ductus deferens........	Umbilical a.
Cremasteric a...................	Inferior epigastric a.
Testicular a....................	Aorta
Pampiniform plexus.............	Testicular v.
Testicular lymphatics...........	Lumbar nodes
Autonomic nerves..............	Spermatic and pelvic plexuses

Table 73

Inguinal layer	Corresponding anterior abdominal layer
Layer of scrotum:	
Skin.....................	Skin
Dartos m.................	Camper's fascia
Colles' fascia..............	Scarpa's fascia
Covering of cord:	
External spermatic fascia....	External oblique aponeurosis
Cremaster m..............	Internal oblique m.
—	Transversus abdominis m.
Internal spermatic fascia....	Transversalis fascia
Constitutents of cord:	
Areolar tissue.............	Extraperitoneal fatty tissue
Tunica vaginalis..........	Peritoneum

SPERMATIC CORD. It extends from the deep inguinal ring to the posterior border of the testis. Its constituents are shown in Table 72.

The cord is enveloped by the internal spermatic fascia, cremasteric muscle, and external spermatic fascia which are derived from the abdominal layers (see Table 73 and Fig. 65-4).

SEMINAL VESICLES (Fig. 81-1). They lie on the back of the bladder. Each is a piriform-shaped, branched, sacculated tube, closed at one end. Its other end is a narrow duct which joins the termination of the seminal vesicle.

The neurovascular supply of the seminal vesicles are supplied by:

arteries: Branches of the vesical and middle rectal aa.

veins: They correspond to the arteries.

nerves: Ln 2 to 4 via the hypogastric plexus.

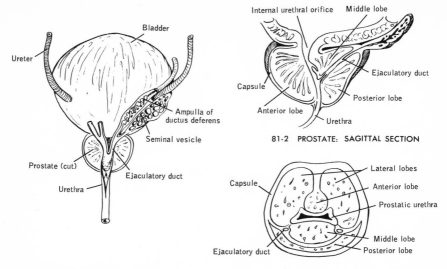

81-1 SEMINAL VESICLE AND EJACULATORY DUCT

81-2 PROSTATE: SAGITTAL SECTION

81-3 PROSTATE: CROSS SECTION AT NECK OF BLADDER

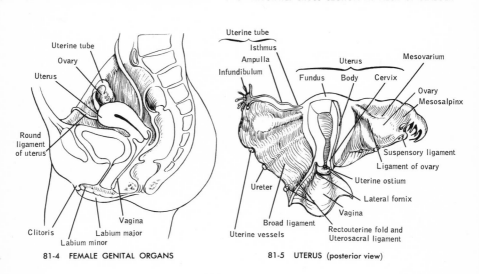

81-4 FEMALE GENITAL ORGANS

81-5 UTERUS (posterior view)

Plate 81

270

EJACULATORY DUCTS (Fig. 81-1). These ducts are formed just above the base of the prostate by the union of the ductus deferens and the duct of the seminal vesicle. They pierce the prostate obliquely and open into the prostatic urethra on both sides of the utricle.

PROSTATE (Fig. 81-2). This gland lies behind the symphysis with its base below the bladder and its apex on the urogenital diaphragm. It is perforated in the center by the urethra and from behind by the ejaculatory ducts. In cross section its (two) lateral and median *lobes* can be seen (Fig. 81-3). The median lobe separates the urethra in front from the ejaculatory ducts behind. The prostate is enclosed by a *capsule* which consists of condensed endopelvic fascia. The glandular tissue is embedded in a fibromuscular stroma. The secretion is eliminated via 20 to 30 *prostatic ducts* which open into the prostatic sinuses.

The neurovascular system of the prostate is supplied by:

arteries: Inferior vesicle and middle rectal aa.

veins: They come from the venous plexus draining to the internal iliac v.

nerves: Pelvic sympathetic plexus.

Bulbourethral Gland (Fig. 84-4). This gland is embedded in the substance of the sphincter urethrae. The ducts pass through the bulb of the penis and open into the spongy urethra.

2. Genital Organs of the Female (Figs. 81-4, 81-5)

The female genitalia consist of the uterus, uterine tubes, ovaries, vagina, and the external genital organs (p. 287).

UTERUS (Fig. 81-5). This pear-shaped, muscular organ is located between the rectum and the bladder. The lowest part, or *cervix,* projecting partly into the vagina, has supra- and intravaginal parts. The major section of the uterus is the *body,* which is connected with the cervix by the constricted *isthmus.* The upper end, or *fundus,* is rounded and blunt. The vesical surface is covered with peritoneum as far as the isthmus; the peritoneum passes down the intestinal surface as far as the vagina. The lateral borders are connected to the broad ligament.

The cavity of the body is triangular. The uterine tubes open into the basal angles; the apex is continuous with the cervical canal. The latter extends from the isthmus to the uterine ostium.

The neurovascular system to the uterus is supplied by:

arteries: Uterine aa., which are branches of the internal iliac a.

veins: They correspond to the arteries.

nerves: Uterovaginal plexus, an extension of the inferior hypogastric plexus.

The three ligaments associated with the uterus are:

Broad Ligament. This mesentery extends from the side of the uterus to the side wall of the pelvis. Enclosed in the medial four-fifths of the upper free end of this ligament is the uterine tube. The suspensory ligament of the ovary (see below) is enclosed in the lateral fifth. The mesovarium, attached to the posterior surface, divides the broad ligament into two parts. The upper part is known as the *mesosalpinx*.

Round Ligament (of the Uterus). This ligament, also known as the ligamentum teres (uteri), is the fibromuscular remnant of the lower part of the gubernaculum. Extending from the superolateral angle of the uterus to the deep inguinal ring, it passes through the inguinal canal, emerges through the superficial inguinal ring, and terminates in the labium majus.

Rectouterine Fold. This fold extends from the sacrum to the cervix of the uterus.

UTERINE TUBE. This tube is divided into a short, narrow *isthmus* and a wider *ampulla*. It begins at the fundus of the uterus and terminates at the *infundibulum*, which consists of a number of finger-like processes, or *fimbriae*.

OVARY. It lies against the lateral pelvic walls. The suspensory ligament extends from the tubal end of the ovary to the pelvic wall. It is enveloped by peritoneum which attaches to the broad ligament by the *mesovarium*.

The neurovascular system of the ovary is supplied by:

arteries: Ovarian a. from the aorta and by branches of the uterine a.

veins: They consist of a pampiniform plexus from which the ovarian v. arises to terminate in the inferior vena cava on the right side and the renal v. on the left.

nerves: Branches of the aortic and renal plexuses.

The two ligaments associated with the ovary are:

Suspensory Ligament of the Ovary. Extending from the tubal end of the ovary to the lateral pelvic wall, it lies at the upper margin of the lateral fifth of the uterine tube. The ovarian vessels and nerves course in this ligament.

Ligament of the Ovary. The ovarian ligament extends from the uterine end of the ovary to the lateral side of the uterus, just below the entrance of the uterine tube. It consists of a fibromuscular cord enclosed by the broad ligament.

VAGINA. This organ lies in the lower part of the pelvis and in the perineum (see p. 283). Its walls are in contact with each other except where the cervix projects into the vaginal cavity at its upper end. This forms the constricted *anterior, lateral,* and *posterior fornices.*

The neurovascular system of the vagina is supplied by:

arteries: Uterine, vaginal, middle rectal, and internal pudendal aa.

nerves: From sympathetic and pelvic splanchnic nn.

PELVIC WALLS

1. Pelvic muscles   *2. Pelvic fascia*

The *pelvic outlet* is closed by the obturator internus and piriformis muscles laterally and by the levator ani and coccygeus muscles posteroinferiorly. The urogenital diaphragm contributes anterosuperiorly.

1. Pelvic Muscles (Fig. 82-1)

OBTURATOR INTERNUS. It leaves the pelvis via the lesser sciatic foramen.
Origin: Inner surface of side wall of the pelvis below the obturator n.
Insertion: Greater trochanter of the femur.
Action: Lateral rotation and abduction of the thigh.
Nerve supply: To obturator internus muscle from the sacral plexus.
PIRIFORMIS. It leaves the pelvis via the greater sciatic foramen.
Origin: Pelvic surface of the second to fourth sacral segments.
Insertion: Greater trochanter of the femur.
Action: Lateral rotation and abduction of the thigh.
Nerve supply: Ventral rami of Sn 1 and 2.
COCCYGEUS. It is triangular in shape.
Origin: Spine of the ischium.
Insertion: Margin of Sv 4, 5, and coccyx.
Action: Draws the coccyx forward.
Nerve supply: Ventral rami of Sn 4 and 5.
LEVATOR ANI. It is composed of three parts.
Puborectalis. It is the most medial portion of the levator ani.
Origin: Dorsum of the pubis.
Insertion: Joins the muscle from the other side behind the rectum.
Pubococcygeus. This is the thickest portion of the levator ani.
Origin: Superior pubic ramus lateralward to the obturator canal.
Insertion: Anococcygeal raphe and terminal parts of the coccyx.
Iliococcygeus. It is the most lateral portion of the levator ani.
Origin: Tendinous arch of levator ani (see p. 275) and ischial spine.
Insertion: Anococcygeal raphe and terminal parts of the coccyx.
Action: Supports and raises the pelvic floor.
Nerve supply: Inferior rectal n.
Pelvic Diaphragm. The levator ani and coccygeus muscles and their fascia form the pelvic floor, which separates the pelvis and the perineum. The pelvic diaphragm is perforated by the urethra and the rectum in both sexes. The vagina in addition perforates the pelvic diaphragm in the female.

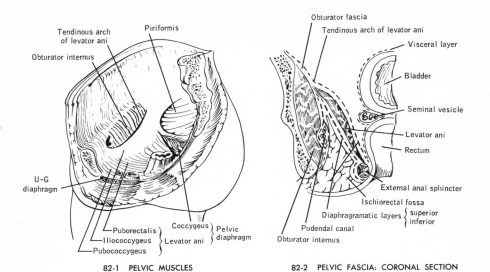

82-1 PELVIC MUSCLES

Tendinous arch of levator ani
Obturator internus
Piriformis
U-G diaphragm
Puborectalis
Iliococcygeus } Levator ani
Pubococcygeus
Coccygeus } Pelvic diaphragm

82-2 PELVIC FASCIA: CORONAL SECTION

Obturator fascia
Tendinous arch of levator ani
Visceral layer
Bladder
Seminal vesicle
Levator ani
Rectum
External anal sphincter
Ischiorectal fossa
Diaphragramatic layers { superior / inferior
Pudendal canal
Obturator internus

82-3 HIP BONE: GLUTEAL ASPECT

Gluteal lines
Posterior Anterior Inferior
Tubercle
Posterior superior spine
ILIUM
Posterior inferior spine
Greater sciatic notch
Acetabular fossa
Ischial spine
Lesser sciatic notch
ISCHIUM
Ischial tuberosity
Ischial ramus
Acetabular notch
Obturator crest
PUBIS
Pubic tubercle
Inferior pubic ramus
Obturator foramen

82-4 HIP BONE: INNER ASPECT

Anterior superior spine
Iliac fossa
Iliac crest
ILIUM
Tuberosity
Anterior inferior spine
Posterior inferior spine
Articular surface
Arcuate line
PUBIS
Pectin
Iliopectineal eminence
ISCHIUM
Ischial ramus
Symphysial surface
Superior pubic ramus
Symphysial surface

Plate 82

2. Pelvic Fascia (Fig. 82-2)

The pelvic viscera, vessels, and muscles are covered with areolar tissue. This fascia is distinguished as three layers:

Visceral Layer. This layer envelops the bladder, the rectum, and the genital organs between. The specific coverings are named accordingly.

Parietal Layer. This downward continuation of the transversalis fascia into the pelvis is divided into two parts:

piriform fascia. This part covers the intrapelvic portion of the muscle and is attached to the front of the sacrum and the side of the greater sciatic foramen.

obturator fascia. This part covers the intrapelvic portion of the muscle except at the lesser sciatic notch, where the muscle leaves the pelvis. The boundary between the intrapelvic and extrapelvic portions of the obturator fascia is thickened from the pubis to the ischial spine. This is known as the *tendinous arch of the levator ani,* since the muscle takes origin from this structure. At the arch, the fascia splits into three sheets: extrapelvic obturator fascia, and the superior and inferior fasciae of the pelvic diaphragm.

Diaphragmatic Layer. Covering the intrapelvic surface of the levator ani and coccygeus muscles, it divides at the tendinous arch into superior and inferior layers. The strong superior layer meets its contralateral counterpart at the *anococcygeal raphe,* and in front of the rectum it contributes to the formation of the deep layer of the urogenital diaphragm. The inferior layer becomes continuous with the superficial layer of the urogenital diaphragm and with the fascia of the sphincter ani muscles.

PELVIC BONES AND JOINTS

1. Ilium   3. Pubis
2. Ischium   4. Joints of pelvis

The pelvis consists, anteriorly and laterally, of the *coxal bones* and, posteriorly, of the sacrum and coccyx. The part above the arcuate line is known as the *false pelvis;* the part below this line is the *true pelvis,* which contains the pelvic viscera. Each of the coxal bones consists of three bones united at the acetabulum: the ilium, ischium, and pubis.

1. Ilium (Figs. 82-3, 82-4)

crest. The margins of the long, arched, upper border are known as the external and internal lips. The anterior and posterior ends of the crest are known respectively as the *anterior* and *posterior superior iliac spines*. The *tubercle* of the crest is located on the outer lip a little behind the anterior superior iliac spine. The ventral abdominal and back muscles are attached to the crest of the ilium.

Anterior Border. It extends from the anterior superior iliac spine to the *iliopectineal eminence*. The anterior inferior iliac spine lies between these two landmarks.

Posterior Border. It extends from the posterior superior spine to the margin of the greater sciatic notch. The posterior inferior iliac spine is on this border.

Gluteal Surface. Three curved lines subdivide this area:

inferior gluteal line. Extends from the anterior inferior spine towards the deepest part of the sciatic notch.

anterior gluteal line. Extends from behind the anterior superior spine towards the sciatic notch.

posterior gluteal line. Extends from a little in front of the posterior superior spine downward to the sciatic notch.

Inner Surface. The iliac fossa is bounded by the crest above and the arcuate line below. Behind the fossa is the smooth articular surface for the sacropelvic joint and the rough iliac tuberosity.

2. Ischium (Fig. 82-3)

Body. The *ischial spine* projects from the posterior border. It divides the border into *greater* and *lesser sciatic notches*. The *ischial tuberosity* is at the end of the posterior border.

Ramus. Extending forward and medially from the tuberosity, it meets the inferior ramus of the pubis and forms the pubic arch.

3. Pubis (Fig. 82-4)

Body. Three surfaces are present: a smooth pelvic surface; a rough femoral surface; and a symphyseal surface. The upper border, the *pectin pubis*, has the *pubic tubercle* at its lateral end.

Superior Ramus. Its medial end is fused with the body of the pubis; its lateral end is fused with the ilium and the ischium to form the acetabulum. The *obturator crest* descends from the pubic tubercle to the acetabular notch.

Inferior Ramus. It descends from the body of the pubis to fuse with the ramus of the ischium.

Acetabulum. This cavity receives the head of the femur. It consists of a rough *acetabular fossa,* which has a gap, the *acetabular notch,* above the obturator foramen. This foramen is surrounded by the bodies and the rami of the ischium and the pubis. It is oval in the male and triangular in the female.

4. Joints of the Pelvis

The joints of the pelvis include the sacroiliac, pubic symphysis, lumbosacral, and sacrococcygeal articulations. The latter two, directly associated with the vertebral column, are discussed elsewhere (p. 364).

Sacroiliac Joint (Fig. 83-1)

Type: It is synovial in type.
Articulating elements: They are the articulating surfaces of the sacrum and the ilium.
Ligaments:
Anterior sacroiliac ligament. Thin short fibers connect the anterior convex margins of the auricular surfaces.
Posterior sacroiliac ligament. The transverse tubercles of the sacrum are connected to the tuberosity of the ilium and the posterior superior iliac spine.
Interosseous sacroiliac ligament. Short, strong fibers connect the tuberosities of the sacrum and the ilium.

Pubic Symphysis (Fig. 83-2)

Type: It is cartilaginous in type.
Articulating elements: They are the bodies of the pubic bones.
Ligaments:
Superior pubic ligament. It extends across the symphysis to the pubic tubercles.
Arcuate pubic ligament. It extends below the symphysis to the inferior pubic rami.
Interpubic disk. It frequently has a sagittal cleft.
Ligaments between sacrum and ischium:
Sacrospinous ligament (Fig. 83-3). This triangular ligament extends between the apex of the ischial spine and the margin of the lowest part of the sacrum and the upper part of the coccyx.
Sacrotuberous ligament (Fig. 83-4). This ligament is broad at its ends and narrow

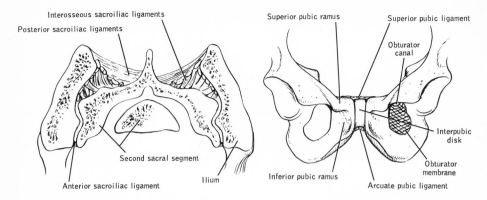

Interosseous sacroiliac ligaments

Posterior sacroiliac ligaments

Second sacral segment

Anterior sacroiliac ligament

Ilium

83-1   SACROILIAC JOINT AND LIGAMENTS

Superior pubic ramus

Superior pubic ligament

Obturator canal

Interpubic disk

Obturator membrane

Inferior pubic ramus

Arcuate pubic ligament

83-2   PUBIC SYMPHYSIS

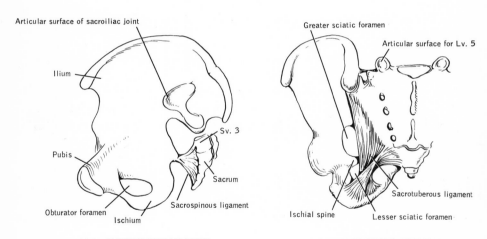

Articular surface of sacroiliac joint

Ilium

Pubis

Obturator foramen

Ischium

Sv. 3

Sacrum

Sacrospinous ligament

83-3   SACROSPINOUS LIGAMENT

Greater sciatic foramen

Articular surface for Lv. 5

Sacrotuberous ligament

Ischial spine

Lesser sciatic foramen

83-4   SACROTUBEROUS LIGAMENT

Plate 83

in the middle. It extends from the posterior iliac spine, the third to fifth transverse sacral tubercles, and the side of the coccyx down to the medial margin of the ischial tuberosity.

PERINEUM

1. Urogenital triangle of the male   2. Urogenital triangle of the female
3. Anal triangle

The perineum (Fig. 84-1) is the diamond-shaped space which, in common with the pelvic outlet, has the following boundaries:

Anterior boundary: pubic symphysis

Anterolateral boundary: inferior ramus of pubis, ramus and tuberosity of ischium

Posterolateral boundary: sacrotuberous ligament

Posterior boundary: coccyx

This region is divided by an imaginary transverse line between the anterior parts of the ischial tuberosities. The urogenital (U-G) triangle lies anteriorly, and the anal triangle lies posteriorly.

1. Urogenital Triangle of the Male

Five layers comprise the male urogenital triangle.

SKIN. The skin has a median raphe which extends from the anus to the scrotum.

SUPERFICIAL PERINEAL FASCIA (Fig. 84-2). This subcutaneous stratum is divided into a superficial fatty layer and a deep membranous layer.

Superficial. This layer is continuous with Camper's fascia of the abdomen, with a similar layer in the anal triangle and with the dartos layer of the scrotum.

Deep. This layer, known as Colles' fascia, is attached behind to the posterior border of the perineal membrane; at the sides, to the ischiopubic rami; and anteriorly, with the dartos of the scrotum, Scarpa's fascia of the abdomen, and the superficial fascia of the penis.

DEEP PERINEAL FASCIA (Fig. 84-2). This layer covers approximately the same triangular area as the preceding layer and thus has similar attachments. It is continuous, anteriorly, with the thin fascia covering the external abdominal oblique muscle, and, laterally, with the fascia lata of the thigh. It invests the superficial perineal muscles and dips between them to become associated with the inferior fascia of the urogenital diaphragm. It extends over the penis as (Buck's) deep penile fascia.

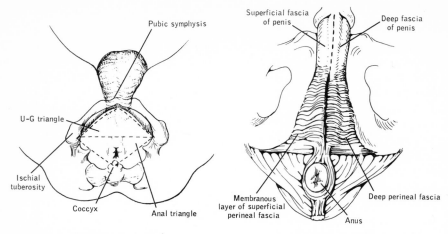

Pubic symphysis

U-G triangle

Ischial
tuberosity

Coccyx

Anal triangle

84-1   MALE PERINEUM: BOUNDARIES

Superficial fascia
of penis

Deep fascia
of penis

Membranous
layer of superficial
perineal fascia

Deep perineal fascia

Anus

84-2   MALE PERINEUM: FASCIA

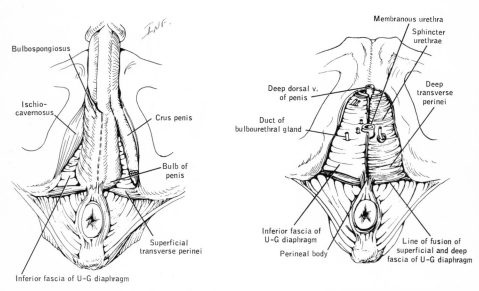

Bulbospongiosus

Ischio-
cavernosus

Crus penis

Bulb of
penis

Superficial
transverse perinei

Inferior fascia of U-G diaphragm

84-3   MUSCLES OF SUPERFICIAL PERINEAL SPACE

Membranous urethra

Sphincter
urethrae

Deep dorsal v.
of penis

Deep
transverse
perinei

Duct of
bulbourethral gland

Inferior fascia of
U-G diaphragm

Perineal body

Line of fusion of
superficial and deep
fascia of U-G diaphragm

84-4   UROGENITAL DIAPHRAGM MALE

Plate 84

SUPERFICIAL PERINEAL SPACE. The area between the deep perineal fascia and the inferior fascia of the urogenital diaphragm is closed, behind, by union of these two layers and, on the side, by the attachment to the margins of the pubic arch. It remains open in front and is filled with the areolar tissue that lies between Scarpa's fascia and the aponeurosis of the external oblique muscle. This space encloses the root of the penis and its associated superficial perineal muscles, branches of the internal pudendal vessels, and the pudendal nerve.

There are four superficial perineal muscles (Fig. 84-3) and they are innervated by the perineal branch of the pudendal n.

Ischiocavernosus. A muscle covers each crus of the penis.

Origin: Ramus of ischium near the tuberosity.

Insertion: Side and undersurface of the crus penis.

Action: Compresses the crus. This prevents the return of blood through the veins and maintains the penis erect.

Bulbospongiosus. This single muscle covers the bulb of the penis.

Origin: Perineal body and median fibrous raphe on the bulb of the penis.

Insertion: Inferior fascia of the urogenital diaphragm, dorsum of the corpus spongiosum, and deep fascia of the dorsum of the penis.

Action: Helps empty the urethra.

Superficial Transverse Perinei

Origin: Ramus of the ischium near the tuberosity.

Insertion: Perineal body.

Action: Fixes the perineal body.

DEEP PERINEAL SPACE. This is the area between the inferior and superior fascia of the urogenital diaphragm.

Inferior Fascia of Urogenital Diaphragm (Fig. 84-3). This strong sheet covers the lower surface of the sphincter urethrae and the deep transverse perineal muscles. Its lower surface is largely covered by the root of the penis. Its posterior border is fused with the posterior border of the superior fascia, the midline of which bears a fibromuscular nodule, the *perineal body*. The fascia is thickened anteriorly to form the transverse perineal ligament. An oval gap separates the membrane from the arcuate ligament of the pubis.

Superior Fascia of the Urogenital Diaphragm. This membrane is derived from the parietal pelvic fascia and covers the pelvic surface of the sphincter urethrae and the deep transverse perineal muscles. It is attached laterally to the obturator fascia. The deep perineal space contains the deep perineal muscles, the membranous part of the urethra, the bulbourethral gland, the internal pudendal vessels, the artery of the bulb of the penis, and the dorsal n. of the penis.

The deep perineal muscles (Fig. 84-4), together with the covering fascial layers, compose the urogenital diaphragm.

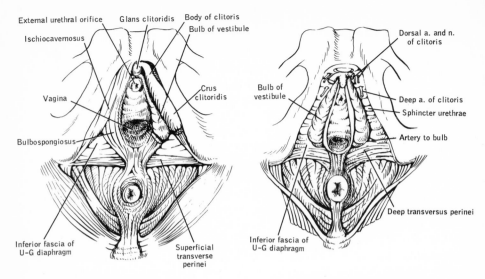

External urethral orifice   Glans clitoridis   Body of clitoris
Bulb of vestibule
Ischiocavernosus
Vagina
Crus clitoridis
Bulbospongiosus
Inferior fascia of U-G diaphragm
Superficial transverse perinei

85-1   FEMALE PERINEUM: MUSCLES

Dorsal a. and n. of clitoris
Bulb of vestibule
Deep a. of clitoris
Sphincter urethrae
Artery to bulb
Inferior fascia of U-G diaphragm
Deep transversus perinei

85-2   UROGENITAL DIAPHRAGM: FEMALE

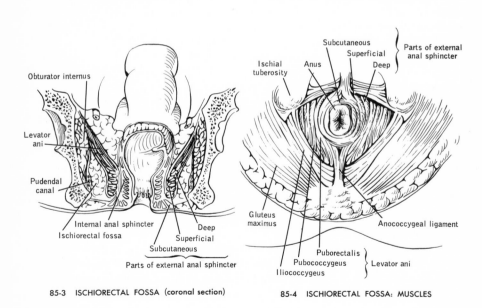

Obturator internus
Levator ani
Pudendal canal
Internal anal sphincter
Ischiorectal fossa
Deep
Superficial
Subcutaneous
Parts of external anal sphincter

85-3   ISCHIORECTAL FOSSA (coronal section)

Subcutaneous
Superficial
Ischial tuberosity
Anus
Deep
Parts of external anal sphincter
Gluteus maximus
Anococcygeal ligament
Puborectalis
Pubococcygeus
Iliococcygeus
Levator ani

85-4   ISCHIORECTAL FOSSA: MUSCLES

Plate 85

282

Sphincter Urethrae

Origin: Inferior ramus of the pubis.

Insertion: Joins the fibers of the other side to encircle the urethra.

Action: Constricts the membranous part of the urethra.

Nerve supply: Dorsal n. of the penis.

Deep Transverse Perinei

Origin: Ramus of the ischium.

Insertion: Posterior margin of the spincter urethrae.

Action: Helps fix the perineal body.

Nerve supply: Dorsal n. of the penis.

2. Urogenital Triangle of the Female

The urogenital triangle of the female is associated with the lower end of the vagina and the female external genitalia, in addition to the urethra. This modifies the region somewhat from the corresponding male triangle, but the basic organization is the same. The five layers are:

SKIN. The orifices of the urethra and vagina are evident. The skin is folded to shape the external genital organs.

SUPERFICIAL PERINEAL FASCIA. This consists of two layers.

Superficial. This fatty layer extends into the labia majora.

Deep. This membranous layer has the same attachments posteriorly and laterally as in the male. The layer unites anteriorly to the vagina to become continuous with Scarpa's fascia.

DEEP PERINEAL FASCIA. It has the same attachments as in the male (p. 279).

SUPERFICIAL PERINEAL SPACE. It has the same boundaries as in the male. It encloses the superficial perineal muscles, the greater vestibular glands, and branches of the internal pudendal vessels and the pudendal n.

The superficial perineal muscles (Fig. 85-1) are:

Ischiocavernosus. This is similar to its homologue in the male but smaller.

Bulbospogiosus. It passes around the vagina.

Origin: Perineal body.

Insertion: Side of the pubic arch and root of the clitoris.

Action: Compresses bulb of vestibule and acts as sphincter of vaginal orifice.

Superficial Transverse Perinei. It is similar to the same muscle in the male.

DEEP PERINEAL SPACE. It has the same boundaries as the corresponding space in the male and is enclosed by the inferior and superior fascia of the urogenital diaphragm. It contains the deep perineal muscles, the membranous part of the urethra, the middle segment of the vagina, the internal pudendal vessels, the artery of the bulb of the vestibule, and the dorsal n. of the clitoris.

The deep perineal muscles (Fig. 85-2) are less developed in the female than in the male.

Sphincter Urethrae

Origin: Inferior ramus of the pubis.

Insertion: Lateral wall of the vagina.

Deep Transverse Perinei

Origin: Ramus of the ischium.

Insertion: Perineal body and lateral wall of the vagina.

3. Anal Triangle

This region is identical in both sexes. It is divided into two lateral ischiorectal fossae and a median area containing the lower part of the anal canal surrounded by the external sphincter ani.

ISCHIORECTAL FOSSAE (Fig. 85-3). Each fossa is wedge-shaped and is filled with fat. Its boundaries are:

Anterior boundary: posterior margin of the urogenital diaphragm

Posterior boundary: sacrotuberous ligament

Lateral boundary: obturator muscle, its fascia, and ischium

Medial boundary: levator ani and external sphincter muscles

ANAL CANAL. Passing through the pelvic floor, it terminates at the anus. Its circular muscular fibers are thickened to form the internal anal sphincter.

EXTERNAL ANAL SPHINCTER (Fig. 85-4). It consists of three parts:

Subcutaneous Part. It surrounds the lowermost part of the anal canal.

Superficial Part. It extends from the tip of the coccyx to the anococcygeal ligament.

Deep Part. It surrounds the upper part of the anal canal.

The neurovascular system of the anal canal is supplied by:

arteries: Middle and inferior rectal aa.

veins: Drain into the rectal plexus.

nerves: From hypogastric plexus.

EXTERNAL GENITALIA

1. *External genital organs of the male*   3. *Superficial perineal arteries and veins*
2. *External genital organs of the female*   4. *Superficial perineal nerves*

The pelvic genital organs have already been discussed (pp. 267 and 271).

1. External Genital Organs of the Male

SCROTUM (Fig. 86-1). This sac is located below and behind the penis. It is divided into two compartments, each of which contains a testicle, the epididymis, the lower part of the spermatic cord, and its coverings. Its layers are:

Skin. Scrotal skin is dark, with a median raphe.

Dartos Muscle. Corresponding to Camper's fascia, it is thin and forms the septum dividing the scrotum. Colles' fascia is part of this layer.

The neurovascular system of the scrotum is supplied by:

arteries: Scrotal branches of the internal and external pudendal aa.

veins: They correspond to the arteries.

nerves: Ilioinguinal, scrotal branch of the perineal, and perineal branch of the posterior femoral cutaneous nn.

PENIS (Fig. 86-2). The male organ of copulation. It is perforated through its length by the spongy urethra and is enclosed by:

Skin. The skin of the penis is devoid of hair except near the pubis.

Superficial (Colles') Fascia. Thin, without fat, and continuous with the dartos of the scrotum, it passes over the superficial perineal muscles to join the superficial perineal fascia. At the base of the penis it receives additional fibers which extend from the dorsal aspect of the penis to the pubic symphysis, thus forming the *fundiform ligament.*

Deep (Buck's) Fascia. This fibrous tubular sheath envelops the erectile tissue masses that comprise the substance of the penis. It extends from the neck of the penis to the ends of the erectile bodies. Where it is continuous with the deep perineal fascia. A triangular fibrous band, the *suspensory ligament of the penis,* extends between the symphysis to the deep fascia at the root of the penis. The substance of the penis consists of masses of erectile tissue. Each tissue mass is enveloped by a fibroelastic coat, the *tunica albuginea.* It forms a septum where the corpora cavernosa are fused.

The penis is divided into three parts:

Root. The part of the penis located in superficial perineal space consists of three masses of erectile tissue: two lateral *crura* and the median *bulb* of the penis. Each crus penis is attached to its adjacent pubic arch and deep perineal fascia and is covered by an ischiocavernosus muscle. The bulb of the penis is also adherent to the deep perineal membrane and is covered by the bulbospongiosus muscle.

Body. The free part of the penis consists of the paired corpora cavernosa and a single corpus spongiosum. Each *corpus cavernosum* is a continuation of the crus, and both are fused together and end bluntly. The *corpus spongiosum* is a continuation of the bulb which lies in the groove along the undersurface of the corpora.

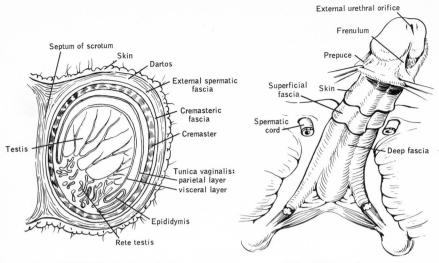

86-1   SCROTUM (longitudinal section)

Septum of scrotum
Skin
Dartos
External spermatic fascia
Cremasteric fascia
Cremaster
Testis
Tunica vaginalis:
parietal layer
visceral layer
Epididymis
Rete testis

86-2   PENIS (muscles removed)

External urethral orifice
Frenulum
Prepuce
Superficial fascia
Skin
Spermatic cord
Deep fascia

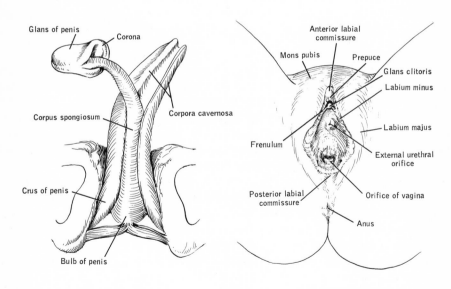

86-3   PENIS (deep dissection)

Glans of penis
Corona
Corpus spongiosum
Corpora cavernosa
Crus of penis
Bulb of penis

86-4   FEMALE EXTERNAL GENITALIA

Anterior labial commissure
Mons pubis
Prepuce
Glans clitoris
Labium minus
Labium majus
Frenulum
External urethral orifice
Posterior labial commissure
Orifice of vagina
Anus

Plate 86

Glans. The expanded end of the corpus spongiosum has a prominent margin, or *corona,* and a concavity which covers the blunted free ends of the corpora cavernosa. The constricted neck of the glans separates it from the body of the penis. The tip of the glans bears the *external urethral orifice.* The *prepuce,* a double layer of skin, extends from the neck to cover the glans, and a *frenulum,* or median fold, extends from the deep layer of the prepuce to a point just below the external orifice.

The neurovascular system of the penis is supplied by:

arteries: Three branches of the internal pudendal a. are on each side. The artery to the bulb supplies the bulb and the corpus spongiosum. The deep artery of penis supplies the corpus cavernosum. The dorsal artery of penis supplies the fascia and skin.

veins: The veins are located outside erectile tissue. The superficial dorsal v. drains the skin and fascia into the superficial external pudendal v. The dorsal v. of penis drains the region beneath deep fascia, it divides and empties into the prostatic plexus.

nerves: These are the dorsal n. of penis, from the pudendal plexus. The deep branches of the perineal nn. enter the bulb. The ilioinguinal n. innervates the skin of the root.

2. External Genital Organs of the Female (Fig. 86-4)

They consist of the mons pubis, labia majora, labia minora, clitoris, and the vestibule of the vagina.

MONS PUBIS. The median elevation in front of the symphysis pubis is produced by the underlying fatty pad. It is covered with hair after puberty.

LABIA MAJORA. This pair of elongated folds extends back from the mons pubis and is separated by the *median pudendal cleft.* The folds are united by an *anterior commissure* at the mons and by the *posterior commissure* in front of the anus. The inner surfaces are smooth and hairless; the outer surfaces are neither.

LABIA MINORA. A pair of thin folds is located on either side of the vagina. Posteriorly in the virgin the folds join a slight transverse ridge of skin, the *frenulum of the labia.* Anteriorly each of the folds divides. The lateral pair forms a cover over the glans clitoris, the *prepuce of the clitoris.* The medial pair unite beneath the clitoris, forming the *frenulum of the clitoris.*

CLITORIS. The female homologue of the penis consists of erectile tissue but is not traversed by a urethra. The clitoris is located behind the anterior commissure

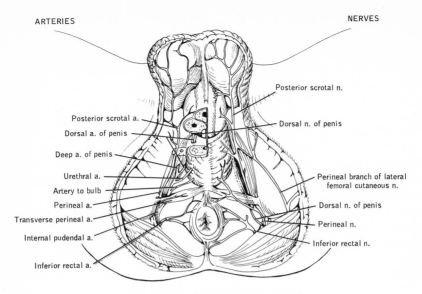

Posterior scrotal n.

Posterior scrotal a.

Dorsal a. of penis

Dorsal n. of penis

Deep a. of penis

Urethral a.

Artery to bulb

Perineal a.

Transverse perineal a.

Internal pudendal a.

Inferior rectal a.

Perineal branch of lateral
femoral cutaneous n.

Dorsal n. of penis

Perineal n.

Inferior rectal n.

87-1   MALE PERINEUM: BLOOD AND NERVE SUPPLY

ARTERIES   NERVES

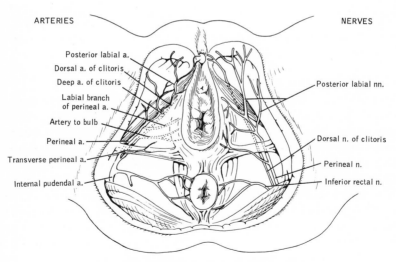

Posterior labial a.

Dorsal a. of clitoris

Deep a. of clitoris

Labial branch
of perineal a.

Artery to bulb

Perineal a.

Transverse perineal a.

Internal pudendal a.

Posterior labial nn.

Dorsal n. of clitoris

Perineal n.

Inferior rectal n.

87-2   FEMALE PERINEUM: BLOOD AND NERVE SUPPLY

Plate 87

of the labia majora and consists of the same components as the penis. Thus, two *crura* of the clitoris are present which continue forward as the *corpora cavernosa*. These form the *body* of the clitoris, the free end of which bears a small rounded elevation, the *glans clitoris*. The *bulb* of the vestibule corresponds to the bulb and corpus spongiosum of the penis in the male. It consists of paired elongated masses of erectile tissue located beneath the bulbospongiosus muscle on the sides of the vaginal opening. They unite in front to form a thin strand that extends along the lower surface of the body of the clitoris to the glans.

VESTIBULE OF THE VAGINA. This cleft between the labia minora, anteriorly continuous with the external urethral orifice, is continuous behind with the vaginal orifice and the shallow vestibular fossa.

Greater Vestibular Glands. They lie on both sides of the lowest part of the vagina, enclosed by the bulbospongiosus muscle. The duct opens into the groove between the hymen and the labium minus.

The neurovascular system of the female external genitalia is supplied by:

arteries: The anterior labial branches of the external pudendal aa. and posterior labial branches of the internal pudendal aa. supply the labia majora and minora. The deep aa. of the clitoris supply the crura and corpora cavernosa of the clitoris. The dorsal aa. of the clitoris supply the glans clitoris. The artery to the bulb of the vestibule supplies the bulb of the vestibule and the greater vestibular gland.

nerves: Ilioinguinal n. to the labia; dorsal n. of the clitoris; uterovaginal plexus to the bulb of the vestibule.

3. Superficial Perineal Arteries and Veins

These vessels supply the external genitalia. They reach the perineal region from the pelvis via the pudendal canal.

Pudendal Canal. This tunnel in the substance of the obturator fascia courses from the lesser sciatic foramen, along the side wall of the ischiorectal fossa to terminate in the deep perineal space at the side of the pubic arch.

INTERNAL PUDENDAL A. (Figs. 87-1, 87-2). One of the two terminal branches of the anterior division of the internal iliac a. passes into the pudendal canal. It courses forward in the side wall of the ischiorectal fossa to enter the deep perineal pouch. It pierces the deep perineal fascia and terminates by dividing into the deep and dorsal aa. of the penis (clitoris). Its branches are shown in Table 74, in their order of origin:

Table 74

Branch	*Course*
Muscular branches................	To pelvic and gluteal mm.
Inferior rectal a..................	To gluteus maximus, levator ani, and external sphincter mm.
Perineal a........................	To the superficial perineal mm.
Posterior scrotal (labial) aa.......	To the skin and dartos of the scrotum
Transverse perineal a............	Anastomoses with opposite artery
Artery to bulb of penis............	To bulb and bulbourethral gland
Artery to bulb of vestibule.........	To bulb of vestibule and greater vestibular gland
Urethral a.......................	Enters corpus spongiosum; to gland penis
Deep a. of penis (clitoris)..........	Enters substance of corpus cavernosum
Dorsal a. of penis (clitoris).........	Pierces urogenital diaphragm and descends on dorsum to glans

The veins are venae comitantes of the arteries.

4. Superficial Perineal Nerves

PUDENDAL N. (Figs. 87-1, 87-2). One of the two terminal branches of the sacral plexus enters the pudendal canal and divides into three branches:

Inferior Rectal N. Passing through the ischiorectal fat pad, it divides to supply the levator ani and external sphincter muscles and the skin around the anus.

Perineal N. It passes into the superficial perineal space, supplies its muscles, and divides into the *posterior scrotal (labial) nn.* which supply the dartos (labia majora) and skin.

Dorsal N. of the Penis (Clitoris). Passing into the deep perineal space, it supplies and pierces the urogenital diaphragm. It emerges on the dorsum of the penis (clitoris), lateral to its artery, and provides branches to the corpus cavernosum and the glans.

THE LOWER EXTREMITY

The external borders of the pelvis and their associated ligaments form the line of demarcation between the trunk and the lower extremity. The lower extremity will be considered in terms of the following regions.

Table 75

Thigh	Leg	Foot
Front of thigh Medial side of thigh Gluteal region Back of thigh Popliteal fossa	Front of leg (and dorsum of foot) Lateral side of leg Back of leg	Sole

THIGH

The thigh extends from the hip to the knee. It has one bone, the femur, whose proximal end articulates with the hip bone at the hip joint. The distal end of the femur articulates with the patella (knee cap) and the proximal end of the tibia at the knee joint. The lower part of the back of the thigh is called the ham, and the depression on the back of the knee is the popliteal fossa.

FRONT OF THIGH

1. Fascia   *3. Femoral triangle*

2. Muscles   *4. Adductor canal*

The front of the thigh extends from the inguinal ligament to the knee. It consists of a group of extensor muscles and their related blood vessels and nerves.

1. Fascia

SUPERFICIAL FASCIA. The covering of the entire thigh consists of adipose and membranous layers that are continuous with the corresponding layers on the anterior abdominal wall. The membranous layer is loosely attached to the deep

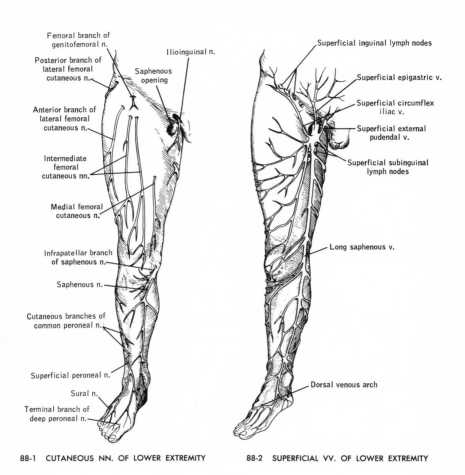

Femoral branch of
genitofemoral n.
Posterior branch of
lateral femoral
cutaneous n.
Anterior branch of
lateral femoral
cutaneous n.
Intermediate
femoral
cutaneous nn.
Medial femoral
cutaneous n.
Infrapatellar branch
of saphenous n.
Saphenous n.
Cutaneous branches of
common peroneal n.
Superficial peroneal n.
Sural n.
Terminal branch of
deep peroneal n.

Ilioinguinal n.
Saphenous
opening

Superficial inguinal lymph nodes
Superficial epigastric v.
Superficial circumflex
iliac v.
Superficial external
pudendal v.
Superficial subinguinal
lymph nodes
Long saphenous v.
Dorsal venous arch

88-1   CUTANEOUS NN. OF LOWER EXTREMITY   88-2   SUPERFICIAL VV. OF LOWER EXTREMITY

Plate 88

fascia by areolar tissue. A little below the inguinal ligament the attachment is linear and firm. The superficial fascia filling the saphenous opening in the deep fascia near the inguinal ligament is known as the *cribriform fascia*.

Cutaneous Nerves (Fig. 88-1). These six nerves can be divided into two groups, according to their site of origin:

The branches from the lumbar plexus are:

ilioinguinal n. Emerging from the abdominal wall through the superficial inguinal ring, it provides branches to the skin of the genital organs and adjacent parts of the thigh.

lumboinguinal n. The femoral branch of the genitofemoral n. pierces the deep fascia laterad to the saphenous opening and a little below the inguinal ligament to innervate the skin of the uppermost part of the thigh.

lateral femoral cutaneous n. Emerging from behind the lateral end of the inguinal ligament, it descends in the deep fascia for a short distance to divide. The anterior branch pierces the deep fascia below its point of origin, it innervates the skin of the anterolateral surface of the thigh. The posterior branch pierces the deep fascia immediately, it descends backward to innervate the skin on the posterolateral surface of the thigh.

The branches from the femoral n. are:

intermediate femoral cutaneous n. Piercing the deep fascia in the midthigh, it innervates the skin down to the patella via its medial and lateral branches.

medial femoral cutaneous n. In its initial course under the deep fascia it gives off filaments which innervate the middle third of the medial side of the thigh. At the apex of the femoral triangle it divides. The anterior branch pierces the deep fascia further down, laterad to the long saphenous v., to innervate the lower, medial side of the thigh. The posterior branch continues down to pierce the deep fascia behind the long saphenous v. near the knee. It descends to innervate the skin on the medial side of the leg.

infrapatellar branch of saphenous n. Piercing the deep fascia on the medial side of the knee, it then curves downwards and forwards to innervate the skin below the patella.

patellar plexus. This network of nerves consists of terminal branches of the medial, intermediate, and lateral femoral cutaneous nn. and the infrapatellar branch of the saphenous n. It is located in the fascia in front of the patella and the patellar ligament.

Superficial Inguinal Aa. (Fig. 89-4). Three arteries arise from the femoral a. below the inguinal ligament and supply the skin:

superficial circumflex iliac a. Piercing the deep fascia laterad to the saphenous opening, it extends to the iliac crest.

superficial epigastric a. Piercing the cribriform fascia, it crosses the midinguinal point and ascends almost to the umbilicus.

superficial external pudendal a. Piercing the cribriform fascia, it passes medially across the spermatic cord, or round ligament, to the external genitalia.

Superficial Inguinal Vv. These correspond to the arteries and terminate in the long saphenous v. just before it pierces the cribriform fascia.

long (great) saphenous v. (Fig. 88-2). This vein begins at the medial end of the dorsal venous arch of the foot and ascends in front of the medial malleolus, along the medial side of the leg and behind the medial condyles of the tibia and femur. On the thigh, it takes an anterolateral course to the saphenous opening, where, having pierced the cribriform fascia, it terminates in the femoral v. The long saphenous v. has numerous valves, communicates through the deep fascia with the deep veins, and has many unnamed tributaries, including the superficial inguinal vv.

Superficial Inguinal Lymph Nodes (Fig. 88-2)

inguinal nodes. The horizontal row of glands lies along the line of fusion of the membranous layer of superficial fascia with the deep fascia of the thigh.

subinguinal nodes. These glands are located on both sides of the upper portion of the long saphenous v.

The afferent vessels of these two groups drain the superficial parts of the lower limb, the anterior abdominal wall, the external genitalia, the perineum, and the gluteal region. The efferent vessels penetrate the cribriform fascia to terminate in the deep inguinal nodes and in the external iliac nodes.

DEEP FASCIA. The fascia lata is attached (directly or indirectly) to all the bony and ligamentous structures of the pelvis and of the knee. It is like a stocking around the thigh. The fascia is thin medially but denser over the popliteal fossa. On the lateral side of the thigh it takes the form of a wide, strong band, the *iliotibial tract,* which extends from the iliac crest to the lateral condyle of the tibia. The *saphenous opening* is an aperture in the fascia lata, a little below the medial end of the inguinal ligament. At this site various structures pierce the cribriform fascia. The *falciform margin* of the saphenous opening is the crescent, which begins at the pubic tubercle and arches laterally to end behind the long saphenous v. The medial margin is formed by the deep fascia over the pectineus muscle that slopes downwards behind the femoral vessels; it is not sharp.

Three *intermuscular septums* lateral, medial, and posterior, extend from the deep surface of the fascia lata to the linea aspera and to its prolongations on the back of the femur. These septums separate the thigh muscles into three compartments, as shown in Table 76.

Table 76

Function	Position	Nerve supply
Extensors........	Anteromedial	Femoral n.
Adductors.......	Medial	Obturator n.
Flexors..........	Posterior	Sciatic n.

The lateral one is the most well developed of these septums, from which secondary septums arise to envelop the individual muscles.

2. Muscles: Extensor Group (Figs. 89-1, 89-2)

The extensors of the thigh are innervated by the femoral n.

SARTORIUS. It descends obliquely across the front and medial sides of the thigh.

Origin: Anterior superior iliac spine.

Insertion: Upper part of the medial surface of the tibia.

Action: Flexes hip and knee joint.

QUADRICEPS FEMORIS. This muscle consists of four distinct parts having a common insertion, innervation, and action.

Insertion: Common tendon which is attached to the base of the patella and which is extended to the tibial tuberosity by means of the patellar ligament.

Action: Extension of the knee.

Nerve supply: Femoral n.

Rectus Femoris. It lies in the middle of the front of the thigh.

Origin: By two tendinous heads which unite in front of the hip joint.

Straight head: Anterior inferior iliac spine.

Reflected head: Above the brim of the acetabulum.

Action: In addition to extension of the knee, flexion of the thigh at the hip joint.

Vastus Lateralis. It is in the lateral side of the thigh.

Origin: From root of the greater trochanter down the lateral lip of the linea aspera, to the beginning of the lateral supracondylar ridge.

Vastus Medialis. It is in the medial side of the thigh.

Origin: From the intertrochanteric line down the spiral line, medial lip of the linea aspera, and upper part of the medial supracondylar line.

Vastus Intermedius

Origin: Anterior and lateral surfaces of the upper two-thirds of the femoral shaft.

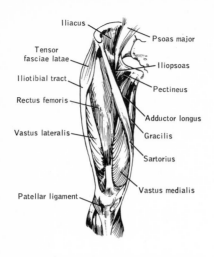

Iliacus

Psoas major

Tensor fasciae latae

Iliopsoas

Iliotibial tract

Pectineus

Rectus femoris

Vastus lateralis

Adductor longus

Gracilis

Sartorius

Patellar ligament

Vastus medialis

89-1   MUSCLES OF THIGH: SUPERFICIAL VIEW

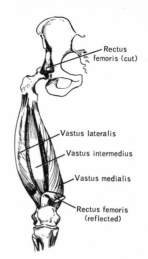

Rectus femoris (cut)

Vastus lateralis

Vastus intermedius

Vastus medialis

Rectus femoris (reflected)

89-2   MUSCLES OF THIGH: DEEP VIEW

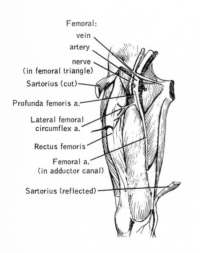

Femoral:
  vein
  artery
  nerve
  (in femoral triangle)

Sartorius (cut)

Profunda femoris a.

Lateral femoral circumflex a.

Rectus femoris

Femoral a. (in adductor canal)

Sartorius (reflected)

89-3   FEMORAL VESSELS AND NERVE

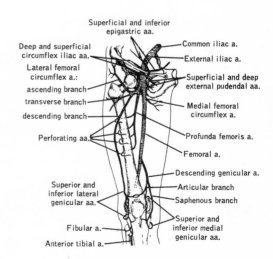

Superficial and inferior epigastric aa.

Common iliac a.

Deep and superficial circumflex iliac aa.

External iliac a.

Lateral femoral circumflex a.:

Superficial and deep external pudendal aa.

  ascending branch

  transverse branch

Medial femoral circumflex a.

  descending branch

Perforating aa.

Profunda femoris a.

Femoral a.

Descending genicular a.

Superior and inferior lateral genicular aa.

Articular branch

Saphenous branch

Superior and inferior medial genicular aa.

Fibular a.

Anterior tibial a.

89-4   ARTERIES OF THE THIGH

Plate 89

Table 77

Compartment	Contents
Lateral....................	Femoral a.
Middle....................	Femoral v.
Medial (femoral canal)......	Deep lymph glands and vessels

Articularis Genu. A distinct bundle of muscle fibers considered to belong to the vastus intermedius muscle.

Origin: Anterior surface of the lower part of the femur.

Insertion: Synovial membrane of the knee joint.

Action: Draws up the synovial membrane during extension of the knee.

Nerve supply: Branch of the nerve to the vastus intermedius muscle.

PECTINEUS. This muscle belongs to the adductor group and is sometimes innervated by a branch of the obturator n. It is included here because it is associated with the femoral triangle.

Origin: iliopectineal line.

Insertion: Line extending from the lesser trochanter to the linea aspera.

Action: Flexes and adducts the thigh.

ILIOPSOAS. See Posterior Wall of Abdomen, p. 253.

3. Femoral Triangle (Fig. 89-1)

This subfascial space in the upper third of the thigh has as its boundaries the following:

Base: inguinal ligament

Apex: where sartorius muscle crosses adductor longus muscle

Roof: fascia lata and cribriform fascia

Floor: anterior surfaces of iliopsoas, pectineus, and adductor longus muscles

The contents of the femoral triangle are the following:

FEMORAL SHEATH. This flattened, fascial funnel lies behind the cribriform fascia and the adjacent fascia lata. It extends from behind the inguinal ligament to the lower margin of the saphenous opening and fuses with the adventitial coat of the femoral vessels. The sheath is composed of a downward prolongation of the transversalis fascia, anteriorly, and of the iliac fascia posteriorly. Two vertical septums divide the interior of the sheath into three compartments, shown in Table 77.

FEMORAL CANAL. The canal lies on the pectineus muscle and is conical in shape. Its oval upper end, the *femoral ring*, faces the peritoneal cavity and is closed by a plug of extraperitoneal connective tissue, the *femoral septum*.

FEMORAL A. (Fig. 89-3). The continuation of the external iliac a. begins behind the inguinal ligament at the mid-inguinal point. It descends almost vertically and slightly backward through the femoral triangle and the adductor canal (see

Table 78

Branch	Course	Area supplied or joined
Profunda femoris a.		
Lateral femoral circumflex a.	Laterally behind rectus femoris m.	
Ascending branch........	Ascends beneath tensor fascia lata	Hip joint
Transverse branch........	Across lateral part of thigh	Gluteal muscles
Descending branch.......	Descends over lower third of thigh	Superior lateral geniculate a.
Medial femoral circumflex a.		
Superficial branch.........	Medially over pectineus m.	Cruciate anastomosis
Deep branch..............	Continuation of stem a.	
Muscular branch........	To muscles	Adductor mm.
Acetabular branch.......	Beneath transacetabular ligament	Hip joint
Ascending branch.......	To trochanteric fossa	Gluteal aa.
Transverse branch.......	Behind adductor magnus m.	Cruciate anastomosis
Perforating aa.		
First.....................	Above adductor brevis m.	Adductor magnus m.
Second...................	Through adductor brevis m.	Hamstring mm.
Third....................	Below adductor brevis m.	Hamstring mm.
Fourth...................	Termination of stem a.	Hamstring mm.

p. 299). The artery passes through the hiatus in the adductor magnus muscle at the junction of the middle and lower thirds of the thigh and becomes the popliteal a. The branches of the femoral a., which arise in the femoral triangle, are:

Superficial Inguinal A. See p. 293.

Deep External Pudendal A. Arising in the femoral sheath from the medial side of the femoral a., it pierces the sheath and courses medialward across the pectineus and adductor longus muscles beneath the deep fascia. It emerges on the medial side of the thigh and is distributed to the skin of the external genitalia.

Profunda Femoris A. (Fig. 89-4). The largest branch arises from the lateral side of the femoral a. shortly after it emerges from the femoral sheath. The artery descends and curves gradually medialwards to pass behind the femoral vessels. It leaves the femoral triangle between the pectineus and adductor longus muscles to enter the medial side of the thigh. Its branches are shown in Table 78 (see also Fig. 89-4).

FEMORAL V. This continuation of the popliteal v. accompanies the femoral a. as it ascends through the upper two-thirds of the thigh. Its tributaries are the long saphenous v. and veins corresponding to branches of the artery (except the superficial inguinal vv.).

Table 79

Muscular branches	Cutaneous branches
To pectineus m............	Medial femoral cutaneous n. (p. 293)
To sartorius m............	Intermediate femoral cutaneous n. (p. 293)
To quadriceps femoris m....	Saphenous n.

FEMORAL N. (Figs. 90-1, 90-2). This nerve originates in the abdomen and enters the thigh behind the inguinal ligament and under the iliac fascia laterad to the femoral a. It ramifies completely into its terminal branches, which are divided into the two groups shown in Table 79.

Saphenous N. The longest branch accompanies the femoral a. through the triangle and the adductor canal. In the middle of the canal it provides a branch that joins those from the obturator and medial femoral cutaneous nn. to form the *subsartorial plexus* around the vessels. Near the end of the canal the saphenous n. provides its *infrapatellar branch* and then emerges to the surface by piercing the deep fascia on the medial side of the knee between the sartorius and gracilis muscles. It descends alongside the long saphenous v. to innervate the skin on the anterior and medial sides of the leg, and finally reaches the foot.

DEEP LYMPH NODES. One to four nodes are located on the medial side of the upper portion of the femoral v.; the highest one lies in the femoral canal. Afferents drain the deep parts of the limb, the penis (or clitoris), and the superficial inguinal lymph nodes. The efferents enter the abdomen alongside the external iliac a.

4. Adductor Canal

An intermuscular, fascial canal, triangular on cross section, is located in the middle third of the medial side of the thigh and extends from the apex of the femoral triangle to the hiatus of the adductor magnus muscle. It has the following boundaries (Fig. 89-2):

Anterolateral boundary: fascial covering of vastus medialis m.

Anteromedial (roof): fascial expansion extending between vastus medialis and adductor longus and magnus mm.; covered by sartorius m.

Posterior (floor): upper two-thirds: adductor longus m.; lower third: adductor magnus m.

The contents of the adductor canal are the following:

Femoral Vessels. The femoral a. provides a branch just before it passes through the hiatus of the adductor magnus muscle. This branch, the descending genicular a., in turn divides immediately into:

articular branch. It courses through the substance of the vastus medialis muscle, and then joins the arterial plexus around the knee.

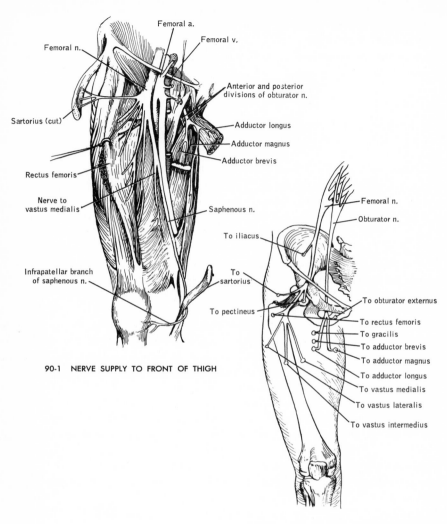

Femoral a.

Femoral v.

Femoral n.

Anterior and posterior
divisions of obturator n.

Sartorius (cut)

Adductor longus

Adductor magnus

Adductor brevis

Rectus femoris

Nerve to
vastus medialis

Saphenous n.

Femoral n.

Obturator n.

To iliacus

To
sartorius

To obturator externus

To pectineus

To rectus femoris

To gracilis

To adductor brevis

Infrapatellar branch
of saphenous n.

To adductor magnus

To adductor longus

To vastus medialis

To vastus lateralis

To vastus intermedius

90-1   NERVE SUPPLY TO FRONT OF THIGH

90-2   FEMORAL AND OBTURATOR NERVES: DISTRIBUTION

Plate 90

saphenous branch. It emerges from the canal along with the saphenous nerve and joins the medial inferior genicular a. on the medial side of the knee.

Saphenous N. See above.

Nerve to the Vastus Medialis. A branch of the femoral n. enters the canal and then passes into the medial aspect of this muscle.

MEDIAL SIDE OF THIGH

1. *Fascia*   3. *Arteries*
2. *Muscles*   4. *Veins*
           5. *Nerves*

The medial side of the thigh is that part from the medial part of the inguinal ligament to the side of the knee.

1. Fascia (see p. 301)

2. Muscles: Adductor Group (Fig. 91-1)

The adductor muscles of the thigh are innervated by the obturator n. and have a common function of adduction, flexion, and lateral rotation of the thigh. The muscles are arranged in three planes, the first of which contains the pectineus (p. 297), adductor longus, and gracilis muscles.

ADDUCTOR LONGUS. It is triangular in shape.

Origin: Body of pubis below its crest.

Insertion: Lower two-thirds of the linea aspera.

GRACILIS: This is the superficial muscle on the medial side of the thigh and knee.

Origin: Margin of the pubic arch.

Insertion: Medial surface of the tibia below the condyle and behind the sartorius muscle.

ADDUCTOR BREVIS. This muscle occupies the middle plane.

Origin: Body and inferior ramus of the pubis between the gracilis and obturator externus muscles.

Insertion: Below the lesser trochanter to the upper part of the linea aspera.

ADDUCTOR MAGNUS. This muscle shares the deepest plane with the obturator externus muscle in front of the pelvis and the neck of the femur. The ischiocondylar portion of the muscle descends vertically and is morphologically part of the hamstrings.

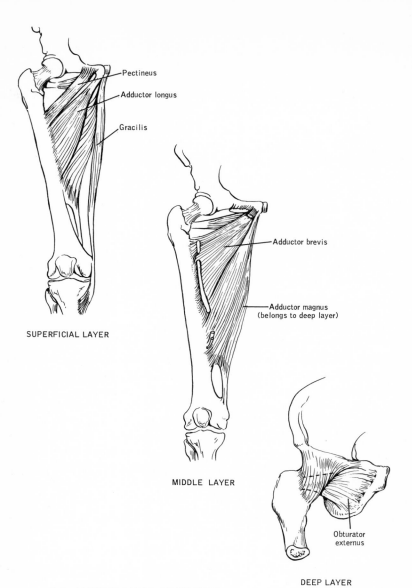

Pectineus

Adductor longus

Gracilis

SUPERFICIAL LAYER

Adductor brevis

Adductor magnus
(belongs to deep layer)

MIDDLE LAYER

Obturator
externus

DEEP LAYER

91-1   ADDUCTOR MUSCLES OF THE THIGH

Plate 91

Origin: Side of the pubic arch and ischial tuberosity.

Insertion: Extends from the medial side of the gluteal tuberosity, down the linea aspera and supracondylar ridge to the adductor tubercle on the medial epicondyle. The aponeurosis of insertion has, adjacent to the femur, four openings for perforating vessels and a large gap, the adductor hiatus, for the femoral vessels.

Action: The greater part of the muscle acts as a typical member of the adductor group; the ischiocondylar portion extends the hip.

Nerve supply: Obturator n.; a branch of the sciatic n. supplies the ischiocondylar portion.

OBTURATOR EXTERNUS. It is flat and triangular.

Origin: Medial half of the obturator membrane and adjacent edge of the obturator foramen.

Insertion: Floor of the trochanteric fossa.

Action: Rotates the thigh laterally.

Nerve supply: Posterior division of the obturator n.

3. Arteries

OBTURATOR A. A branch of the internal iliac a. accompanies the nerve through the obturator foramen and divides into its anterior and posterior terminal branches. These form an arterial circle on the obturator membrane beneath the obturator externus muscle. Both branches supply neighboring muscles. The posterior branch also provides an articular branch to the hip joint.

PROFUNDA FEMORIS A. (Fig. 89-4). Arising from the lateral side of the femoral a., it curves downward, behind it, to leave the femoral triangle by passing through its floor between the pectineus and adductor longus muscles. It descends, close to the femur, between the adductor longus and magnus muscles and terminates in the lower third of the thigh by piercing the adductor magnus muscle to supply the hamstring muscles. The terminal portion is also called the *fourth perforating a.* The branches of the profunda femoris are listed in Table 78.

Cruciate Anastomosis. This cross-shaped junction is located at the upper part of the back of the thigh. Its components are:

Horizontal arm: transverse branches of circumflex femoral aa.

Upper limb: descending branches of inferior gluteal a.

Lower limb: ascending branch of the first perforating a.

4. Veins

OBTURATOR V. The veins that accompany the branches of the obturator a. unite. This vein pierces the obturator membrane, enters the pelvis, and terminates in the internal iliac v.

PROFUNDA FEMORIS V. The fourth perforating v. runs with its corresponding artery to join the femoral v. at a point lower than the origin of the artery. Its tributaries correspond to the branches of the profunda femoris a. The circumflex branches enter the femoral v. directly.

5. Nerves

OBTURATOR N. (Fig. 90-2). In the abdomen, the lumbar plexus provides a branch which enters the thigh through the obturator foramen. It divides into two parts which are separated by the adductor brevis muscle:

Anterior Division. It passes across the obturator externus and the adductor brevis muscles, behind the pectineus and adductor longus muscles, to terminate in the subsartorial plexus. It provides:

articular branches. Pass through the acetabular notch to the hip joint.

muscular branches. Innervate the gracilis and adductor longus and brevis muscles.

Posterior Division. This portion of the obturator n. supplies and pierces the obturator externus muscle, passes behind the adductor brevis muscle, and reaches the anterior surface of the adductor magnus muscle, where it terminates as:

muscular branch. Innervates the adductor magnus muscle.

articular branch. Passes to the knee joint.

GLUTEAL REGION

1. Fascia	*3. Deep arteries*
2. Muscles	*4. Deep nerves*

The gluteal region, or buttock, lies over the posterior surface of the hip bone.

1. Fascia

SUPERFICIAL. The superficial fascia of the gluteal region is heavily laden with fat. It is tough and stringy over the ischial tuberosity and contains vessels and nerves.

Unnamed Arteries and Veins. These are terminal branches and tributaries of deep vessels.

Cutaneous Nerves

posterior branch of lateral femoral cutaneous n. This nerve pierces the deep fascia to supply the skin over the greater trochanter and the adjacent parts of the thigh and gluteal region.

lateral cutaneous branch of subcostal n. Piercing the deep fascia immediately above the tubercle of the iliac crest, it descends across the gluteal region to the greater trochanter.

lateral cutaneous branch of iliohypogastric n. Appearing behind the tubercle, it courses parallel to the preceding branch.

superior cluneal nn. These are branches from the very small ventral rami of Ln 1 to 3. They approach the surface a little above the highest point of the iliac crest and descend almost to the gluteal fold.

middle cluneal nn. These are branches from the small ventral rami of Sn 1 to 3. They pierce the gluteus maximus muscle and approach the surface between the posterior superior iliac spine and the coccyx to ramify over the medial surface of the gluteal region.

perforating cutaneous nn. Originating in the pelvis from the very fine rami of Sn 2 and 3, they perforate the sacrotuberous ligament, gluteus maximus muscle, and deep fascia midway between the coccyx and the ischial tuberosity. The course is laterad to the lower medial side of the gluteal region.

inferior cluneal nn. These are gluteal branches of the posterior femoral cutaneous n. They pierce the deep fascia at the middle third of the lower border of the gluteal region.

DEEP. The dense anterior portion of the fascia lies over the anterior part of the gluteus medius muscle. It splits to enclose the gluteus maximus muscle and sends septums into the muscle which divide it into coarse bundles.

2. Muscles (Figs. 92-1, 92-2)

GLUTEUS MAXIMUS. It is the heaviest muscle in the body.

Origin: Upper part of the ilium behind the posterior gluteal line, the dorsum of the sacrum and coccyx, the posterior surface of the sacrotuberous ligament, and from the deep fascia overlying the gluteus medius.

Insertion: Lower fourth by fleshy fibers into the gluteal tuberosity, upper three-fourths by an aponeurosis into the iliotibial tract.

Action: Extends and abducts the thigh, and rotates it laterally.

Nerve supply: Inferior gluteal n.

GLUTEUS MEDIUS. Its posterior portion lies deep to the gluteus maximus muscle.

Origin: Area of the gluteal surface of the ilium bounded by the anterior and posterior gluteal line and the iliac crest.

Insertion: Lateral surface of the greater trochanter.

Action: Abducts the thigh.

Nerve supply: Superior gluteal n.

GLUTEUS MINIMUS. It lies deep to the gluteus medius muscle.

Origin: Gluteal surface of the ilium, between the anterior and inferior gluteal lines.

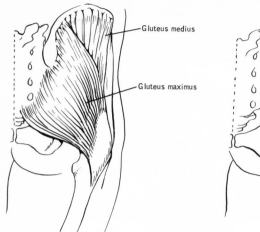

92-1   GLUTEAL REGION: SUPERFICIAL MUSCLES

Gluteus medius

Gluteus maximus

Gluteus medius (cut)

Gluteus minimus

Piriformis

Superior gemellus

Obturator internus tendon

Inferior gemellus

Quadratus femoris

92-2   GLUTEAL REGION: DEEP MUSCLES

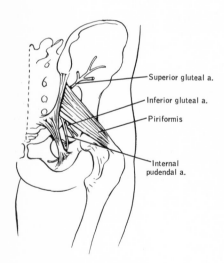

Superior gluteal a.

Inferior gluteal a.

Piriformis

Internal pudendal a.

92-3   GLUTEAL REGION: ARTERIES

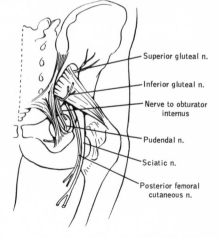

Superior gluteal n.

Inferior gluteal n.

Nerve to obturator internus

Pudendal n.

Sciatic n.

Posterior femoral cutaneous n.

92-4   GLUTEAL REGION: NERVES

Plate 92

Insertion: Anterior surface of the greater trochanter.

Action: Abducts the thigh.

Nerve supply: Superior gluteal n.

OBTURATOR INTERNUS. It emerges from the pelvis through the lesser sciatic foramen.

Origin: Pelvic surface of the obturator membrane and neighboring bones.

Insertion: Medial surface of the greater trochanter.

Action: Abductor of flexed thigh; lateral rotator of extended thigh.

Nerve supply: Nerve to obturator internus muscle.

GEMELLUS SUPERIOR. It lies above the obturator internus muscle.

Origin: Ischial spine.

Insertion: Tendon of the obturator internus muscle.

Action: Lateral rotator of the thigh.

Nerve supply: Nerve to obturator internus muscle.

GEMELLUS INFERIOR. It lies below the obturator internus muscle.

Origin: Ischial tuberosity.

Insertion: Tendon of the obturator internus muscle.

Action: Lateral rotator of thigh.

Nerve supply: Nerve to quadratus femoris muscle.

QUADRATUS FEMORIS. It is quadrilateral and covers the obturator externus muscle.

Origin: Lateral margin of ischial tuberosity.

Insertion: Trochanteric crest, quadrate tubercle, and a line extending downward from the tubercle.

Action: Adductor and lateral rotator of the thigh.

Nerve supply: Nerve to quadratus femoris muscle.

TENSOR FASCIAE LATAE

Origin: Anterior part of outer lip of iliac crest.

Insertion: Iliotibial tract.

Action: Assists in flexion, abduction and medial rotation of thigh.

Nerve supply: Superior gluteal n.

3. Deep Arteries (Fig. 92-3)

These deep arteries, veins, and nerves emerge from the pelvis through the greater sciatic foramen and enter the glutal region above or below the piriformis muscle.

SUPERIOR GLUTEAL A. A branch of the internal iliac a. appears in the gluteal region accompanied by its corresponding vein and divides immediately into two divisions:

Superficial Division. This division ramifies immediately and supplies the gluteus maximus muscle.

Deep Division. This division runs forward between the gluteus medius and minimus muscles and divides into superior and inferior branches which accompany their corresponding nerves.

INFERIOR GLUTEAL A. This branch of the internal iliac a. passes through the gluteal region into the thigh.

muscular branches. To the gluteus maximus and other neighboring muscles.

cutaneous branches. To the skin of the buttock and back of the thigh.

anastomotic branches. Joins the cruciate anastomosis and supplies the capsule of the hip joint.

coccygeal branches. Pierce the sacrotuberous ligament to supply the skin over the coccyx.

companion artery of sciatic n. Courses on the surface of the nerve and then enters it.

INTERNAL PUDENDAL A. A branch of the internal iliac a., it emerges inferior to the piriformis muscle between the nerve to the obturator internus muscle and the pudendal nerve. It accompanies the pudendal nerve into the perineum.

4. Deep Nerves (Fig. 92-4)

SUPERIOR GLUTEAL N. Arising from the sacral plexus, it enters the gluteal region above the piriformis muscle. It passes forward between the gluteus medius and minimus muscles to divide into two branches.

superior branch. Terminates the gluteus medius muscle.

inferior branch. Innervates the gluteus medius and minimus muscles and terminates in the tensor fascia lata.

INFERIOR GLUTEAL N. Another branch of the sacral plexus, it emerges into the gluteal region inferior to the piriformis muscle and ramifies immediately to innervate the gluteus maximum muscle.

SCIATIC N. A terminal branch of the sacral plexus, it enters the gluteal region inferior to the piriformis muscle and crosses the gemelli and obturator internus muscles to enter the thigh at the lower border of the quadratus femoris muscle. It usually provides no branches in the gluteal region.

POSTERIOR FEMORAL CUTANEOUS N. This branch of the sacral plexus enters the gluteal region on or at the medial side of the sciatic n. In the gluteal region it provides:

gluteal branch. Innervates the skin of the buttocks.

perineal branch. Passes medially on the back of the hamstring muscles to innervate the skin of the scrotum or labium majus.

NERVE TO QUADRATUS FEMORIS. This branch of the sacral plexus also enters the gluteal region below the piriformis muscle, deep to the tendon of the obturator internus and gemelli muscles. It provides branches to the inferior gemellus and hip joint, and terminates in the deep surface of the quadratus femoris muscle.

NERVE TO OBTURATOR INTERNUS. This branch of the sacral plexus emerges below the piriformis muscle medial to the sciatic n., crosses the root of the ischial spine, and provides a branch to innervate the superior gemellus muscle. It leaves the gluteal region to reenter the pelvis through the lesser sciatic foramen to innervate the obturator internus muscle.

PUDENDAL N. This terminal branch of the sacral plexus is the most medial structure to emerge below the piriformis muscle. It passes over the root of the ischial spine, enters the pelvis through the lesser sciatic foramen, and then runs through the pudendal canal which leads it to the perineum.

BACK OF THIGH

1. *Fascia*	3. *Deep arteries*
2. *Muscles*	4. *Deep nerves*

The back of the thigh extends from the gluteal fold to the upper border of the popliteal fossa (p. 311).

1. Fascia

SUPERFICIAL. The superficial fascia of the back of the thigh has no unusual characteristics. It contains:

Cutaneous Nn. They are branches of the medial, lateral, and posterior femoral cutaneous nn.

Cutaneous Blood Vessels. They have come to the surface from deep vessels, after piercing the deep fascia.

DEEP. The deep fascia of the back of the thigh is thin but strong.

2. Muscles: Flexor Group (Hamstrings) (Fig. 93-1)

The flexor muscles of the thigh are innervated by the sciatic n.

BICEPS FEMORIS. It is the most laterally situated muscle of this group.

Origin:

Long head: By a common tendon together with the semitendinosus muscle, from the upper medial part of the ischial tuberosity.

Short head: From the linea aspera and the lateral supracondylar line.

Insertion: Head of the fibula.

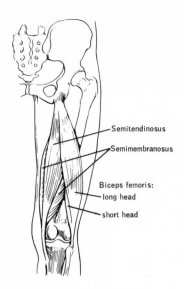

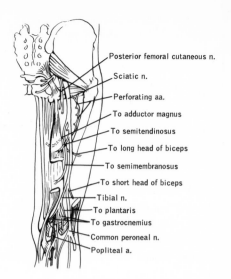

93-1   BACK OF THIGH: MUSCLES

- Semitendinosus
- Semimembranosus
- Biceps femoris:
  - long head
  - short head

93-2   BACK OF THIGH: ARTERIES AND NERVES

- Posterior femoral cutaneous n.
- Sciatic n.
- Perforating aa.
- To adductor magnus
- To semitendinosus
- To long head of biceps
- To semimembranosus
- To short head of biceps
- Tibial n.
- To plantaris
- To gastrocnemius
- Common peroneal n.
- Popliteal a.

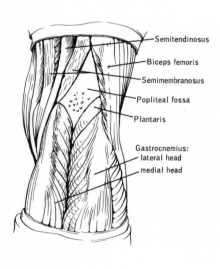

93-3   POPLITEAL FOSSA: BOUNDARIES

- Semitendinosus
- Biceps femoris
- Semimembranosus
- Popliteal fossa
- Plantaris
- Gastrocnemius:
  - lateral head
  - medial head

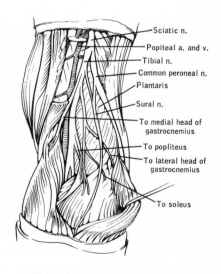

93-4   POPLITEAL FOSSA: CONTENTS

- Sciatic n.
- Popiteal a. and v.
- Tibial n.
- Common peroneal n.
- Plantaris
- Sural n.
- To medial head of gastrocnemius
- To popliteus
- To lateral head of gastrocnemius
- To soleus

Plate 93

Action: Flexor and lateral rotator of the leg.

SEMITENDINOSUS. It is fusiform in shape.

Origin: In common with long head of the biceps from the ischial tuberosity.

Insertion: Medial surface of the tibia, below the insertion of the sartorius and gracilis muscles.

Action: Flexor and medial rotator of the leg extends the thigh.

SEMIMEMBRANOSUS. It lies deep to the semitendinosus muscle.

Origin: Upper lateral part of the ischial tuberosity.

Insertion: Groove on the back of the medial tibial condyle; as the oblique posterior ligament into the capsule of the knee joint (p. 343); the fascia covering the popliteus muscle.

Action: Flexor and lateral rotator of the leg.

3. Deep Arteries (Fig. 93-2)

perforating and muscular branches of profunda femoris a. (p. 298).
muscular branches of the popliteal a. (p. 312).

4. Deep Nerves (Fig. 93-2)

SCIATIC N. Entering the thigh at the lower border of the quadratus femoris muscle from the gluteal region (p. 266) it runs down the midline of the thigh on the posterior surface of the adductor magnus muscle and terminates by dividing, near the upper apex of the popliteal fossa, into the medial and lateral popliteal nn. Other branches supply the hamstrings and the ischial part of the adductor magnus muscle.

POSTERIOR FEMORAL CUTANEOUS N. Emerging from under the gluteus maximus muscle, it descends in the midline of the thigh beneath the deep fascia on the long head of the biceps. In the middle of the popliteal fossa it pierces the deep fascia and continues down to the middle of the leg in the superficial fascia, accompanied by the short saphenous v. Its branches in the gluteal region were described (p. 308). Its branches in the thigh are cutaneous and they supply the skin on the back and medial side of the thigh. Its branches in the leg are also cutaneous and they supply the skin of the upper half of the back of the leg.

POPLITEAL FOSSA

> *1. Fascia*   *2. Boundaries*
> *3. Contents*

The popliteal fossa is the diamond-shaped space behind the lower part of the femur, the knee joint, and the upper part of the tibia.

1. Fascia

SUPERFICIAL. The superficial fascia of the popliteal fossa contains the terminal part of the posterior femoral cutaneous n., posterior branch of the medial femoral cutaneous n., sural communicating n., and short saphenous v.

DEEP. The deep fascia of the popliteal fossa is thin and strong.

2. Boundaries (Fig. 93-3)

The popliteal fossa is diamond-shaped; it has four sides, a roof, and a floor, as follows:

Superior lateral boundary: biceps femoris muscle
Superomedial boundary: semitendinosus, semimembranosus muscle
Inferior lateral boundary: lateral head of gastrocnemius and plantaris muscle
Inferior medial boundary: medial head of gastrocnemius muscle
Floor: popliteal surface of femur, capsule of knee, popliteus muscle and its fascia
Roof: deep fascia

3. Contents (Fig. 93-4)

POPLITEAL A. This continuation of the femoral a. begins at the hiatus in the adductor magnus muscle and descends vertically through the popliteal fossa to terminate by dividing at the distal borders of the popliteus muscle.

Branches. In addition to the terminal branches, the popliteal a. has the following:

muscular branches. They supply the muscles on the back of the thigh and leg, and provide cutaneous branches.

articular branches. They join the circumpatellar anastomoses.

terminal branches. Anterior and posterior tibial aa.

Circumpatellar Anastomosis (Fig. 89-4). It establishes a collateral circulation that links the femoral a. with the popliteal and anterior tibial arteries.

POPLITEAL V. It is formed by the union of the venae comitantes of the anterior and posterior tibial arteries at the distal border of the popliteus muscle.

Tributaries

short saphenous v. (p. 321) *and veins corresponding to the arteries.*

TIBIAL N. A terminal branch of the sciatic n. (p. 308), it enters the fossa at its upper angle, laterad to the popliteal vessels. The nerve crosses behind the vessels to leave the fossa at its lower angle.

cutaneous branch. Sural n. (p. 321).

muscular branches. They supply the muscles on the back of the leg.

genicular branches. The superior, medial, middle, and inferior branches innervate the synovial membrane of the knee joint.

COMMON PERONEAL N. The other terminal branch of the sciatic n. enters the fossa at its upper angle and descends along the medial side of the biceps. It leaves the fossa at the lateral angle and crosses the lateral head of the gastrocnemius muscle and the head of the fibula. It winds around the neck of the fibula deep to the peroneus longus muscle and divides into its terminal branches.

Sural Communicating N. Arising just above the lateral angle of the fossa, it exits by passing out over the lateral head of the gastrocnemius muscle. It soon pierces the deep fascia and descends to join the sural n. at the middle of the back of the leg.

Lateral Sural Cutaneous N. Arising at the lateral angle of the fossa, it also passes out over the lateral head of the gastrocnemius muscle. It immediately pierces the deep fascia to supply the skin on the lateral side of the proximal part of the leg.

Genicular Branches. Superior lateral and inferior lateral branches arise in the fossa and accompany the corresponding vessels to the knee joint. The recurrent genicular branch originates outside the fossa (p. 317).

POSTERIOR FEMORAL CUTANEOUS N. See p. 265.

LEG

The leg extends from the knee joint to the angle joint. The calf represents the fleshy part at the back of the leg. The bones of the leg are the tibia and the fibula. The muscles, attached to the fibula, are called peroneal muscles. Both bones articulate with each other at their proximal and distal ends, forming two tibiofibular joints. The distal ends of the tibia and fibula also articulate with the talus to form the ankle joint. The upper surface of the foot is called the dorsum.

FRONT OF LEG AND DORSUM OF FOOT

1. Fascia	*3. Deep arteries*
2. Muscles	*4. Deep nerves*

This region extends from the knee to the tips of the digits.

1. Fascia

SUPERFICIAL. The superficial fascia of the front of the leg and the dorsum of the foot contains some fat, vessels, and nerves.

Superficial Veins

dorsal digital vv. Two veins are present on each side of the dorsum of every toe. The veins from adjacent sides of two toes unite to form the dorsal metatarsal vv., which terminate in the *dorsal venous arch* that lies across the shafts of the metatarsals.

long saphenous v. The lateral dorsal digital v. of the fifth toe unites with the lateral end of the dorsal arch.

Cutaneous Nerves

infrapatellar branch of saphenous n. It supplies the skin on the uppermost part of the front of the leg.

lateral sural cutaneous n. It supplies the skin on the middle third of the front of the leg.

cutaneous branches of superficial peroneal n. They innervate the lower third of the leg, the dorsum and medial side of the foot, and the first digit and contiguous sides of the second to fifth digits.

terminal branch of deep peroneal n. It innervates contiguous sides of the first and second digits.

sural n. It courses along the lateral side of the foot and supplies the lateral side of the fifth toe.

DEEP FASCIA. The downward continuation of the fascia lata envelops the leg. It is attached to all the bony structures around the knee and fuses with the periosteum of the subcutaneous surface of the tibia and fibula. Intramuscular septums from the deep fascia serve to subdivide the leg into three compartments (Fig. 94-1), as shown in Table 80.

The *anterior intermuscular septum* is attached to the anterior border of the fibula and separates the anterior and lateral compartments. The *posterior intermuscular septum* is attached to the posterior border of the fibula and separates the lateral and posterior compartments. The latter is subdivided by a transverse septum into superficial and deep parts.

The deep fascia above the ankle and on the dorsum of the foot is thickened by transverse fibers to form bands, or retinacula. These act as pulleys for the deep tendons and maintain their position during muscle contraction. The two retinacula are:

Superior Extensor Retinaculum. These fibers are attached to the anterior borders of the tibia and fibula just above the ankle joint. The band bridges all the anterior compartment muscles of the leg. The tibialis anterior tendon is enclosed in its own synovial sheath and is separated from the other tendons by a septum.

Inferior Extensor Retinaculum. The stem of this Y-shaped band is attached to the anterior part of the calcaneus. The upper limb is attached to the medial malleolus, and the lower limb curves around the medial side of the foot to blend with the deep fascia of the sole. The tendons, enclosed in their synovial sheaths, pass beneath this retinaculum in three tunnels. They contain, from lateral to medial, (1) the extensor digitorum longus and peroneus tertius muscles, (2) the extensor hallucis longus muscle, and (3) the tibialis anterior muscle.

Table 80

Compartment	Nerve supply
Anterior..................	Deep peroneal n.
Lateral (peroneal).........	Superficial peroneal n.
Posterior.................	Tibial n.

2. Muscles (Fig. 94-2)

The muscles of the leg are innervated by the tibial n.

TIBIALIS ANTERIOR. It is just laterad to the tibia.

Origin: Upper two-thirds of lateral surface of the tibia and interosseous membrane.

Insertion: First cuneiform and first metatarsal bones.

Action: Dorsiflexion and supination.

EXTENSOR DIGITORUM LONGUS. It lies on the lateral side of the leg.

Origin: Lateral tibial condyle, upper three-fourths of the fibula and adjacent interosseous membrane.

Insertion: Middle and distal phalanges of the lateral four digits.

Action: Extension of toes and dorsiflexion of the foot.

PERONEUS TERTIUS. It is continuous at its origin with the extensor digitorum longus and may be considered as part of this muscle.

Origin: Distal third of anterior surface of the fibula.

Insertion: Dorsum of base of fifth metatarsal.

Action: Eversion and dorsiflexion of the foot.

EXTENSOR HALLUCIS LONGUS. It reaches the surface in the lower half of the leg.

Origin: Middle half of the anterior surface of the fibula.

Insertion: Dorsum of base of distal phalanx of the first digit.

Action: Extension of the first digit and dorsiflexion of the foot.

EXTENSOR DIGITORUM BREVIS. Lying on the lateral part of the dorsum of the foot, it divides into four segments; the medialmost may be considered a separate muscle, the *extensor hallucis brevis*.

Origin: Stem of inferior extensor retinaculum and calcaneus.

Insertion: Tendon of extensor hallucis brevis muscle; base of the proximal phalanx of first digit; adjacent three tendons; and extensor expansion of second, third, and fourth digits.

Action: Extends first metatarsophalangeal joint, and helps extend the metatarsophalangeal and interphalangeal joints of second, third, and fourth digits.

Extensor Expansions (see Fig. 43-3). The tendons of the long and short extensors on the dorsum of the proximal phalanx form an expansion which also receives the

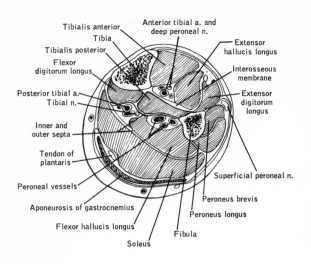

94-1   CROSS SECTION OF LEG

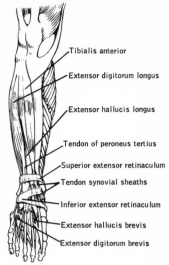

94-2   FRONT OF LEG: MUSCLES

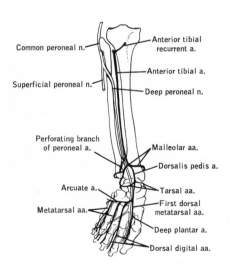

94-3   FRONT OF LEG: ARTERIES AND NERVES

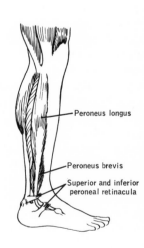

94-4   PERONEAL MUSCLES

Plate 94

insertions of the tendons of the lumbricals and the interossei at the sides. At the distal end of the phalanx, the expansion splits into three parts: the central part inserts into the base of the middle phalanx; the two collateral parts unite and insert into the base of the terminal phalanx.

Synovial Sheaths

sheath of tibialis anterior. Extends from the upper edge of the superior retinaculum to the tendinous insertion.

sheath of extensor hallucis longus. Commences between the retinacula and extends to a point above the middle of the shaft of the first metatarsal.

sheath of extensor digitorum longus and peroneus tertius. Extends from the lower edge of the superior retinaculum to a little below the inferior retinaculum.

3. Deep Arteries (Fig. 94-3)

ANTERIOR TIBIAL A. A terminal branch of the popliteal a., it arises in the back of the leg at the lower border of the popliteus muscle. It passes over the proximal border of the interosseous membrane medial to the neck of the fibula and enters the anterior compartment of the leg. It descends vertically, passes deep to the superior extensor retinaculum, reaches the ankle joint midway between the malleoli, and continues onto the foot as the dorsalis pedis a. Two venae comitantes accompany it.

Branches. See Table 81.

DORSALIS PEDIS A. A continuation of the anterior tibial a., it descends on the dorsum of the foot to the proximal end of the first intermetatarsal space, where it terminates by dividing into the first dorsal metatarsal and deep plantar aa.

Branches. See Table 81.

PERFORATING BRANCH OF THE PERONEAL A. This branch arises in the back of the leg and pierces the interosseous membrane near its distal end to enter the anterior compartment. It descends behind the superior retinaculum and anastomoses with the lateral malleolar and tarsal aa. It establishes a collateral circulation between the posterior and anterior tibial aa.

4. Deep Nerves (Fig. 94-3)

COMMON PERONEAL N. This nerve becomes superficial behind the head of the fibula and winds around the lateral side of the neck of the fibula deep to the peroneus longus muscle.

recurrent genicular n. To the knee joint.

terminal branches. Deep peroneal and superficial peroneal (p. 319) nn.

Table 81

Branches	Course	Area supplied or artery joined
Anterior tibial a.		
Muscular branches.........	At irregular intervals	Muscles of anterior compartment
Circumflex fibular a........	Around neck of fibula	Lateral inferior genicular a.
Anterior tibial recurrent a...	Pierces tibialis anterior m.	Genicular branch of popliteal a.
Medial and lateral malleolar aa.	Medial and lateral across ankle	Knee joint and adjacent skin
Dorsalis pedis a.		
Medial and lateral tarsal aa.	Medial and lateral across foot	Tarsal joints
Arcuate a.................	Across base of metatarsals	Lateral tarsal a.
Second–fourth dorsal metatarsal aa..........	Between metatarsal aa.	
Anterior perforating a...	Via proximal intermetatarsal space	Same branch of plantar metatarsal a.
Posterior perforating a.	Via distal intermetatarsal space	Same branch of plantar metatarsal a.
Dorsal digital aa.......	Between digits	Adjacent sides of digits
First dorsal metatarsal a....	In first intermetatarsal space	
Digital aa................	On adjacent sides of digits	Adjacent sides of first and second digits
Medial digital a...........	Over first metatarsal bone	Medial side of first digit
Deep plantar a............	Into sole of foot	Plantar arch

DEEP PERONEAL N. This nerve enters the anterior compartment by piercing the anterior intermuscular septum and the extensor digitorum longus muscle. It meets and follows the anterior tibial a. to the ankle joint and terminates by dividing between the malleoli.

muscular branches. To the muscles of the anterior compartment.

articular branches. To the ankle joint.

medial terminal branch. Continues down to the first intermetatarsal space, where it divides to supply the adjacent sides of the first and second digits. It provides articular branches to the tarsometatarsal and metatarsophalangeal joints of the first digit.

lateral terminal branch. Passes laterally to terminate on the dorsum of the foot as a ganglion-like mass. It innervates the extensor digitorum brevis muscle and the adjacent tarsal joints.

LATERAL SIDE OF LEG

1. Peroneal retinacula   *2. Peroneal muscles*

3. Deep nerve

The lateral side of the leg extends from the lateral side of the knee to the lateral side of the ankle.

1. Peroneal Retinacula

Superior Peroneal Retinaculum. This band is attached to the back of the lateral malleolus and the lateral surface of the calcaneus. It holds down the tendons of the peroneous longus and brevis muscles.

Inferior Peroneal Retinaculum. This band extends from the anterior part of the upper surface of the calcaneus to the lateral surface of the calcaneus. It holds down the peroneal tendons and provides a septum between the muscles.

2. Peroneal Muscles (Fig. 94-4)

The two muscles in this group are innervated by the superficial peroneal n. and serve as plantar flexors of the foot.

PERONEUS LONGUS. It is the more superficial of the two muscles.

Origin: Upper two-thirds of the lateral surface of the fibula, intermuscular septums, and deep fascia.

Its tendon passes behind the lateral malleolus, along the lateral surface of the calcaneus to the base of the fifth metatarsal. It enters the groove on the plantar surface of the cuboid bone and courses obliquely.

Insertion: Lateral side of the base of the first metatarsal and adjoining part of the medial cuneiform.

PERONEUS BREVIS. It lies deep to the peroneus longus muscle.

Origin: Distal two-thirds of the lateral surface of the fibula and intermuscular septums.

Its tendon also passes behind the lateral malleolus and forward over the lateral surface of the calcaneus.

Insertion: Tuberosity of the fifth metatarsal.

Synovial Sheath. This tube begins somewhat above the lateral malleolus and jointly encloses both the peroneal tendons. The sheath divides between the peroneal retinacula, and each of the tendons is individually enveloped as far as its insertion.

3. Deep Nerve

SUPERFICIAL PERONEAL N. (Fig. 94-3). A terminal branch of the common peroneal n., it originates on the lateral side of the neck of the fibula and descends through the substance of the peroneus longus muscle to the upper end of the peroneus brevis muscle, innervating both muscles. It passes obliquely over the anterior border of the brevis and descends between this muscle and the anterior intermuscular septum directly under the deep fascia. It pierces the fascia at the distal third of the leg and divides immediately into its lateral and medial terminal branches.

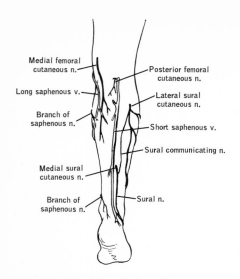

Medial femoral cutaneous n.

Posterior femoral cutaneous n.

Long saphenous v.

Lateral sural cutaneous n.

Branch of saphenous n.

Short saphenous v.

Sural communicating n.

Medial sural cutaneous n.

Branch of saphenous n.

Sural n.

95-1   BACK OF LEG: CUTANEOUS VEINS AND NERVES

Gastrocnemius (medial head)

Gastrocnemius (lateral head)

Tendo calcaneus

95-2   BACK OF LEG: SUPERFICIAL MUSCLE LAYER

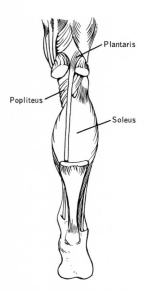

Plantaris

Popliteus

Soleus

95-3   BACK OF LEG: MIDDLE MUSCLE LAYER

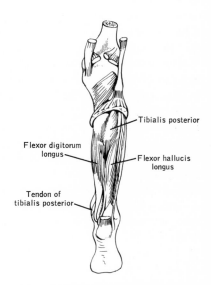

Tibialis posterior

Flexor digitorum longus

Flexor hallucis longus

Tendon of tibialis posterior

95-4   BACK OF LEG: DEEP MUSCLE LAYER

Plate 95

BACK OF LEG

1. *Fascia*   3. *Deep arteries*
2. *Muscles*   4. *Deep nerve*

The back of the leg extends from the lower border of the popliteal fossa to the back of the ankle.

1. Fascia

SUPERFICIAL FASCIA. The superficial fascia of the back of the leg contains (Fig. 95-1):

Cutaneous Vv.

long saphenous v. (p. 294)

short saphenous v. Ascends along the midline of the back of the leg to pierce the fascia over the popliteal fossa and terminate in the popliteal v.

Cutaneous Nerves

sural communicating n. See p. 313.

lateral sural cutaneous n. See p. 313.

sural n. Arising in the middle of the popliteal fossa, it descends under the deep fascia in the midline between the heads of the gastrocnemius muscle. It pierces the fascia in the middle of the leg and descends alongside the short saphenous v., around the lateral malleolus, and along the lateral side of the foot and fifth digit to innervate the leg, the lateral side of the foot, and the fifth toe.

posterior femoral cutaneous n. It pierces the popliteal fascia to innervate the skin of the upper half of the back of the leg.

posterior branch of medial femoral cutaneous n. Extending down from the thigh, it pierces the deep fascia somewhat above the knee and descends along the medial side of the back of the leg to innervate the upper third of this region.

DEEP FASCIA. This is thin in the proximal part of the back of the leg and thicker in the distal portion.

Flexor Retinaculum (Fig. 94-4). This thickened fascial band on the medial side of the ankle extends from the medial malleolus to the medial tubercle of the calcaneus. It holds down the tendons, nerves, and blood vessels that pass from the back of the leg to the sole of the foot. Septums extend from the deep aspect of the retinaculum to the tibia and ankle joint to form four tunnels, which contain, from medial to lateral, the tibialis posterior tendon, the flexor digitorum longus tendon, the posterior tibial vessels and nerve, and the flexor hallucis longus tendon.

Fascial Septums (Fig. 94-1). The posterior osteofascial compartment of the leg is bounded anteriorly by the tibia, interosseous membrane, and fibula, and posteriorly

by the investing deep fascia. This compartment is further subdivided by two septums. The *outer septum* extends from the medial border of the tibia to the posterior
border of the fibula and separates the deep flexors. The *inner septum* (deep transverse fascia) covers the tibialis posterior, separates it from the deep flexors, and extends between the vertical ridge on the posterior surface of the tibia and the medial
crest of the fibula.

2. Muscles

Superficial Group (Figs. 95-2, 95-3)

The superficial group is innervated by the tibial n. and act as plantar flexors.
GASTROCNEMIUS. The gastrocnemius is a two-headed muscle.
Origin:
  Lateral head: Upper part of lateral condyle of the femur.
  Medial head: Popliteal surface of the femur above the medial condyle.
Insertion: Tendo calcaneus (a bursa intervenes at the calcaneus).
Action: Also flexes knee.
PLANTARIS. A belly with a long tendon, it lies between the gastrocnemius and
soleus muscles.
Origin: Popliteal surface of femur above the lateral condyle.
Insertion: Medial tubercle of the calcaneus.
SOLEUS. It extends beneath the gastrocnemius muscle.
Origin:
  Fibular origin: Back of the head and upper third of the shaft of the fibula.
  Tibial origin: Soleal line and its continuation along the middle third of the
medial border of the tibia.
Insertion: Tendo calcaneus.

Deep Group (Fig. 95-4)

POPLITEUS. It is thin, flat, and triangular.
Origin: Anterior part of the groove on the lateral condyle of the femur.
Insertion: Posterior surface of the tibia above the soleal line.
Action: Flexes the leg and rotates it medially.
Nerve supply: Tibial n.
FLEXOR DIGITORUM LONGUS
Origin: Middle of posterior surface of the tibia distal to the soleal line and medial
to the vertical line.
Its tendon descends behind the distal part of the tibia and runs behind and to
the lateral side of the tendon of the tibialis posterior muscle. Both tendons curve

into the sole by passing behind the medial malleolus, deep to the flexor retinaculum in a common groove but in their individual passageways.

Insertion: As four tendons into the bases of the terminal phalanges of the second to fifth digits.

Action: Flexor of the lateral four toes.

Nerve supply: Tibial n.

FLEXOR HALLUCIS LONGUS.

Origin: Lower two-thirds of the posterior surface of the fibula.

Its tendon passes behind the ankle joint, along a groove on the back of the talus beneath the sustentaculum tali, and under the flexor retinaculum to enter the sole of the foot.

Insertion: Base of the distal phalanx of the first digit.

Action: Flexion of the big toe and plantar flexion of the foot.

Nerve supply: Tibial n.

TIBIALIS POSTERIOR. It is the deepest muscle of this group.

Origin: Posterior surface of the interosseous membrane, below the soleal line and laterad to the vertical line of the tibia as far as the middle of the shaft; and the upper two-thirds of the medial surface of the fibula.

Its tendon descends in a groove around the medial malleolus and enters the sole of the foot just above the sustentaculum tali under cover of the flexor retinaculum.

Insertion: Chiefly into the tuberosity of the navicular and medial cuneiform; fibers also insert on all other tarsals (except the talus) and to the bases of the second, third, and fourth metatarsals.

Action: Inverter and plantar flexor of the foot.

Nerve supply: Tibial n.

SYNOVIAL SHEATHS

sheath of tibialis posterior. Extends from a little above the flexor retinaculum almost to the insertion.

sheath of flexor hallucis longus. Extends from a little above the flexor retinaculum to the middle of the sole. Each of the tendons is enclosed in its own digital sheath.

3. Deep Arteries (Fig. 96-1)

ANTERIOR TIBIAL A. A terminal branch of the popliteal a., it provides the *circumflex fibular a.* and the *posterior tibial recurrent a.,* and passes to the front of the leg through a gap at the proximal border of the interosseous membrane.

POSTERIOR TIBIAL A. The direct continuation of the popliteal a. under the outer septum, it passes behind the medial malleolus and under the flexor retinaculum into the sole to divide into its terminal branches.

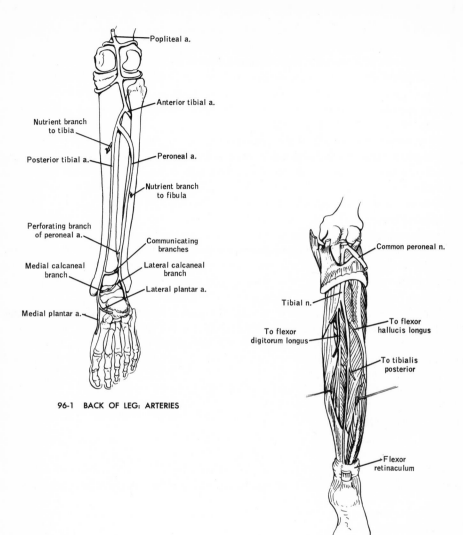

Popliteal a.

Anterior tibial a.

Nutrient branch
to tibia

Posterior tibial a.

Peroneal a.

Nutrient branch
to fibula

Perforating branch
of peroneal a.

Communicating
branches

Medial calcaneal
branch

Lateral calcaneal
branch

Lateral plantar a.

Medial plantar a.

96-1   BACK OF LEG: ARTERIES

Common peroneal n.

Tibial n.

To flexor
hallucis longus

To flexor
digitorum longus

To tibialis
posterior

Flexor
retinaculum

96-2   BACK OF LEG: NERVES

Plate 96

muscular branches. To the soleus muscle and deep flexors.

cutaneous branches. To the skin on the medial side of the leg.

nutrient branch. Enters the nutrient foramen of the tibia.

communicating branch. Anastomoses with the corresponding branch of the peroneal a.

medial calcaneal branch. To the region behind the tendo calcaneus and around the heel.

terminal branches. Lateral and medial plantar aa.

Peroneal A. The largest branch of the posterior tibial a. arises a little below the origin of its parent artery and descends obliquely and laterally behind the soleus muscle towards the fibula. It passes behind the ankle joint to terminate as a number of lateral calcaneal branches. It provides:

muscular branches. To the peroneal muscles.

nutrient branch. It enters the nutrient foramen of the fibula.

perforating branch. It runs just above the inferior tibiofibular joint to the front of the leg (p. 317).

communicating branch. It anastomoses with the corresponding branch from the posterior tibial a.

lateral calcaneal branches. They pass to the lateral side of the heel, anastomosing with the corresponding branches from the medial side.

4. Deep Nerves (Fig. 96-2)

TIBIAL N. This extends from the lower border of the popliteus muscle to terminate beneath the flexor retinaculum.

muscular branches. Innervate the soleus muscle and deep flexors.

medial calcaneal nn. Innervate the skin of the heel.

articular branches. Innervate the ankle joint.

terminal branches. Medial and lateral plantar branches.

FOOT

The distal part of the lower extremity extends from the heel to the toes. Its upper surface is the dorsum; its lower surface is the sole. The foot is divided into:

tarsus. Consists of seven tarsal bones.

metatarsus. Consists of five metatarsal bones.

digits. Five in number; the first is known as the *hallux*.

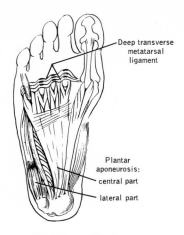

97-1 PLANTAR FASCIA

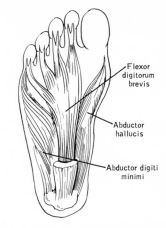

97-2 MUSCLES OF FOOT: SUPERFICIAL LAYER

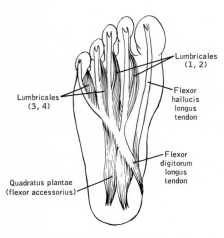

97-3 MUSCLES OF FOOT: MIDDLE LAYER

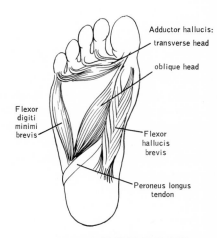

97-4 MUSCLES OF FOOT: DEEP LAYER

Plate 97

326

SOLE OF THE FOOT

1. *Fascia*   3. *Arteries*
2. *Deep layers of sole*   4. *Nerves*

The sole, or plantar surface, of the foot extends from the heel to the tips of the digits.

1. Fascia

SUPERFICIAL. A considerable amount of fat infiltrates between the tough, fibrous strands extending from the skin to the deep fascia. It is especially thick on the heel, the lateral margin of the foot, the ball of the foot, and the ends of the toes. This fascia also contains the medial calcaneal nn. and aa. and cutaneous branches of the medial and lateral plantar nn. and aa.

DEEP. This fascia is thin on the medial and lateral sides of the sole of the foot and thickened in the center (to form the plantar aponeurosis) and over the toes (forming the fibrous flexor sheaths).

Plantar Aponeurosis (Fig. 97-1). Attached proximally to the medial tubercle of the calcaneus, it widens as it extends forward and divides into five slips, one for each digit, near the heads of the metatarsals. Transverse fibers interconnect these slips. Each slip has a thin superficial layer that terminates in the skin of the crease between the sole and the toes. The remaining deep layer of each slip divides into two processes, forming an arch, under which the flexor tendons pass to the digits. The distal edges of each pair of processes fuses with the proximal end of a fibrous flexor sheath. The slips terminate by attaching to the deep transverse metatarsal ligaments.

Fibrous Flexor Sheaths. A sheath for each digit is attached to the margins of the plantar ligaments of the joints, to the margins of the proximal and middle phalanges, and to the plantar surface of the distal phalanges beyond the insertion of the flexor tendons, forming osseoaponeurotic canals. Opposite the bodies of the phalanges, the sheath is strong and has transverse fibers. Opposite the interphalangeal joints, it is thin and has oblique fibers. The outer layer of the synovial sheaths that envelop the tendons serve as linings of the fibrous sheaths.

2. Deep Layers of Sole

Intramuscular septums pass upward into the sole from both the medial and lateral margins of the plantar aponeurosis to either side of the flexor digitorum brevis muscle and partition the sole into three compartments. This muscle is located centrally below the plantar aponeurosis. This region is described in terms of four layers of muscles and tendons.

Superficial (First) Layer (Fig. 97-2)

ABDUCTOR HALLUCIS. It covers the long tendons that enter the sole.

Origin: Medial tubercle of the calcaneus, plantar aponeuroses, and flexor retinaculum.

Insertion: Medial side of the base of the proximal phalanx of the first digit.

Action: Abducts and flexes the hallux.

Nerve supply: Medial plantar n.

FLEXOR DIGITORUM BREVIS. It lies deep to the plantar aponeurosis.

Origin: Medial tubercle of the calcaneus.

The muscle divides into four fleshy bellies, the tendons of which enter a fibrous flexor sheath to be perforated by a long flexor tendon and then divide.

Insertion: Margins distal to the base of the middle phalanx of the lateral four digits.

Action: Flexor of the middle and proximal phalanges of the lateral four digits.

Nerve supply: Medial plantar n.

ABDUCTOR DIGITI MINIMI

Origin: Lateral tubercle of the calcaneus and plantar aponeurosis.

Insertion: Lateral side of the base of the proximal phalanx of the fifth digit.

Action: Abducts and flexes the little toe.

Nerve supply: Lateral plantar n.

Middle (Second) Layer (Fig. 97-3)

FLEXOR DIGITORUM LONGUS TENDON. It passes behind the medial malleolus to enter the sole. It then crosses obliquely superficial to the tendon of the flexor hallucis longus muscle, from which a fibrous slip joins it. It receives the insertion of the quadratus plantae muscle and divides into its four digital tendons, which enter the fibrous flexor sheaths. Each tendon is enclosed in a common synovial sheath together with the tendon of the flexor digitorum brevis that it pierces to reach its insertion.

QUADRATUS PLANTAE (FLEXOR ACCESSORIUS). It is quadrangular in shape.

Origin:

Medial head: Muscular from the medial surface of the calcaneus.

Lateral head: Tendinous from the lateral surface of the calcaneus.

Insertion: Tendon of the flexor digitorum longus muscle.

Action: Flexes the terminal phalanges of the lateral four digits.

Nerve supply: Lateral plantar n.

LUMBRICALES. These four, fusiform muscles are numbered from medial to lateral.

Origin: Adjacent sides of the tendons of the flexor digitorum longus muscle. The first arises from the medial side of the tendon for the second digit. The others lie between the flexor tendons.

They pass forward under the deep transverse metatarsal ligament which separates them from the interossei muscles.

Insertion: Medial side of the dorsal digital expansions (p. 315).

Action: Flexes proximal phalanx; extends middle and distal phalanges.

Nerve supply: Medial plantar n. to second; lateral plantar n. to third, fourth, and fifth.

FLEXOR HALLUCIS LONGUS TENDON. It enters the sole from the back of the leg by descending in the lateralmost passageway under the flexor retinaculum. It crosses deep to the tendon of the flexor digitorum longus and continues forward to enter the fibrous flexor sheath of the first digit and insert at the base of its distal phalanx.

Deep (Third) Layer (Fig. 97-4)

FLEXOR HALLUCIS BREVIS. Two bellies lie on the plantar surface of the first metatarsal.

Origin: Cuboid bone and a tendinous prolongation of the tibialis posterior muscle which reaches the medial cuneiform bone.

Insertion:

Medial belly: Medial side of the base of the proximal phalanx of the first digit.

Lateral belly: Lateral side of the base of the distal phalanx of the first digit.

Action: Flexion of the first digit.

Nerve supply: Medial plantar n.

ADDUCTOR HALLUCIS. Two heads of origin fuse before they insert.

Origin:

Oblique head: Bases of the second, third, and fourth metatarsals and the sheath of the tendon of the peroneous longus muscle.

Transverse head: Plantar ligaments of the metatarsophalangeal joints of the third, fourth, and fifth digits.

Insertion: Lateral side of the base of the proximal phalanx of the big toe.

Action: Adducts and flexes the first digit.

Nerve supply: Lateral plantar n.

FLEXOR DIGITI MINIMI BREVIS. It lies on the plantar surface of the fifth digit.

Origin: Base of fifth metatarsal bone.

Insertion: Lateral side of the base of the first phalanx of the fifth digit.

Action: Flexes the little toe.

Nerve supply: Lateral plantar n.

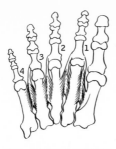

98-1 DORSAL INTEROSSEI

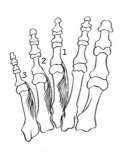

98-2 PLANTAR INTEROSSEI

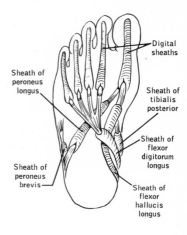

Digital
sheaths

Sheath of
peroneus
longus

Sheath of
tibialis
posterior

Sheath of
flexor
digitorum
longus

Sheath of
peroneus
brevis

Sheath of
flexor
hallucis
longus

98-3 SYNOVIAL SHEATHS OF THE SOLE OF THE FOOT

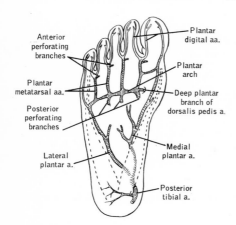

Anterior
perforating
branches

Plantar
metatarsal aa.

Posterior
perforating
branches

Lateral
plantar a.

Plantar
digital aa.

Plantar
arch

Deep plantar
branch of
dorsalis pedis a.

Medial
plantar a.

Posterior
tibial a.

98-4 ARTERIES OF THE SOLE OF THE FOOT

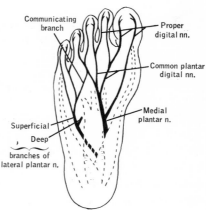

Communicating
branch

Proper
digital nn.

Common plantar
digital nn.

Medial
plantar n.

Superficial

Deep

branches of
lateral plantar n.

98-5 NERVES OF THE SOLE OF THE FOOT

Plate 98

Deepest (Fourth) Layer

INTEROSSEI. There are seven interossei muscles; four dorsal and three plantar. Their tendons pass above the deep transverse ligaments and insert into the bases of the proximal phalanges. They are innervated by the lateral plantar n.

Dorsal Interossei (Fig. 98-1)

Origin: Two heads from the adjacent sides of the metatarsals between which they lie.

Insertion: Medial side of base of proximal phalanx of the second digit, lateral side of this bone of the second, third, and fourth digits.

Action: Abduct digits from the longitudinal axis of the second toe.

Plantar Interossei (Fig. 98-2)

Origin: Medial surfaces of the third, fourth, and fifth metatarsals.

Insertion: Medial side of the proximal phalanges of the same toes.

Action: Adduct digits towards the longitudinal axis of the second toe.

PERONEUS LONGUS TENDON. It curves from the lateral side of the leg around the side of the cuboid and passes medially forward in a fibrous canal formed by the groove on the plantar surface of the cuboid and a "sheath" derived from the long plantar ligament. It continues across the lateral and intermediate cuneiform bones to insert on the medial cuneiform and the base of the first metatarsal.

Digital Synovial Sheaths (Fig. 98-3). The long flexor tendon sheaths begin near the middle of the metatarsals. They extend to the bases of the terminal phalanges where the long flexor tendons insert. The sheath of the fifth digit is continuous with the one that envelops the main tendon of the flexor digitorum longus muscle. Vincula, or vascular folds, representing duplications between the outer and inner synovial sheaths, can be seen at a number of points within the fibrous flexor sheaths of each digit. The *vincula longa* extend between the tendons and the proximal phalanges. The triangular *vincula breve* are located near the insertion of each tendon.

3. Arteries (Fig. 98-4)

The medial and lateral plantar aa. course between the muscles of the first and second layers; the deep branches of the lateral plantar a. course medially between the muscles of the third and fourth layer.

MEDIAL PLANTAR A. The smaller branch of the posterior tibial a. passes forward on the medial side of the foot to the head of the first plantar metatarsal a. The artery provides *superficial digital branches,* which accompany corresponding branches of the nerve.

LATERAL PLANTAR A. The larger terminal branch of the posterior tibial a. passes obliquely lateralward and forward from its point of origin under the flexor retinaculum to the base of the fifth metatarsal bone. It curves medially as the *plantar arch* with the deep branch of the lateral plantar n. between the third and fourth muscle layers and terminates at the base of the first metatarsal bone. It unites with the deep plantar branch of the dorsalis pedis a.

muscular branches. They supply the adjacent muscles.

articular branches. They supply the tarsal joints.

posterior perforating branches. Three branches ascend through the proximal end of the lateral three intermetatarsal spaces to anastomose with the corresponding branches from the dorsal metatarsal aa.

plantar metatarsal aa. The second, third and fourth arteries pass forward on the plantar surface of the interossei muscles between the metatarsal bones. Each provides an anterior perforating branch and divides into a pair of plantar digital aa. The anterior perforating branches ascend through the distal end of the intermetatarsal spaces of the lateral four digits to anastomose with a corresponding branch from the dorsal metatarsal a. The plantar digital aa. supply adjacent sides of the lateral four toes. The proper plantar digital a. to the lateral side of the fifth digit arises where the lateral plantar a. becomes the plantar arch.

first plantar metatarsal a. It arises at the junction of the deep plantar branch of the dorsalis pedis a. and plantar arch. At the first cleft it provides a plantar digital a. to the medial side of the digit and divides into a pair of plantar digital aa. for the adjacent sides of the first and second digits.

All the digital arterial branches lie dorsal to their corresponding nerves. They supply the plantar surfaces and sides of the digits and form plexuses in their digital pads.

4. Nerves (Fig. 98-5)

MEDIAL PLANTAR N. This is the terminal branch of the tibial n. (p. 325). It enters the sole beneath the abductor hallucis muscle and passes forward to provide a proper plantar digital n. to the hallux. It terminates by dividing into three common digital nn. near the bases of the metatarsals.

cutaneous branches. Innervate the skin on the medial side of the sole.

muscular branches. Innervate the abductor hallucis and flexor digitorum brevis muscles.

articular branches. Innervate the tarsal and metatarsal joints.

proper digital n. Provides a muscular branch to the flexor hallucis brevis muscle, pierces the plantar aponeurosis, and descends to the medial side of the foot and big toe to supply the skin.

common digital nn. Three nerves pass between the processes of the plantar aponeurosis. Each splits into two proper digital nerves.

First common digital n. Provides a muscular branch to the first lumbrical muscle
and supplies the skin on adjacent sides of the first and second digits.

Second common digital n. Supplies the skin on the adjacent sides of the second
and third digits.

Third common digital n. Gives off a communicating branch to the lateral plantar
n., and supplies the skin on the adjacent sides of the third and fourth digits.

LATERAL PLANTAR N. The other terminal branch of the tibial n. (p. 325)
enters the sole, passes obliquely lateralwards, between the first and second muscle
layers, between the flexor digitorum brevis and the abductor digiti quinti muscles,
and terminates by dividing into superficial and deep branches.

cutaneous branches. Innervate the skin on the lateral side of the sole.

muscular branches. Innervate the quadratus plantae and abductor digiti minimi
muscles.

articular branches. Innervate the calcaneocuboid joint.

superficial branch. Divides into two rami, a medial branch, the fourth common
digital n. which provides a communicating branch to the medial plantar n. and in
turn divides into two proper digital nn. which supply the adjacent sides of the
fourth and fifth digits. The lateral branch provides a proper digital branch to the
skin on the lateral side of the fifth digit and muscular branches to the flexor digiti
minimi, third plantar, and fourth dorsal interossei muscles.

deep branch. It curves across the bases of the metatarsal bones together with the
palmar arch between the third and fourth layers. It provides muscular branches
for the second, third, and fourth lumbricals, all the remaining interossei, and both
heads of the adductor hallucis muscle and articular branches for the tarsometatarsal
and intermetatarsal joints.

BONES OF LOWER EXTREMITY

1. *Hip bone*   3. *Leg: tibia and fibula*
2. *Thigh: femur and patella*   4. *Foot: tarsus, metatarsus and phalanges*

Each of the four regions of the lower extremity has its bony framework.

1. Hip Bone

See Pelvic Bones, p. 275.

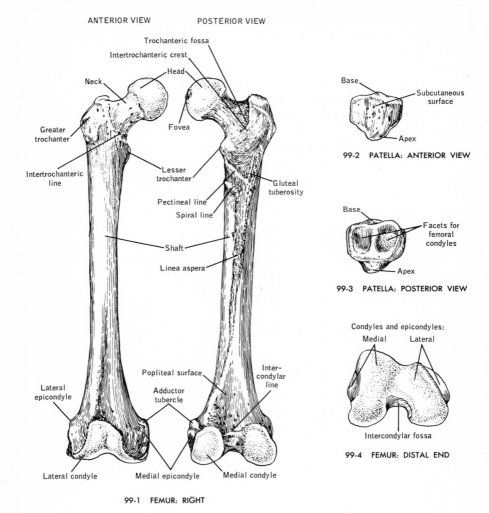

ANTERIOR VIEW   POSTERIOR VIEW

Trochanteric fossa

Intertrochanteric crest

Neck   Head

Greater
trochanter

Fovea

Intertrochanteric
line

Lesser
trochanter

Gluteal
tuberosity

Pectineal line

Spiral line

Shaft

Linea aspera

Lateral
epicondyle

Popliteal surface

Adductor
tubercle

Inter-
condylar
line

Lateral condyle

Medial epicondyle   Medial condyle

99-1   FEMUR: RIGHT

Base

Subcutaneous
surface

Apex

99-2   PATELLA: ANTERIOR VIEW

Base

Facets for
femoral
condyles

Apex

99-3   PATELLA: POSTERIOR VIEW

Condyles and epicondyles:

Medial   Lateral

Intercondylar fossa

99-4   FEMUR: DISTAL END

Plate 99

334

2. Thigh

Femur (Figs. 99-1, 99-2)

The femur is the longest and strongest bone in the body.

Proximal End. It articulates with the acetabulum of the hip bone.

head. The spherical head has a *fovea* below its center.

neck. A thick bar connects the head with the trochanters.

greater trochanter. A rough, quadrilateral eminence projects from the junction of the lateral part of the neck and the proximal end of the shaft. The trochanteric fossa is situated on its inner surface.

lesser trochanter. A conical eminence projects medially backwards from the junction of the medial part of the neck and the posterior proximal end of the shaft.

intertrochanteric line. A ridge on the anterior surface of the base of the neck descends obliquely from the greater trochanter into the linea aspera. The upper part of the line is rough; the lower part is less prominent (see "spiral line," below).

intertrochanteric crest. A prominent ridge on the posterior surface extends between the two trochanters. The *quadrate line* extends downward from the middle of the crest.

Shaft. Generally the shaft is smooth and cylindrical.

linea aspera. A prominent ridge on the back of the middle third of the shaft exhibits medial and lateral lips.

gluteal tuberosity. The upward prolongation from the lateral lip to the base of the greater trochanter.

pectineal line. The upward prolongation of the intermediate ridge to the base of the lesser trochanter.

spiral line. The upward continuation of the medial lip winds around below the lesser trochanter to become continuous with the less prominent part of the intertrochanteric line.

medial and *lateral supracondylar lines.* The downward prolongations to the condyles of the lips of the linea aspera.

popliteal surface. The triangular area between the supracondylar lines forms the upper part of the floor of the popliteal fossa.

nutrient foramen. Near the linea aspera in the middle of the shaft the nutrient foramen is directed upward.

Distal End. It articulates with the tibia.

medial and *lateral condyles.* They are united anteriorly and laterally by a shallow articular depression, the patellar surface. The condyles bulge beyond the plane of the shaft posteriorly, separated by the intercondylar notch.

intercondylar line. A ridge on the posterior surface separates the popliteal surface of the shaft from the intercondylar fossa.

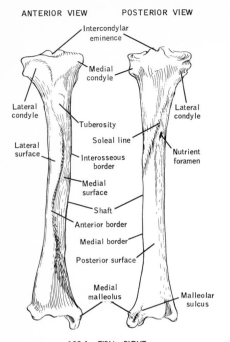

Intercondylar
eminence

Medial
condyle

Lateral
condyle

Lateral
condyle

Tuberosity

Soleal line

Lateral
surface

Nutrient
foramen

Interosseous
border

Medial
surface

Shaft

Anterior border

Medial border

Posterior surface

Medial
malleolus

Malleolar
sulcus

100-1   TIBIA: RIGHT

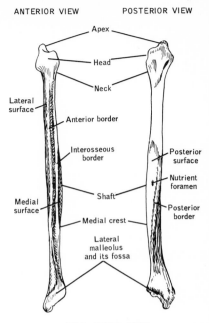

Apex

Head

Neck

Lateral
surface

Anterior border

Interosseous
border

Posterior
surface

Nutrient
foramen

Medial
surface

Shaft

Posterior
border

Medial crest

Lateral
malleolus
and its fossa

100-2   FIBULA: RIGHT

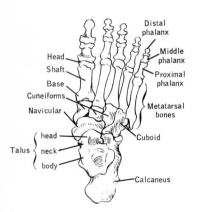

Distal
phalanx

Head

Middle
phalanx

Shaft

Base

Proximal
phalanx

Cuneiforms

Navicular

Metatarsal
bones

head
Talus { neck
body

Cuboid

Calcaneus

100-3   BONES OF FOOT: DORSAL VIEW

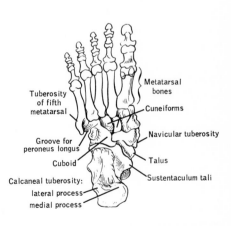

Metatarsal
bones

Tuberosity
of fifth
metatarsal

Cuneiforms

Navicular tuberosity

Groove for
peroneus longus

Cuboid

Talus

Sustentaculum tali

Calcaneal tuberosity:
lateral process
medial process

100-4   BONES OF FOOT: PLANTAR VIEW

Plate 100

medial and *lateral epicondyles*. Eminences project from the sides of the condyles.

adductor tubercle. On the medial epicondyle at the termination of the medial lip of the linea aspera.

Patella (Figs. 99-3, 99-4)

The patella is the sesamoid bone developed in the quadriceps tendon.

anterior surface. The convex surface has numerous small nutrient foramens. It is roughened by vertical ridges.

posterior surface. The upper, smooth articular area is subdivided by a vertical ridge into a large lateral and a smaller medial facet. The lower nonarticular area is rough.

base. The thick superior border.

apex. The inferior end of the patella.

3. Leg

Tibia (Fig. 100-1)

This is the larger, medial leg bone.

Proximal End. The proximal end of the tibia is large and expanded.

medial and *lateral condyles*. The upper surface has two smooth, articular facets separated from each other by a wide, irregular strip, the intercondylar strip. This strip contains the *intercondylar eminence* in the middle, and the anterior and posterior *intercondylar areas* in front and behind. The sides of the eminence are prolonged proximally to form the medial and lateral *intercondylar tubercles*.

tibial tuberosity. This tubercle is situated anteriorly where the lower margins of the condyles converge downwards. Its upper part is smooth and its lower part is rough.

Shaft. The shaft of the tibia presents three borders and three surfaces.

anterior border. The border extends from the tuberosity down to the anterior margin of the malleolus.

medial border. The blunt border extends from the medial condyle to the back of the medial malleolus.

interosseous border. The thin prominent border extends from in front of the fibular facet to the apex of the fibular notch (p. 338), where it bifurcates.

medial surface. This surface is bounded by the anterior and medial borders. It is subcutaneous except near its upper end.

lateral surface. This surface is bounded by the medial and interosseous borders. It is slightly concave above but becomes convex below.

posterior surface. This surface is bounded by the medial and interosseous borders.

The *soleal line* crosses its upper third and extends obliquely down from the fibular facet to the medial border. The *vertical line* extends distally from the soleal line, dividing the middle third of the posterior surface into lateral and medial parts. A large nutrient foramen, directed downward, lies below the soleal line.

Distal End. The distal end of the tibia presents five surfaces.

medial surface. This subcutaneous surface is prolonged downwards to form the medial malleolus.

medial malleolus. The posterior surface is grooved by the *malleolar sulcus.*

lateral surface. The upper part of this depressed surface is rough; the lower part is smooth. Both parts form the triangular *fibular notch.*

anterior surface. Smooth and rounded.

posterior surface. This rounded surface contains a shallow oblique groove.

inferior articular surface. This quadrilateral surface is wider in front than behind and is concave anteroposteriorly. It is continuous with the malleolar articular surface.

Fibula (Fig. 100-2)

This is the smaller, lateral leg bone.

Proximal End. It consists of three parts.

head. It occupies almost the entire proximal end. It has an articular facet superiorly for articulation with the posteroinferior aspect of the lateral condyle of the tibia. The blunt apex projects upward from the posterolateral aspect of the head. It is the site of attachment for a ligament and a muscle tendon.

neck. The constricted portion is below the head.

styloid process. It is blunt and conical.

Shaft. The shaft of the fibula has three borders and three surfaces.

anterior border. This sharp border descends from the neck.

interosseous border. This ill-defined border descends parallel to the anterior border. It bifurcates at the apex of a triangular area above the articular facet on the lateral malleolus.

posterior border. This blunt border descends to the medial margin of the posterior surface of the malleolus.

medial surface. This surface represents the area between the anterior border and the medial crest and includes the interosseous border.

lateral surface. The continuation of the anterior surface of the shaft lies between the anterior and posterior borders.

posterior surface. This surface lies between the medial crest and the posterior border.

Distal End

lateral malleolus. The distal end of the fibula consists of the lateral malleolus. The medial surface presents a triangular articular facet. Below the facet is the *malleolar fossa.*

anterior surface. This surface is narrow above, wide below, and lies between the rough anterior border and the interosseous border.

medial surface. This surface presents a triangular articular facet. The malleolar fossa lies below the facet.

lateral surface. The continuation of the anterior surface of the shaft lies between the anterior and posterior borders. It is convex and subcutaneous and it spirals posteriorly in its lower third to become continuous with the posterior aspect of the lateral malleolus.

posterior surface. The continuation of the lateral surface of the shaft lies between the interosseous and the posterior area and is continuous inferiorly with the medial surface of the lateral malleolus. It is divided into unequal parts by a *medial crest* that extends down from the neck and presents a nutrient foramen.

4. Foot (Figs. 100-3, 100-4)

TARSUS. The posterior half of the foot consists of seven tarsal bones. One of these, the *talus,* articulates with the leg bones by means of three surfaces presented by the trochlea, a part of the body of the talus, which also has a narrow neck and a round head. The inferior surface of the talus rests in part on the *calcaneus,* the bone of the heel. The head of the talus articulates with the concave posterior surface of the *navicular.* Four bones, placed side by side, articulate with the anterior surfaces of the navicular and calcaneus bones. The navicular faces the three *cuneiform* bones; the calcaneus articulates with the *cuboid.* The various prominences of the individual tarsal bones are illustrated.

METATARSUS. Five metatarsal bones are set side by side between the tarsal bones and the digits. They are numbered from one to five, from the big to the little toe. The three medial metatarsals articulate with the corresponding cuneiforms; two lateral metatarsals meet the cuboid. Each *metatarsal* consists of three parts. The base is the larger posterior wedge-shaped end with apex facing upward. It bears articular facets behind for its corresponding tarsal bone and on the sides for the adjacent metatarsals. The dorsal and plantar surfaces are rough. The shaft is narrow, prismoid, convex above, and concave below. The head is anterior and articulates with the base of the proximal phalanx by a convex articular facet. Its sides are flattened, and on its dorsal surface, at the junction of the head and shaft, are tubercles. Its plantar surface is notched.

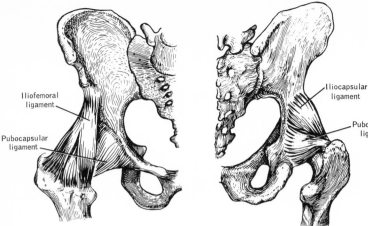

101-1 HIP VIEW: ANTERIOR VIEW

Iliofemoral ligament

Pubocapsular ligament

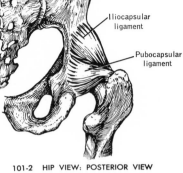

101-2 HIP VIEW: POSTERIOR VIEW

Iliocapsular ligament

Pubocapsular ligament

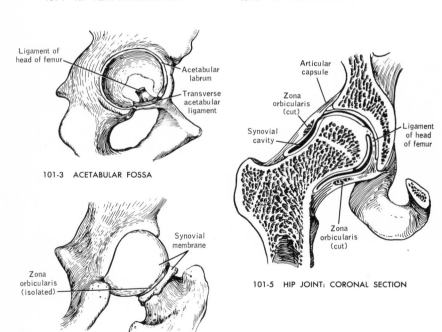

Ligament of head of femur

Acetabular labrum

Transverse acetabular ligament

101-3 ACETABULAR FOSSA

Articular capsule

Zona orbicularis (cut)

Synovial cavity

Ligament of head of femur

Zona orbicularis (cut)

101-5 HIP JOINT: CORONAL SECTION

Synovial membrane

Zona orbicularis (isolated)

101-4 POSTERIOR ASPECT OF SYNOVIAL MEMBRANE

Plate 101

PHALANGES. Each digit has three phalanges, except the first, which has two. They are called proximal, middle, and distal. Each phalanx consists of a base, a short shaft, and a pulley-like head.

JOINTS OF LOWER EXTREMITY

1. *Hip joint*   3. *Tibiofibular joints*
2. *Knee joint*   4. *Ankle joint*
          5. *Joints of the foot*

The joints of the lower extremity are classified into five groups.

1. Hip Joint (Figs. 101-1, 101-2)

Type: The hip joint is spheroidal, or of the ball-and-socket type.

Articulating elements: The head of the femur articulates with the acetabulum of the coxal bone. The cup is deepened by the *acetabular labrum,* a fibrocartilaginous ring of triangular cross section that is attached to the rim of the acetabulum.

Ligaments:

Transverse ligament. Extending across the acetabular notch, it forms a foramen.

Articular capsule. The capsular ligament extends from the rim of the acetabulum, and the transverse ligament to the intertrochanteric line, anteriorly, and to the middle of the neck of the femur, posteriorly. It has both longitudinal and circular fibers. The circular fibers are deeper and form a collar, the *zona orbicularis.* The synovial membrane of the capsule (Figs. 101-4, 101-5) is reflected on to the intracapsular part of the neck of the femur and envelops it up to the articular head. It also continues over both surfaces of the labrum and the fat of the acetabular fossa and forms a tubular sheath around the ligament of the head of the femur (see below).

Iliofemoral ligament. A Y-shaped band in front of the joint has its apex at the anterior inferior iliac spine. Its two limbs are attached below to the upper and lower ends of the intertrochanteric line.

Pubofemoral ligament. It extends from the pubic part of the acetabular rim and blends with the capsule.

Ischiofemoral ligament. Extending from the ischium below and behind the acetabulum, it blends with the capsule.

Ligament of head of femur (Fig. 101-3). This flattened triangular intracapsular ligament is attached at its apex to the fovea of the head of the femur, and at its base to the transverse ligament and margins of the acetabular notch.

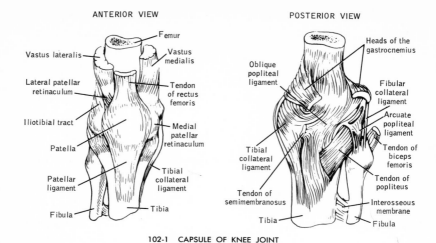

Femur

Vastus lateralis

Vastus medialis

Lateral patellar retinaculum

Tendon of rectus femoris

Iliotibial tract

Medial patellar retinaculum

Patella

Patellar ligament

Tibial collateral ligament

Fibula

Tibia

Heads of the gastrocnemius

Oblique popliteal ligament

Fibular collateral ligament

Arcuate popliteal ligament

Tibial collateral ligament

Tendon of biceps femoris

Tendon of popliteus

Tendon of semimembranosus

Interosseous membrane

Tibia

Fibula

102-1   CAPSULE OF KNEE JOINT

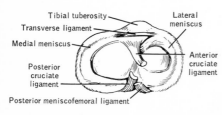

Posterior meniscofemoral ligament

Anterior and posterior cruciate ligaments

Lateral meniscus

Medial meniscus

102-2   KNEE JOINT (opened from behind)

Tibial tuberosity

Lateral meniscus

Transverse ligament

Medial meniscus

Anterior cruciate ligament

Posterior cruciate ligament

Posterior meniscofemoral ligament

102-3   SUPERIOR ARTICULAR SURFACE OF TIBIA

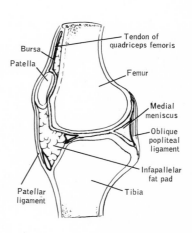

Bursa

Patella

Tendon of quadriceps femoris

Femur

Medial meniscus

Oblique popliteal ligament

Infapallelar fat pad

Patellar ligament

Tibia

102-4   SAGITTAL SECTION OF KNEE JOINT

Plate 102

Movements: The hip joint provides for movement in all possible directions.

The blood supply to the hip joint is provided by the superior and inferior gluteal, medial femoral circumflex, and obturator aa. The joint is innervated by branches from the femoral n., obturator n., and n. to the quadratus femoris muscle.

2. Knee Joint

Type: The knee joint is comprised of medial and lateral condylar joints and a semiplane patellar joint.

Articulating elements: The condyles of the femur articulate with the condyles of the tibia, through the mediation of the corresponding menisci; the patella articulates with the femur.

Extracapsular ligaments (Fig. 102-1)

Articular capsule. This thin, strong membrane is deficient anteriorly, where it is replaced by the quadriceps femoris muscle, the patella, and the patellar ligament. It is reinforced by two retinacula and five ligaments. The synovial membrane lines the articular capsule, is reflected onto the bones, and extends as far as their articular margins. Its anterior portion extends a short distance upward onto the deep surface of the quadriceps tendon from behind the patella. It covers the deep surface of the infrapatellar fat pad and passes upward and forward as a triangular duplication, the infrapatellar synovial fold. The apex of the fold is attached to the front of the intercondylar notch. The lower margins project sideways as the alar folds.

Medial and lateral patellar retinacula. They are expansions from the vasti and fascia lata.

Oblique popliteal ligament. It is a flat band derived from the tendon of the semimembranosus muscle.

Patellar ligament. This strong, thick band extends from the apex and the lower part of the deep surface of the patella to the upper part of the tuberosity of the tibia. Its superficial fibers are continuous with the central part of the common tendon of the quadriceps femoris muscle over the front of the patella. The posterior surface of the ligamentum patellae is separated from the synovial membrane of the joint by the infrapatellar fat pad, and from the upper end of the tibia by a bursa.

Tibial collateral ligament. This flat band extends from the medial femoral epicondyle to the medial condyle and surface of the body of the tibia.

Fibular collateral ligament. This cordlike band extends from the posterior part of the lateral femoral epicondyle to the head of the fibula.

Arcuate popliteal ligament. This ligament arches downwards from the lateral femoral condyle on the back of the capsule and is connected to the styloid process of the head of the fibula by two converging bands.

Intracapsular ligaments and cartilages (Figs. 102-2, 102-3):

Anterior cruciate ligament. It extends upward, backward, and laterally from the anterior part of the intercondylar fossa of the tibia to the posterior part of the medial surface of the lateral condyle of the femur.

Posterior cruciate ligament. This ligament extends upward, forward, and medially from the posterior part of the intercondylar fossa of the tibia to the anterior part of the lateral surface of the medial condyle of the femur.

Medial and lateral menisci. The semilunar cartilages deepen the articulating surface of the condyles and act as shock absorbers. They are crescentic fibrocartilages with flat lower surfaces and concave upper surfaces. The peripheral margins are thick, convex, and attached to the capsule. The inner margins are thin, concave, and free. Their horns, or fibrous ends, are attached to the tibia in front and to the intercondylar eminence behind. The medial cartilage is nearly semicircular; the lateral one is almost circular.

Posterior meniscofemoral ligament. A fasciculus from the lateral meniscus which joins the posterior cruciate ligament to be inserted on the medial condyle of the femur. A comparable anterior ligament is sometimes present.

Transverse genicular ligament. This ligament connects the anterior convex margins of the two menisci.

Movements: The knee joint is capable of a gliding movement, combined with rotation around a vertical axis. The terminal part of flexion is accompanied by medial rotation of the tibia on the femur. Extension is accompanied by lateral rotation and terminates in it. Independent rotation occurs best when the knee is flexed at right angles. The patella maintains a shifting contact with the femur in all positions of the knee. It protects the front of the joint and increases the traction angle of the tendon of the quadriceps muscle.

The blood supply to the knee joint is provided by the superior genicular branch of the femoral a.; genicular branches of the popliteal a.; recurrent branches of the anterior tibial a.; descending branch of the lateral femoral circumflex a. The joint is innervated by branches of the femoral n. to the vasti; branches of the tibial and common peroneal nn., recurrent branch of the common peroneal n., and the genicular branch of the obturator n.

3. Tibiofibular Joints

Superior Tibiofibular Joint

Type: This is the plane type of joint.

Articulating elements: The head of the fibula articulates with the lateral condyle of the femur.

Ligaments:

Articular capsule. The capsule is thicker in front and is attached to the articular margins of the bones. It is lined with a synovial membrane.

Anterior ligament. A few bands pass obliquely from the front of the head of the fibula to the front of the lateral femoral condyle.

Posterior ligament. A broad band passes obliquely from the back of the head of the fibula to the back of the lateral femoral condyle.

Movement: The joint provides for a slight gliding movement.

The arterial blood supply to the superior tibiofibular joint is provided by the lateral inferior genicular and anterior recurrent tibial aa. This joint is innervated by the nerve to the popliteus muscle and the recurrent branch of the common peroneal n.

Interosseous membrane. This extends between the interosseous borders of the tibia and fibula. Its upper margin has a concave border and does not reach the superior tibiofibular joint. It is continuous with the interosseous ligament of the inferior tibiofibular joint and is perforated by numerous small vessels.

Inferior Tibiofibular Joint

Type: This joint provides a syndesmotic type of articulation.

Articulating elements: The lower end of the fibula articulates with the lateral side of the tibia.

Ligaments:

Anterior ligament. This flat band passes obliquely from the anterior border of the fibular notch of the tibia to the lateral malleolus.

Posterior ligament. This flat band passes obliquely from the posterior border of the fibular notch of the tibia to the lateral malleolus.

Transverse ligament. This wide band crosses the back of the joint. It extends from the inferior border of the posterior surface of the tibia to the upper end of the malleolar fossa of the fibula.

Interosseous ligament. This continuation of the interosseous membrane consists of short thick bands extending from the floor of the fibular notch of the tibia to above the articular surface of the lateral malleolus.

Movement: This joint accommodates the talus during ankle movement.

The blood supply to the inferior tibiofibular joint is provided by the perforating branch of the peroneal a. This joint is innervated by the anterior tibial n.

4. Ankle Joint (Fig. 103-1)

Type: The ankle joint is of the ginglymus (hinge) type.

Articulating elements: The malleoli at the distal end of the tibia articulate with the talus.

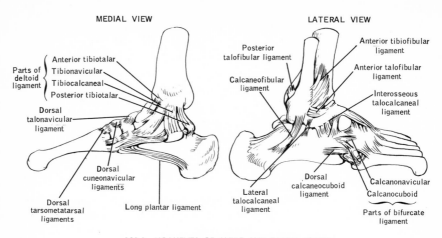

MEDIAL VIEW

Parts of deltoid ligament {
Anterior tibiotalar
Tibionavicular
Tibiocalcaneal
Posterior tibiotalar

Dorsal talonavicular ligament

Dorsal cuneonavicular ligaments

Dorsal tarsometatarsal ligaments

Long plantar ligament

LATERAL VIEW

Posterior talofibular ligament

Calcaneofibular ligament

Anterior tibiofibular ligament

Anterior talofibular ligament

Interosseous talocalcaneal ligament

Lateral talocalcaneal ligament

Dorsal calcaneocuboid ligament

Calcanonavicular

Calcaneocuboid

Parts of bifurcate ligament

103-1 LIGAMENTS OF ANKLE AND TARSAL JOINTS

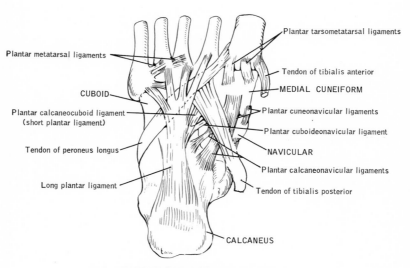

Plantar metatarsal ligaments

CUBOID

Plantar calcaneocuboid ligament (short plantar ligament)

Tendon of peroneus longus

Long plantar ligament

Plantar tarsometatarsal ligaments

Tendon of tibialis anterior

MEDIAL CUNEIFORM

Plantar cuneonavicular ligaments

Plantar cuboideonavicular ligament

NAVICULAR

Plantar calcaneonavicular ligaments

Tendon of tibialis posterior

CALCANEUS

103-2 LIGAMENTS OF THE SOLE OF THE FOOT

Plate 103

Ligaments:

Articular capsule. It is thin in front and behind and is attached to the margins of the articular surfaces. The synovial membrane lines the deep surfaces of the ligaments and extends upward between the distal ends of the tibia and fibula into the inferior tibiofibular joint as far as the interosseous ligament.

Deltoid ligament. A triangular ligament on the medial side of the joint is attached by its blunted apex to the margins and tip of the medial malleolus above. Its extensive inferior attachment stretches from the neck of the talus along the tuberosity of the navicular and sustentaculum tali to the medial side of the body of the talus.

The three lateral collateral ligaments are:

Anterior talofibular ligament. This short ligament extends forwards from the anterior border of the lateral malleolus to the lateral side of the neck of the talus.

Calcaneofibular ligament. A rounded cord extends downward and backward from the tip of the lateral malleolus to the middle of the lateral surface of the calcaneus.

Posterior talofibular ligament. A strong horizontal band extends from the floor of the malleolar fossa of the fibula to the posterior tubercle of the talus.

Movements: This joint provides for dorsiflexion and plantar flexion.

The blood supply to the ankle joint is provided by the malleolar branches of the anterior and posterior tibial and perineal aa. The joint is innervated by the anterior tibial and lateral branch of the deep peroneal aa.

5. Joints of the Foot (Fig. 103-2)

Intertarsal Joints

These joints are all plane and have dorsal, plantar, and interosseous ligaments. They are lined with a synovial membrane and permit gliding movements. Their blood supply obtains from adjacent branches of the dorsalis pedis and medial and lateral plantar aa. Their innervation is derived from the deep peroneal and medial and lateral plantar nn.

SUBTALAR JOINT

Articulating elements: The inferior surface of the talus articulates with the superior surface of the calcaneus.

Ligaments: The ligaments of this joint are the articular capsule and the medial, lateral, posterior, and interosseous talocalcaneal ligaments.

TALOCALCANEONAVICULAR JOINT.

Articulating elements: The head of the talus articulates with a socket formed by the posterior surface of the navicular, the anterior articular surface of the calcaneus, and the upper surface of the plantar calcaneonavicular ligament.

ligaments: The ligaments of this joint are the articular capsule, dorsal and plantar calcaneonavicular ligament (spring ligament), and the calcaneocuboid part of the bifurcated ligament.

CALCANEOCUBOID JOINT

Articulating elements: A facet on the anterior surface of the calcaneus articulates with a facet on the posterior surface of the cuboid.

Ligaments: The ligaments of this joint are the articular capsule, dorsal and plantar calcaneocuboid (short plantar) ligament, and two especially significant ligaments:

Long plantar ligament (Fig. 103-3). The longest tarsal ligament extends from the plantar surface of the calcaneus in front of the tuberosity to the tuberosity of the cuboid bone. Its superficial fibers are continued forward to the bases of the third, fourth, and fifth metatarsal bones.

Bifurcated ligament. The stem of this Y-shaped ligament is attached to the dorsal surface of the calcaneus laterad to the facet for the head of the talus. The calcaneo-cuboid part is attached to the medial surface of the cuboid. The calcaneonavicular part extends to the lateral surface of the navicular.

The transverse tarsal joint is the irregular articular plane that extends across the width of the foot. It is composed of the talonavicular joint, medially, and the cal-caneocuboid joint laterally. Inversion and eversion of the foot take place primarily at this joint. Additional ligaments unite the cuboid and navicular bones. These are the dorsal, plantar, and interosseous cuboideonavicular ligaments.

The three distal intertarsal joints are:

CUNEONAVICULAR JOINT

Articulating elements: Facets on the anterior surface of the navicular articulate with facets on the posterior surface of the three cuneiform bones.

Ligaments: The ligaments of this joint are the dorsal and plantar cuneonavicular ligaments.

CUNEOCUBOID JOINT

Articulating elements: A facet on the medial surface of the cuboid articulates with the posterior facet on the lateral surface of the lateral cuneiform.

Ligaments: The ligaments of this joint are the dorsal, plantar, and interosseous cuneocuboid ligaments.

INTERCUNEIFORM JOINTS. They provide for two articulations.

Articulating elements: A facet on the medial side of the lateral cuneiform articu-lates with a facet on the lateral side of the middle cuneiform. A facet on the lateral side of the second cuneiform articulates with a facet on the medial side of the medial cuneiform.

Ligaments: The ligaments of these joints are the dorsal, plantar, and interosseous intercuneiform ligaments.

Tarsometatarsal Joints

Type: The tarsometatarsal joints are of the plane type.

Articulating elements: The base of the first metatarsal articulates with the medial cuneiform; the base of the second metatarsal with all three cuneiforms; the base of the third metatarsal with the lateral cuneiform; the base of the third metatarsal with the cuboid and lateral cuneiform; the base of the fifth metatarsal with the distal surface of the cuboid.

Ligaments: The ligaments of these joints are the dorsal, plantar, and interosseous tarsometatarsal ligaments.

Movement: These joints provide for a slight gliding movement.

Intermetatarsal Joints

Type: The intermetatarsal joints are also of the plane type.

Articulating elements: They are the bases of the metatarsal bones.

Ligaments: The ligaments of these joints are the dorsal, plantar, and interosseous intermetatarsal ligaments. The first and second metatarsals are interconnected by interosseous fibers only.

Metatarsophalangeal Joints

Type: The metatarsophalangeal joints are condyloid in type.

Articular elements: The rounded heads of the metatarsals articulate with the shallow cavities at the bases of the proximal phalanges.

Ligaments:

Articular capsule. The loose capsule is lined with synovial membrane.

Plantar ligaments. Each fibrocartilaginous plate is attached loosely to the neck of a metatarsal and firmly to the base of the phalanx. The plantar ligament of the first metatarsophalangeal joint is replaced by sesamoid bones in the tendon of the flexor hallucis brevis muscle.

Collateral ligaments. These extend from the tubercles on each side of the head of a metatarsal bone to the side of the base of the phalanx and to the margins of its plantar ligament. The extensor expansions on the dorsal surface take the place of the dorsal ligaments.

Deep transverse metatarsal ligament. A band connects the head and joint capsules of all the metatarsal bones.

Movements: These joints permit dorsi- and plantar flexion, abduction, and adduction.

Interphalangeal Joints

Type: The interphalangeal joints are of the ginglymus (hinge) type.

Articulating elements: The heads of the proximal and middle phalanges articulate with the shallow cavities at the bases of the middle and distal phalanges respectively.

Ligaments: The articular capsule and the plantar and collateral ligaments are arranged like those of the metatarsophalangeal joints.

Movements: These joints provide for dorsi- and plantar flexion.

BACK

The back is the posterior part of the trunk, extending from the neck to the pelvis.

FASCIA AND MUSCLES OF THE BACK

1. Fascia　　　　　　*2. Muscles*

The cutaneous innervation of the back has been discussed on p. 119.

1. Fascia

NUCHAL FASCIA. This cervical portion of the fascia of the back is attached to the skull beneath the superior nuchal line, to the ligamentum nuchae, and to the spinous processes of Cv 7 and Tv 1 to 6, and is continuous with the thoracolumbar fascia below.

THORACOLUMBAR FASCIA (Fig. 104-1). This downward prolongation of the nuchal fascia is attached to all the vertebral spines below Tv 7, their supraspinous ligaments, and the medial crest of the sacrum. Below, it is attached to the iliac crest. Laterally, it is thin in the thoracic region and attaches to the angles of the ribs. In the lumbar region it is thick and continuous with the aponeurosis of origin of the transversus abdominis muscle. The aponeurosis splits into two layers to enclose the deep vertebral muscles.

Posterior Layer. This tough, thick layer of the thoracolumbar fascia passes behind the deep muscles to attach to the lumbar spines. It is strengthened by the aponeurosis of the latissimus dorsi muscle.

Anterior Layer. This strong, thin layer passes between the deep muscles and the quadratus lumborum muscle to attach to the lumbar transverse processes.

2. Muscles

The muscles of the back may be divided into three groups, as shown in Table 82 (Figs. 39-4, 104-3):

Superficial Group

The superficial muscles of the back have been discussed earlier (p. 121).

Intermediate Group

The intermediate group consists of two flat quadrilateral muscles.

351

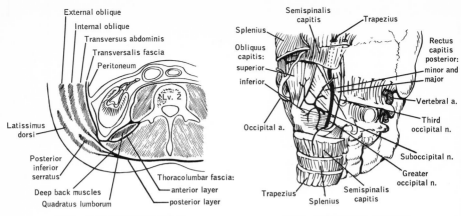

Labels for figure 104-1 (THORACOLUMBAR FASCIA):

External oblique
Internal oblique
Transversus abdominis
Transversalis fascia
Peritoneum

Latissimus dorsi

Posterior inferior serratus

Deep back muscles
Quadratus lumborum

Lv. 2

Thoracolumbar fascia:
— anterior layer
— posterior layer

104-1 THORACOLUMBAR FASCIA

Labels for figure 104-2 (SUBOCCIPITAL TRIANGLE):

Semispinalis capitis
Splenius
Obliquus capitis:
superior
inferior
Occipital a.

Trapezius
Rectus capitis posterior: minor and major
Vertebral a.
Third occipital n.
Suboccipital n.
Greater occipital n.
Semispinalis capitis
Splenius
Trapezius

104-2 SUBOCCIPITAL TRIANGLE

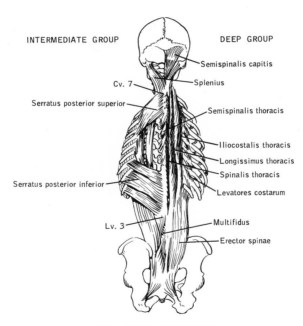

INTERMEDIATE GROUP   DEEP GROUP

Semispinalis capitis
Cv. 7
Splenius
Serratus posterior superior
Semispinalis thoracis
Iliocostalis thoracis
Longissimus thoracis
Spinalis thoracis
Levatores costarum
Serratus posterior inferior
Lv. 3
Multifidus
Erector spinae

104-3 MUSCLES OF THE BACK

Plate 104

Table 82

Superficial group: acting on limbs
 Trapezius
 Latissimus dorsi
 Levator scapulae
 Rhomboideus major and minor
Intermediate group: respiratory
 Serratus posterior superior
 Serratus posterior inferior
Deep group: intrinsic
 Splenius
 Suboccipital muscles
 Longitudinal muscles:
  iliocostalis, longissimus, spinalis
 Oblique muscles:
  semispinalis, multifidus, rotatores
 Minor muscles:
  interspinales, intertransversarii, levatores costarum

SERRATUS POSTERIOR SUPERIOR. It is thin and quadrilateral.

Origin: Spines of Cv 6 and 7 and Tv 1 and 2.

Insertion: Second to fifth ribs beyond the angle.

Action: Raises ribs.

Nerve supply: Branches of the ventral rami of Tn 1 to 4.

SERRATUS POSTERIOR INFERIOR. It is irregularly quadrilateral.

Origin: Spines of Tv 1 to 2 and Lv 1 to 3.

Insertion: Ninth to twelfth ribs beyond the angle.

Action: Draws ribs outward.

Nerve supply: Branches of ventral rami of Tn 9 to 12.

Deep Muscles

SPLENIUS. The splenius muscle is the detached part of this group; it is divided into two parts.

Origin: Lower half of the nuchal ligament and spines of Tv 1 to 6.

Insertion:

 Capitis: Superior nuchal line and mastoid process.

 Cervicis: Posterior tubercles of Cv 1 to 3.

Action: Draws head and neck backward and lateralward.

Nerve supply: Lateral branches of the dorsal rami of Cn 2 to 5.

SUBOCCIPITAL MUSCLES. See p. 355.

LONGITUDINAL MUSCLES. A broad thick muscle mass, the *erector spinae*, is attached to the posterior aspect of the sacrum, the iliac crest, and the lumbar spinous processes. A little below the last rib it splits into three columns:

Iliocostalis. This lateralmost column consists of the lumborum, thoracis and cervicis muscles.

Origin: Crest of the ilium.

Insertion: Angles of ribs and cervical transverse processes.

Longissimus. This intermediate column consists of the thoracis, cervicis and capitis muscles.

Origin: Transverse processes of lower level.

Insertion: Transverse processes of higher level.

Spinalis: Thoracis, Cervicis, Capitis. It is the medialmost column.

Origin: Upper lumbar spinous processes.

Insertion: Upper thoracic spinous processes.

OBLIQUE MUSCLES. They are covered by the erector spinae muscle and its fibers. They extend obliquely from the transverse processes to the spinous processes.

Semispinalis: Thoracis, Cervicis, Capitis. It spans from four to six segments.

Origin: Transverse proceses from Tv 12 and upward.

Insertion: Spinous processes as far as the occipital bone.

Multifidus. It spans three segments.

Origin: Posterior aspects of the sacrum to the transverse process of Cv 4.

Insertion: Lower border of every spinous process to Cv 2.

Rotatores: Cervicis, Thoracis, Lumborum. They span one segment.

Origin: Root of one transverse process.

Insertion: Root of the spinous process above it.

MINOR MUSCLES

Interspinales: Cervicis, Thoracis, Lumborum

Origin: Spinous processes of the cervical and lumbar vertebrae.

Insertion: Spinous process above it.

Intertransversarii: Lumborum, Cervicis. They are absent in the thoracic region.

Origin: Transverse processes of the cervical and lumbar vertebrae.

Insertion: Transverse process above it.

Levatores Costarum. They are present only in the thoracic region (p. 195).

Nerves of the Deep Back Muscles (Figs. 39-3, 39-4). The dorsal rami of the spinal nn. divide into medial and lateral branches. In the upper half of the trunk the medial branches become cutaneous while the lateral branches are muscular. The lateral branches become cutaneous in the lower half of the trunk where the medial branches are muscular. The dorsal rami of Cn 1, 6, 7, lower lumbar, sacral, and coccygeal nerves have no cutaneous distribution (see Table 46).

SUBOCCIPITAL TRIANGLE

1. Boundaries   2. Suboccipital muscles
3. Contents

The suboccipital triangle is located at the upper portion of the back of the neck beneath the occipital bone and adjacent muscles of the back.

1. Boundaries (Fig. 104-2)

The suboccipital triangle has the following boundaries:
Superomedial boundary: rectus capitis posterior major
Superolateral boundary: obliquus capitis superior
Inferolateral boundary: obliquus capitis inferior
Roof: semispinalis capitis
Floor: posterior occipitoatlantal membrane and posterior arch of the atlas
It contains the four suboccipital muscles, two nerves, and two arteries.

2. Suboccipital Muscles (Fig. 104-2)

OBLIQUUS CAPITIS INFERIOR
Origin: Spine of the axis.
Insertion: Tip of the transverse process of the atlas.
Action: Rotates the atlas and thereby the head.
Nerve supply: Branch of the dorsal ramus of the suboccipital n.
OBLIQUUS CAPITIS SUPERIOR
Origin: Tip of the transverse process of the atlas.
Insertion: Between the nuchal lines on the occipital line.
Action: Extends the head.
Nerve supply: Branch of the dorsal ramus of the suboccipital n.
RECTUS CAPITIS POSTERIOR MINOR
Origin: Posterior tubercle of the atlas.
Insertion: Between the inferior nuchal line and the foramen magnum.
Action: Extends the head.
Nerve supply: Branch of the dorsal ramus of the suboccipital n.
RECTUS CAPITIS POSTERIOR MAJOR
Origin: Spine of the axis.
Insertion: Between the inferior nuchal line and the foramen magnum.
Action: Extends the head.
Nerve supply: Branch of the dorsal ramus of the suboccipital n.

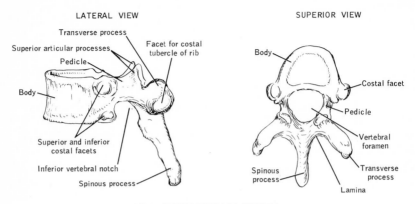

LATERAL VIEW   SUPERIOR VIEW

Transverse process

Superior articular processes

Pedicle

Facet for costal
tubercle of rib

Body

Body

Costal facet

Pedicle

Vertebral
foramen

Superior and inferior
costal facets

Inferior vertebral notch

Spinous process

Spinous
process

Transverse
process

Lamina

105-1   TYPICAL THORACIC VERTEBRA

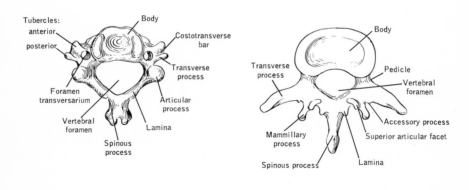

Tubercles:
anterior
posterior

Body

Costotransverse
bar

Transverse
process

Foramen
transversarium

Articular
process

Vertebral
foramen

Lamina

Spinous
process

Transverse
process

Body

Pedicle

Vertebral
foramen

Accessory process

Mammillary
process

Superior articular facet

Spinous process

Lamina

105-2   TYPICAL CERVICAL VERTEBRA   105-3   TYPICAL LUMBAR VERTEBRA

Plate 105

356

3. Contents (Fig. 104-2)

OCCIPITAL A. This artery arises from the internal carotid a. in the upper part of the neck. In the anterior triangle of the neck it lies in front of the sternomastoid. It passes deep to this muscle in the occipital groove on the back of the skull, pierces the trapezius muscle, and ascends with the greater occipital n. to the scalp.

VERTEBRAL A. Arising in the neck from the first part of the subclavian a., it ascends through the foramina transversaria of Cv 1 to 6 and then pierces the posterior atlantooccipital membrane to enter the skull through the foramen magnum.

SUBOCCIPITAL N. The dorsal ramus of Cn 1 emerges above the posterior arch of the atlas and innervates the suboccipital muscles and the semispinalis capitis muscle. It has no cutaneous branches.

GREATER OCCIPITAL N. The dorsal ramus of Cn 2 emerges below the obliquus capitis inferior muscle and divides. The lateral branch serves to innervate the splenius and semispinalis capitis muscles; the larger medial branch is known as the greater occipital n. It pierces the semispinalis capitis and trapezius muscles, ascends to the vertex of the skull, and supplies the skin of the scalp.

VERTEBRAL COLUMN

1. Components of a vertebra	*4. Lumbar vertebrae*
2. Cervical vertebrae	*5. Sacrum*
3. Thoracic vertebrae	*6. Coccyx*

The vertebral column supports the weight of the head, acts as the central pillar of the body, connects the upper and lower segments of the trunk, provides attachments for the ribs, reduces shock impact on the body, and protects the spinal cord. It consists of 33 vertebrae: 7 cervical, 12 thoracic, 5 lumbar, 5 fused sacral, and 4 fused coccygeal vertebrae.

1. Components of a Vertebra

Each vertebra consists of three parts (Fig. 105-1)

Body. The body is a short cylindrical structure with a smooth rim.

Vertebral Arch. It consists of *pedicles* which project back from the body and have intended borders that form the vertebral notches. The other components of an arch are the *laminae,* the flat, sloping plates that meet in the median plane and form the pedicles laterally.

Processes. There are three types:

spinous process. Projects backward from the junction of the laminae.

Table 83

Component	Cervical: 3–6	Thoracic: 2–11	Lumbar: 1–4
Body............	Small, rectangular	Heart-shaped	Large, kidney-shaped
Pedicles.........	Short		
Lamina.........			
Vertebral foramen.	Triangular	Circular, small	Triangular
Spine...........	Short, bifid	Long	Thick
Transverse process	Short, bifid with foramina transversaria	Thick	Bears accessory process

transverse process. Projects sideways from the junction of the pedicle and the lamina.

articular process. Projects above and below from the junction of the pedicle and the lamina.

The vertebrae of each region may be separated into typical and atypical forms. The characteristics of the typical vertebrae of each major region are listed in Table 83.

2. Cervical Vertebrae (Fig. 105-2)

The vertebrae of the neck are characterized by the *foramina transversaria* of the transverse processes. The two parts of the transverse processes are united by a *costotransverse bar* and terminate in anterior and posterior tubercles. The atypical cervical vertebrae are:

First Cervical Vertebra (Fig. 106-1). The *atlas* has no body or spine. It consists of an *anterior arch*, which bears a facet and an *anterior tubercle; lateral masses,* which bear superior and inferior articular facets; medial tubercles; transverse processes; and a *posterior arch*, which bears a *posterior tubercle.*

Second Cervical Vertebra (Fig. 106-2). The *axis* is characterized by its *dens,* which bears facets on the anterior and posterior sides of its root.

Seventh Cervical Vertebra. The *vertebra prominens* is characterized by a very long spine, for which it is named.

3. Thoracic Vertebrae (Fig. 104-1)

The facets on the sides of the bodies for the head of the ribs and the facets on most of the transverse processes for the tubercles of the ribs characterize the thoracic vertebrae. The atypical thoracic vertebrae are:

First Thoracic Vertebra. It resembles the cervical vertebra but has an entire facet on its superior surface for the first rib and a demifacet inferiorly.

Eleventh Thoracic Vertebra. It has an entire facet on the side and none on the rudimentary transverse process.

Twelfth Thoracic Vertebra. It resembles a lumbar vertebra but has an entire facet on the side. Its transverse process is rudimentary, and superior, inferior, and lateral tubercles are present.

4. Lumbar Vertebrae (Fig. 105-3)

The large size, absence of costal facets, and presence of foramens in the transverse processes characterize the lumbar vertebrae. The fifth is atypical.

Fifth Lumbar Vertebra. It is the largest of all the vertebrae; it has a small spine and a thick transverse process.

5. Sacrum (Figs. 106-3, 106-4)

A median portion of five fused sacral vertebrae and a pair of lateral masses, composed of the fused costal elements and transverse processes, comprise the sacrum. It is triangular in shape and thus presents:

Base. The anterior margin projects forward as the *promontory*. Posteriorly the triangular vertebral foramen marks the beginning of the *sacral canal*. The *ala* of the sacrum extends from the side of the body.

Apex. The apex is the oval inferior surface of the body of Sv 5.

Pelvic Surface. The concave surface consists of the bodies and ossified disks which are represented by four transverse ridges. The *pelvic sacral foramens* are located at the ends of the lines.

Dorsal Surface. The convex surface has two vertical rows of four *dorsal sacral foramens*. The *median sacral crest* is formed from the reduced spinous processes. Lateral to the foramens is the *lateral sacral crest*, formed from the transverse processes. The lower end of the sacral canal is the oblique *sacral hiatus*, at the sides of which a pair of *sacral horns* projects.

Lateral Surface. Its upper part contains the auricular surfaces.

6. Coccyx (Figs. 106-3, 106-4)

The coccyx is frequently a single bone resulting from the fused coccygeal vertebrae. Its pelvic surface is concave. The dorsal surface is irregular and presents a pair of *coccygeal horns*, which articulate with those of the sacrum.

VERTEBRAL JOINTS

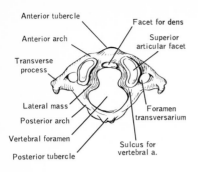

Anterior tubercle

Anterior arch

Facet for dens

Superior articular facet

Transverse process

Lateral mass

Posterior arch

Foramen transversarium

Vertebral foramen

Posterior tubercle

Sulcus for vertebral a.

106-1   ATLAS: SUPERIOR VIEW

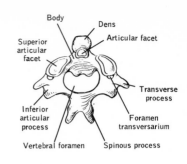

Body

Dens

Superior articular facet

Articular facet

Transverse process

Inferior articular process

Foramen transversarium

Vertebral foramen

Spinous process

106-2   AXIS: POSTEROSUPERIOR VIEW

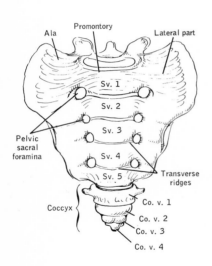

Ala

Promontory

Lateral part

Sv. 1

Sv. 2

Sv. 3

Sv. 4

Sv. 5

Pelvic sacral foramina

Coccyx

Co. v. 1

Co. v. 2

Co. v. 3

Co. v. 4

Transverse ridges

106-3   SACRUM: ANTERIOR VIEW

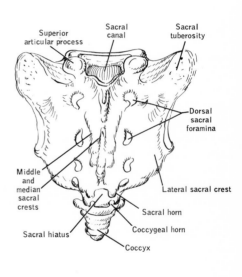

Superior articular process

Sacral canal

Sacral tuberosity

Dorsal sacral foramina

Middle and median sacral crests

Lateral sacral crest

Sacral hiatus

Sacral horn

Coccygeal horn

Coccyx

106-4   SACRUM: POSTERIOR VIEW

Plate 106

The joints of the vertebral column provide for its flexibility.

1. Joints between the Vertebral Bodies (Fig. 107-1)

Type: These joints are cartilaginous.

Articulating elements: The bodies of adjacent vertebrae articulate with one another.

Ligaments:

Anterior longitudinal ligament. Extending from the anterior arch of the atlas to the sacrum, it is attached to the fronts of the bodies and disks.

Posterior longitudinal ligament. Extending from the axis to the sacrum, it is attached to the backs of the bodies and disks.

Intervertebral disk. A fibrocartilaginous pad that is adherent to the hyaline cartilage covering the surfaces of the bodies, it consists of an outer, firm annulus fibrosus and an inner, soft nucleus pulposus.

2. Joints between the Vertebral Arches

Type: These joints are synovial.

Articulating elements: Articulation is provided by the articulating processes of adjacent vertebrae.

Ligaments:

Articular capsules. They enclose the synovial joints between the articular processes.

Ligamenta flava. This pair of elastic ligaments connects the laminae of adjacent vertebrae.

Interspinous ligament. It extends between adjacent spines from the base to the tip.

Supraspinous ligament. It extends between the tips of all the spinous processes. In the neck it is specialized as the nuchal ligament, which extends from the exterior occipital protuberance to Cv 7.

Intertransverse ligament. It extends between the transverse processes of adjacent vertebrae.

3. Atlantoaxial Joint (Figs. 107-2, 107-3)

This joint consists of three articulations.

Lateral Atlantoaxial Joints (2)

Type: The lateral atlantoaxial joints are of the plane type.

Articular elements: Articulation is provided by the articular processes of the atlas and axis.

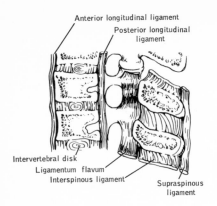

Anterior longitudinal ligament

Posterior longitudinal ligament

Intervertebral disk
Ligamentum flavum
Interspinous ligament
Supraspinous ligament

107-1   VERTEBRAL JOINTS

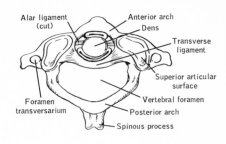

Alar ligament (cut)
Anterior arch
Dens
Transverse ligament
Superior articular surface
Vertebral foramen
Foramen transversarium
Posterior arch
Spinous process

107-2   MEDIAN ATLANTOAXIAL JOINT

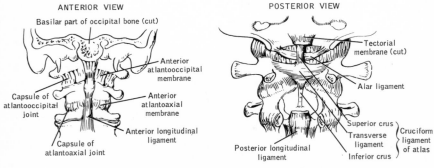

ANTERIOR VIEW

Basilar part of occipital bone (cut)

Anterior atlantooccipital membrane

Capsule of atlantooccipital joint

Anterior atlantoaxial membrane

Anterior longitudinal ligament

Capsule of atlantoaxial joint

POSTERIOR VIEW

Tectorial membrane (cut)

Alar ligament

Superior crus
Transverse ligament } Cruciform ligament of atlas
Inferior crus

Posterior longitudinal ligament

107-3   ATLANTOOCCIPITAL AND ATLANTOAXIAL JOINTS

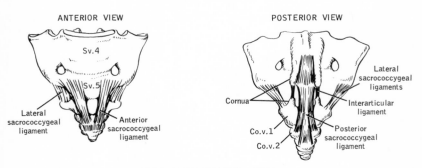

ANTERIOR VIEW

Sv.4

Sv.5

Lateral sacrococcygeal ligament

Anterior sacrococcygeal ligament

POSTERIOR VIEW

Lateral sacrococcygeal ligaments

Cornua

Interarticular ligament

Co.v.1

Co.v.2

Posterior sacrococcygeal ligament

107-4   SACROCOCCYGEAL JOINT

Plate 107

Median Atlantoaxial Joint (1)

Type: The median atlantoaxial joint is trochoid in type.

Articular elements: Articulation is provided by the dens of the axis and the ring formed by the anterior arch and the transverse ligament of the atlas.

Ligaments:

Articular capsule. It extends between the lateral masses of the atlas and the margins of the articular surface of the axis.

Anterior atlantoaxial membrane. It extends between the anterior arch of the atlas and the front of the body of the axis.

Posterior atlantoaxial membrane. It extends between the posterior arch of the atlas and the laminae of the axis.

Transverse ligament of atlas. It extends between the lateral masses and behind the dens. The superior crus extends from this ligament to the basilar part of the occipital bone. The inferior crus descends to the body of the axis. The crura and the transverse ligament constitute the cruciform ligament of the atlas.

Accessory ligaments. These ligaments are occipitoaxial (Fig. 107-3).

Tectorial membrane. It extends between the basilar part of the occipital bone and the body of axis where it is continuous with the posterior longitudinal ligament. Thus it serves to cover the dens and its ligaments.

Alar ligaments. They extend between the tip of the dens and the medial sides of the occipital condyles.

Apical dental ligament. It extends from the apex of the dens to the middle of the anterior margin of the foramen magnum.

Movement: The atlantoaxial joint provides for rotation of the skull and atlas.

4. Atlantooccipital Joint (Fig. 107-3)

Type: The atlantooccipital joint is synovial.

Articulating elements: They are the superior articular facet of the lateral masses of the atlas and the condyle of the occipital bone.

Ligaments:

Articular capsule. It envelops the joint.

Anterior atlantooccipital membrane. It extends between the anterior margin of the foramen magnum and the upper border of the anterior arch of the atlas.

Posterior atlantooccipital membrane. It extends from the posterior margin of the foramen magnum to the upper border of the posterior arch of the atlas.

Movement: The atlantooccipital joint provides for flexion, extension, and lateral bending.

5. Lumbosacral Joint

Type: The lumbosacral joint is cartilaginous.

Articulating elements: They are the fifth lumbar vertebra and the sacrum.

Ligaments: They are the anterior and posterior longitudinal ligaments and an intervertebral disk.

6. Sacrococcygeal Joint (Fig. 107-4)

Type: The sacrococcygeal joint is cartilaginous.

Articulating elements: They are the apex of the sacrum and the base of the coccyx.

Ligaments:

Intervertebral disk. This is reinforced on all sides by sacrococcygeal ligaments and interarticular ligaments between the cornua of the sacrum and coccyx.

Movements of Vertebral Column. Motion occurs in the intervertebral disks and at the joints of the articular processes. Although the extent of movement between adjacent vertebrae is small, the entire column has a considerable range of motion, including flexion, extension, lateral bending, and rotation.

VERTEBRAL CANAL. A vertebral arch and the posterior surface of its body enclose a *vertebral foramen*. All the vertebral foramens and the associated ligaments comprise the *vertebral* (spinal) *canal*. It is triangular in the cervical and lumbar regions and circular in the thoracic region. The vertebral canal contains the spinal meninges, the spinal cord and its vessels, and the roots of the spinal nerves and their sheaths. These are discussed in detail in textbooks of neuroanatomy.

INDEX

Anatomic terms used in the text are arranged generically (e.g., to find the reference for femoral artery, see Artery, femoral).